Exploring
Anatomy&Physiology
in the Laboratory
Core Concepts

Erin C. Amerman

MORTON
PUBLISHING

925 W. Kenyon Avenue, Unit 12
Englewood, CO 80110

www.morton-pub.com

Book Team

Publisher:	Douglas N. Morton
President:	David M. Ferguson
Acquisitions Editor:	Marta R. Martins
Project Manager:	Melanie Stafford
Associate Project Manager:	Rayna Bailey
Production Manager:	Joanne Saliger
Production Assistant:	Will Kelley
Illustrations:	Imagineering Media Services, Inc.
Cover Design:	Imagineering Media Services, Inc.

Printed in the United States of America

10   9   8   7   6   5   4   3   2   1

ISBN: 978-1-61731-158-1

Library of Congress Control Number: 2013944119

Preface

I first started writing lab procedures for my students 13 years ago in response to frustration my students and I were feeling with the anatomy and physiology lab and the accompanying lab manual. My students wanted—and needed—focused activities, clear objectives and explanations, and exercises that enabled them to appreciate the often-missed "big picture" of A&P. None of the available lab manuals provided this, so I was left with no choice but to write my own lab procedures. The results of my efforts were well worth it, as my students were engaged and active the entire lab period. Their lab and class grades improved.

In 2003, I met with David Ferguson, now the president of Morton Publishing Company, and he offered me a dream opportunity: to share my exercises with students and instructors throughout the country. The result of that meeting was the text *Exercises for the Anatomy and Physiology Laboratory*, a simple black-and-white manual with focused activities. My goal with this book was to solve the teaching problems in the A&P lab and to enhance the experience for my colleagues and our students.

Exercises was enthusiastically received, suggesting that we had indeed provided instructors and students something that they had been needing. We were so encouraged that we set out to produce an expanded, full-color version of the exercises that included more explanations, new activities, a complete art program, and new pedagogy. This book became *Exploring Anatomy and Physiology in the Laboratory*, or *EAPL*. Like its predecessor, it was warmly received.

EAPL was originally intended for both one and two-semester anatomy and physiology courses. But we have received feedback that there is simply too much content in *EAPL* for the one-semester course. I have taught one-semester anatomy and physiology, and I agree—the book was too big. So we now present *EAPL, Core Concepts,* which retains all of the enhanced features of *EAPL, 2e,* but is streamlined for use in one-semester courses. Whereas in *EAPL, 2e,* anatomy and physiology chapters are separate, in *Core Concepts* they are consolidated into one chapter on each organ system. In addition, the number of key terms for students to learn has been reduced significantly, and the focus is more on the foundational principles of anatomy and physiology instead of details.

As you peruse the book, please notice the following features:

▌ **Pre-Lab Exercises.** *Core Concepts* has similar pre-lab exercises to *EAPL*, 2e, but they are tailored for the one-semester course. In addition, the exercises have checkbox lists of the terms to be learned so that students can easily keep track of their progress. Note that we now offer the pre-lab exercises to instructors in an electronic format so that they may be assigned online and graded much more efficiently.

▌ **New Pronunciation Guide.** *Core Concepts* includes pronunciations for most of the major anatomy and physiology terms students will need to learn, both in the text in parentheses following the term and in a comprehensive guide in the next few pages.

▌ **Active learning activities.** *Core Concepts* features many of the same active learning activities as *EAPL*, including model inventories, tracing exercises, and hands-on procedures. However, all activities have been modified to best meet the learning outcomes for the one-semester course.

- **Engaging art program.** The same engaging art found in *EAPL*, 2e, is found in *Core Concepts*. We've also added two brand-new figures to *Core Concepts:* Figure 2.4, an example of a pH paper test; and Figure 8.7, an organizational chart of the nervous system.

- **Critical thinking questions.** Critical thinking questions have been incorporated into nearly every unit quiz in the book to help students tie together the information they are learning and help them "see the forest for the trees."

- **Student assessment.** As with *EAPL*, 2e, every unit ends with a quiz. The quizzes are specific for the one-semester course and emphasize core structures and principles covered in the unit. We also have a number of additional questions available that instructors may assign online.

- **The following pages offer a walk-through of the key features in *Exploring Anatomy & Physiology in the Laboratory, Core Concepts*.**

We hope that you enjoy the first edition of *EAPL, Core Concepts*. Please share your feedback with us about ways we can continue to improve this text so that it provides an optimal learning experience for your students.

—Erin C. Amerman

Be Prepared

OBJECTIVES set learning goals to prepare students for what they are expected to know after completing the lab. They also aid in the review of material.

PRE-LAB EXERCISES encourage students to actively prepare for the lab by defining key terms, doing labeling and coloring exercises to learn anatomical structures, and reviewing vital material from previous units, saving instructors from having to spend excessive time reviewing material from the lecture. These exercises can be completed using information available in the lab manual and will help students move through the lab more effectively. By asking students to draw their own leader lines and write out definitions, the pre-lab exercises are designed to help students retain information and build a deeper understanding of the content.

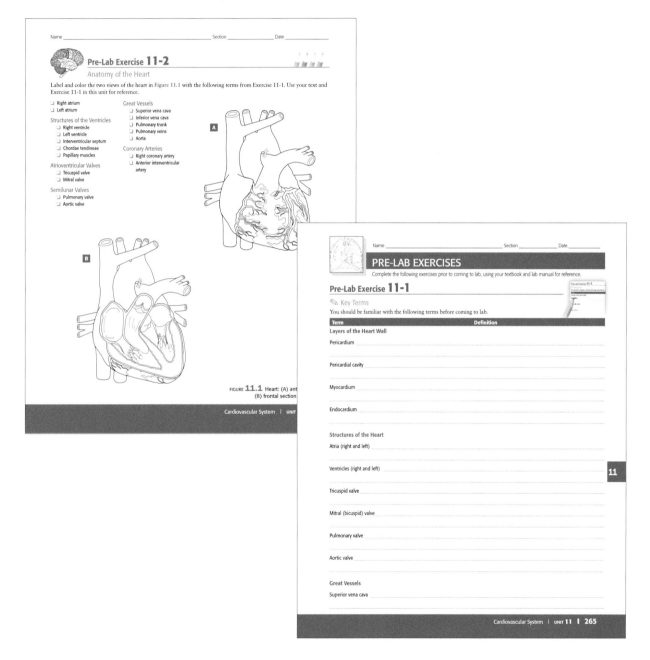

Be Organized

MODEL INVENTORIES provide organized and easily referenced lists of anatomical structures that students are responsible for identifying. These lists help students catalog the specimens they see in the lab. The emphasis on examination, description, pronunciation, and writing the names of anatomical structures encourages students to be actively involved in the learning process and allows them to better retain the material.

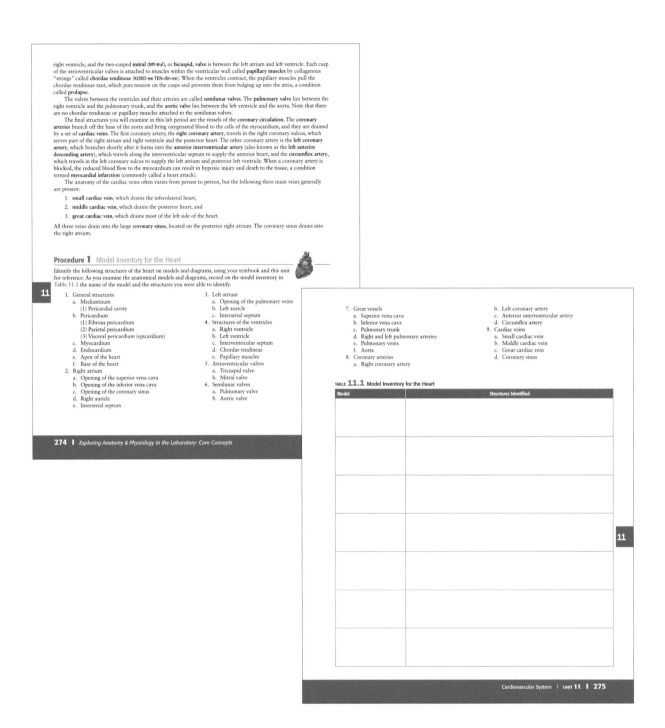

Be Focused

ILLUSTRATIONS and **PHOTOGRAPHS** in *Exploring Anatomy & Physiology in the Laboratory, Core Concepts*, were specifically designed for use in the laboratory setting. The clear photographs and photomicrographs, coupled with carefully drawn illustrations, provide a detailed view of anatomical structures to improve student retention of the material and to aid in the understanding of important concepts.

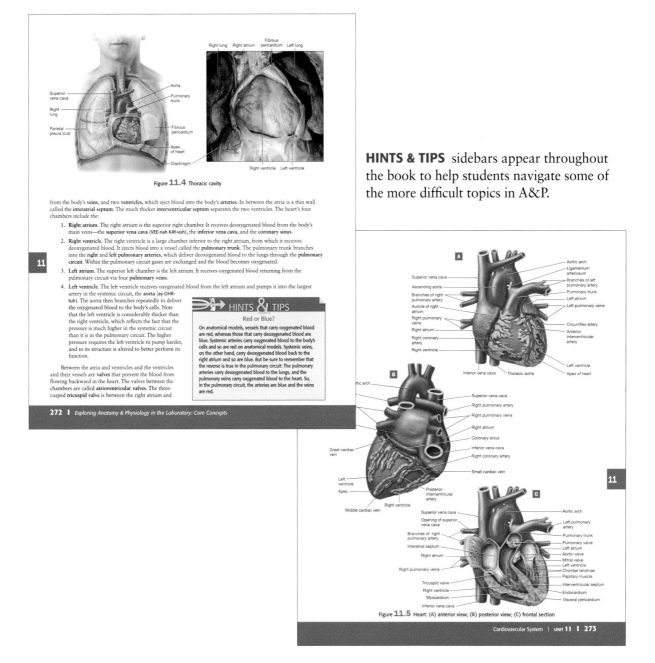

Figure **11.4** Thoracic cavity

from the body's **veins**, and two **ventricles**, which eject blood into the body's **arteries**. In between the atria is a thin wall called the **interatrial septum**. The much thicker **interventricular septum** separates the two ventricles. The heart's four chambers include the:

1. **Right atrium**. The right atrium is the superior right chamber. It receives deoxygenated blood from the body's main veins—the **superior vena cava** (VEE-nah KAY-vuh), the **inferior vena cava**, and the **coronary sinus**.

2. **Right ventricle**. The right ventricle is a large chamber inferior to the right atrium, from which it receives deoxygenated blood. It ejects blood into a vessel called the **pulmonary trunk**. The pulmonary trunk branches into the **right** and **left pulmonary arteries**, which deliver deoxygenated blood to the lungs through the **pulmonary circuit**. Within the pulmonary circuit gases are exchanged and the blood becomes oxygenated.

3. **Left atrium**. The superior left chamber is the left atrium. It receives oxygenated blood returning from the pulmonary circuit via four **pulmonary veins**.

4. **Left ventricle**. The left ventricle receives oxygenated blood from the left atrium and pumps it into the largest artery in the systemic circuit, the **aorta** (ay-OHR-tuh). The aorta then branches repeatedly to deliver the oxygenated blood to the body's cells. Note that the left ventricle is considerably thicker than the right ventricle, which reflects the fact that the pressure is much higher in the systemic circuit than it is in the pulmonary circuit. The higher pressure requires the left ventricle to pump harder, and so its structure is altered to better perform its function.

Between the atria and ventricles and their vessels are **valves** that prevent the blood from flowing backward in the heart. The valves between the chambers are called **atrioventricular valves**. The three-cusped **tricuspid valve** is between the right atrium and

HINTS & TIPS
Red or Blue?

On anatomical models, vessels that carry oxygenated blood are red, whereas those that carry deoxygenated blood are blue. Systemic arteries carry oxygenated blood to the body's cells and so are red on anatomical models. Systemic veins, on the other hand, carry deoxygenated blood back to the right atrium and so are blue. But be sure to remember that the reverse is true in the pulmonary circuit: The pulmonary arteries carry deoxygenated blood to the lungs, and the pulmonary veins carry oxygenated blood to the heart. So, in the pulmonary circuit, the arteries are blue and the veins are red.

HINTS & TIPS sidebars appear throughout the book to help students navigate some of the more difficult topics in A&P.

Figure **11.5** Heart: (A) anterior view; (B) posterior view; (C) frontal section

Be Active

FOCUSED ACTIVITIES are the guiding philosophy of this lab manual. Students learn best when they are actively engaged in the laboratory. In this manual, students are asked to be active by describing, labeling, writing, coloring, and drawing. Each activity has been designed to align with the material covered in a one-semester course.

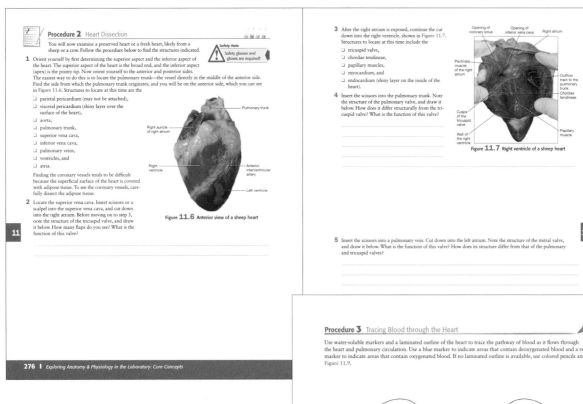

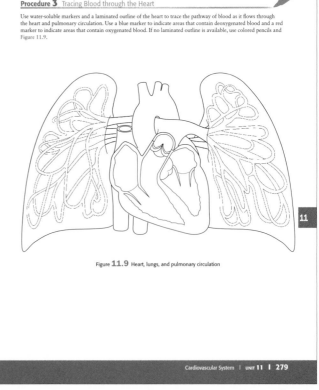

TRACING EXERCISES ask students to write step-by-step, turn-by-turn directions to follow substances (blood cells, food molecules, waste by-products, electrical events) through the human body, then trace the substances' path on a "map" of the body. These exercises allow students to see the big picture of how the body systems interact and to understand the relationship between structure and function.

Be Sure

UNIT QUIZZES consist of labeling, fill-in-the-blank, multiple choice, and sequencing questions that test students' ability to retain the material they completed in the lab. These sheets can be used as graded lab quizzes and/or to check attendance in the lab.

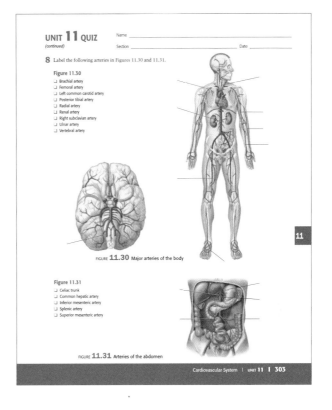

8 Label the following arteries in Figures 11.30 and 11.31.

Figure 11.30
- ❏ Brachial artery
- ❏ Femoral artery
- ❏ Left common carotid artery
- ❏ Posterior tibial artery
- ❏ Radial artery
- ❏ Renal artery
- ❏ Right subclavian artery
- ❏ Ulnar artery
- ❏ Vertebral artery

FIGURE **11.30** Major arteries of the body

Figure 11.31
- ❏ Celiac trunk
- ❏ Common hepatic artery
- ❏ Inferior mesenteric artery
- ❏ Splenic artery
- ❏ Superior mesenteric artery

FIGURE **11.31** Arteries of the abdomen

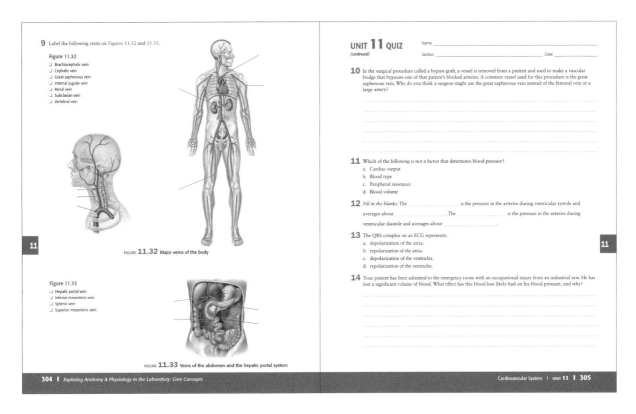

9 Label the following veins on Figures 11.32 and 11.33.

Figure 11.32
- ❏ Brachiocephalic vein
- ❏ Cephalic vein
- ❏ Great saphenous vein
- ❏ Internal jugular vein
- ❏ Renal vein
- ❏ Subclavian vein
- ❏ Vertebral vein

FIGURE **11.32** Major veins of the body

Figure 11.33
- ❏ Hepatic portal vein
- ❏ Inferior mesenteric vein
- ❏ Splenic vein
- ❏ Superior mesenteric vein

FIGURE **11.33** Veins of the abdomen and the hepatic portal system

10 In the surgical procedure called a bypass graft, a vessel is removed from a patient and used to make a vascular bridge that bypasses one of that patient's blocked arteries. A common vessel used for this procedure is the great saphenous vein. Why do you think a surgeon might use the great saphenous vein instead of the femoral vein or a large artery?

_____

_____

_____

_____

11 Which of the following is *not* a factor that determines blood pressure?
- a. Cardiac output
- b. Blood type
- c. Peripheral resistance
- d. Blood volume

12 *Fill in the blanks:* The _____ is the pressure in the arteries during ventricular systole and averages about _____. The _____ is the pressure in the arteries during ventricular diastole and averages about _____.

13 The QRS complex on an ECG represents:
- a. depolarization of the atria.
- b. repolarization of the atria.
- c. depolarization of the ventricles.
- d. repolarization of the ventricles.

14 Your patient has been admitted to the emergency room with an occupational injury from an industrial saw. He has lost a significant volume of blood. What effect has this blood loss likely had on his blood pressure, and why?

_____

_____

_____

_____

Be Aware

Textbooks are expensive, and the last thing a student needs is to spend too much for a lab manual. Morton Publishing is committed to providing high-quality products at reasonable prices.

It is our sincere hope that *Exploring Anatomy & Physiology in the Laboratory, Core Concepts*, will provide you with the tools necessary for a productive and interesting laboratory experience. *We welcome all comments and suggestions for future editions of this book. Please feel free to contact us at* eapl@morton-pub.com or visit us at www.morton-pub.com.

Be Choosy

MortyPak Options

Bundle *Exploring Anatomy & Physiology in the Laboratory, Core Concepts*, with one or more of the following supplemental titles:

- *A Visual Analogy Guide to Human Anatomy*
- *A Visual Analogy Guide to Human Physiology*
- *A Visual Analogy Guide to Human Anatomy and Physiology*
- *A Visual Analogy Guide to Chemistry*
- *A Photographic Atlas of Histology*
- *A Photographic Atlas for the A&P Laboratory*
- *A Dissection Guide and Atlas to the Rat*
- *A Dissection Guide and Atlas to the Fetal Pig*
- *A Dissection Guide and Atlas to the Mink*
- *Mammalian Anatomy: The Cat*
- *An Illustrated Atlas of the Skeletal Muscles*

Morton CustomLab

In an effort to lower the prices of books, and to provide instructors and students books tailored to their needs, we offer the enhanced Morton CustomLab program. With CustomLab, instructors can remove or combine material from our existing lab manuals or photographic atlases, or may use photographs and illustrations from our extensive online library, to create their own, personalized lab manual. Enrollment minimums apply.

E-books

As higher education continues to evolve and incorporate technology, we are pleased to now offer our titles as e-books for students who prefer an e-format. Students may purchase our titles through one of our e-book partners.

Acknowledgments

Although it is my name on the cover of this text, textbooks are never a solo effort. Many people were integral to the production and development of this book, and I would like to take this brief opportunity to express my gratitude.

First and foremost I would like to thank my family, particularly Elise, my mother Cathy, and Chris. Without your unwavering support, this text would not have been possible. And to Elise, thank you especially for being patient with me being behind my computer screen so often. Also, I can't forget my animals, particularly my cats, who unfailingly managed to be completely in the way of whatever I was doing.

Next I would like to extend my gratitude to the talented book team with whom I was fortunate enough to work: Joanne Saliger, who expertly designed and produced the book; Carolyn Acheson, who skillfully compiled the index; Melanie Stafford and Rayna Bailey, who carefully edited the manuscript; the team at Imagineering Media Services, Inc., who provided the beautiful illustrations; and Photo Researchers, Justin Moore, Mike Leboffe, and John Crawley, who allowed me to use their excellent photos and photomicrographs. I truly appreciate all of your hard work and generosity.

I would also like to thank the following reviewers for their valuable suggestions that helped to shape the contents of this book:

Diana M. Coffman, Lincoln Land Community College

Angela Corbin, Nicholls State University

Dr. Cassy Cozine, University of Saint Mary

Molli Crenshaw, Texas Christian University

Jill E. Feinstein, Richland Community College

Elizabeth Hodgson, York College of Pennsylvania

Steven Leadon, Durham Technical Community College

Eddie Lunsford, Southwestern Community College

Dr. Shawn Macauley, Muskegon Community College

Darren Mattone, Muskegon Community College

Justin Moore, American River College

Michele Robichaux, Nicholls State University

Deanne Roopnarine, Nova Southeastern University

Amy Fenech Sandy, Columbus Technical College, Columbus, GA

Lori Smith, American River College

Valory Thatcher, Mt. Hood Community College

Cathy Whiting, Gainesville State College

The acknowledgments would be incomplete without thanking Doug Morton, who has been kind enough to provide me with another opportunity to publish with his company. And finally, I extend a special thank you to President David Ferguson for his support, patience, friendship, and willingness to cheer for the Florida Gators.

About the Author

Erin C. Amerman has been involved in anatomy and physiology education for more than 13 years as an author and professor, most recently at Florida State College in Jacksonville, Florida. She received a B.S. in Cellular and Molecular Biology from the University of West Florida and a doctorate in Podiatric Medicine from Des Moines University. *Exploring Anatomy & Physiology in the Laboratory, Core Concepts*, is her third book with Morton Publishing.

Pronunciation Guide

Note: Accented syllables are capitalized; for example, "a-NAT-oh-mee and fiz-ee-AHL-oh-jee."

abdominal (ab-DAH-min-ul)

abducens (ab-DOO-senz)

acetabulum (ass-e-TAB-yoo-lum)

acromial (ah-KROH-mee-ul)

acromioclavicular (ah-KROH-mee-oh-cla-VIK-yoo-lur)

acromion (ah-KROH-mee-ahn)

adipocytes (AD-ih-poh-sytz)

adrenocorticotropic (a-DREE-noh-kohr-tih-koh-TROH-pik)

albuginea (al-byoo-JIN-ee-uh)

aldosterone (al-DAHS-tur-ohn)

alveoli (al-vee-OH-lye)

amnion (AM-nee-ahn)

amylase (AM-uh-layz)

antebrachial (an-tee-BRAY-kee-ul)

antigens (AN-tih-jenz)

aorta (ay-OHR-tuh)

arachnoid mater (ah-RAK-noyd MAH-tur)

arcuate (AHR-kyoo-it)

areola (air-ee-OH-lah)

arrector pili (ar-EK-tur PEE-lee)

atria (AY-tree-uh)

auricle (OHR-ik-ul)

auscultation (aw-skul-TAY-shun)

axillary (AX-il-air-ee)

axon (AX-ahn)

basale (bay-ZAY-lee)

basal lamina (BAY-zul LAM-in-uh)

basilar (BAY-sih-lur)

basophils (BAY-soh-filz)

biceps brachii (BY-seps BRAY-kee-eye)

brachial (BRAY-kee-ul)

brachiocephalic (bray-kee-oh-sef-AL-ik)

brachioradialis (bray-kee-oh-ray-dee-AL-is)

bronchi (BRAHNK-eye)

bronchial (BRAHNK-ee-ul)

bronchioles (BRAHNK-ee-ohlz)

buccal (BYOO-kul)

bursae (BUR-see)

calcaneal (kal-KAY-nee-ul)

calvaria (kal-VAIR-ee-uh)

calyces (KAL-ih-seez)

canaliculi (kan-uh-LIK-yoo-lee)

capitulum (ka-PIT-yoo-lum)

cardiac (KAR-dee-ak)

carotid (kuh-RAH-tid)

carpals (KAR-pulz)

cauda equina (CAW-duh ee-KWYNE-uh)

cecum (SEE-kum)

celiac (SEE-lee-ak)

centrioles (SEN-tree-ohlz)

cephalic (sef-AL-ik)

cerebellum (sair-e-BEL-um)

cerebrospinal (sair-ee-broh-SPY-nul)

cerebrum (sair-EE-brum)

cervical (SUR-vih-kul)

chiasma (ky-AZ-muh)

chondrocytes (KAHN-droh-sytz)

chordae tendineae (KORD-ee TEN-din-ee)

chorion (KOHR-ee-ahn)

choroid (KOHR-oyd)

chromosomes (KROH-moh-somz)

chylomicrons (ky-loh-MY-krahnz)

cilia (SIL-ee-uh)

cisterna chyli (sis-TUR-nuh KY-lee)

cisternae (sis-TUR-nee)

clitoris (KLIH-tohr-us)

coccyx (CAHX-iks)

conchae (KAHN-kee)

conjunctiva (kahn-junk-TEE-vuh)

coracoid (KOHR-uh-koyd)

corneum (KOHR-nee-um)

coronal (koh-ROH-nul)

coronoid (KOHR-oh-noyd)

corpus luteum (KOHR-pus LOO-tee-um)

cortisol (KOHR-tih-sahl)

cranial (KRAY-nee-ul)

cricoid (KRY-koyd)

cricothyroid (kry-koh-THY-royd)

crista galli (KRIS-tuh GAH-lee)

cruciate (KROO-shee-it)

crural (KROO-rul)

cystic (SIS-tik)

cytokinesis (SY-toh-kin-EE-sis)

cytoplasm (SY-toh-plaz-m)

cytosol (SY-toh-sahl)

deferens (DEF-ur-unz)

dendrites (DEN-drytz)

detrusor (de-TROO-sohr)

diaphragm (DY-uh-fram)

diaphysis (dy-AF-ih-sis)

diastolic (dy-uh-STAH-lik)

diencephalon (dy-en-SEF-uh-lahn)

digital (DIJ-it-ul)

dorsalis pedis (dohr-SAL-iz PEE-diz)

ductus arteriosus (DUK-tus ahr-tih-ree-OH-sus)

ductus venosus (DUK-tus vee-NOH-sus)

duodenum (doo-AH-den-um)

dura (DUR-uh MAH-tur)

dysrhythmia (dis-RITH-mee-uh)

emulsification (ee-mul-sih-fih-KAY-shun)

endometrium (en-doh-MEE-tree-um)

endomysium (en-doh-MY-see-um)

endoplasmic reticulum (en-doh-PLAZ-mik re-TIK-yoo-lum)

endosteum (en-DAHS-tee-um)

eosinophils (ee-oh-SIN-oh-filz)

epididymis (ep-ih-DID-ih-mis)

epidural (ep-ih-DOO-rul)

epiglottis (ep-ih-GLAH-tis)

epimysium (ep-ih-MY-see-um)

epiphyseal (e-PIF-iz-ee-ul)

epiphysis (e-PIF-ih-sis)

epithalamus (ep-ih-THAL-uh-mus)

epithelial (ep-ih-THEE-lee-ul)

erythropoietin (e-rith-roh-POY-e-tin)

ethmoid (ETH-moyd)

erythrocytes (e-RITH-roh-sytz)

esophagus (e-SAH-fuh-gus)

fascicles (FAS-ih-kulz)

femoral (FEM-oh-rul)

femur (FEE-mur)

fibroblasts (FY-broh-blastz)

fibula (FIB-yoo-luh)

fimbriae (FIM-bree-ay)

flagella (fla-JEL-uh)

follicle (FAH-lih-kul)

fontanels (fahn-tuh-NELZ)

foramen ovale (foh-RAY-men oh-VAL-ee)

fovea centralis (FOH-vee-uh sen-TRAL-iz)

frontal (FRUHN-tul)

gametes (GAM-eetz)

gametogenesis (gam-e-toh-JEN-e-sis)

ganglia (GAYN-glee-uh)

gastrocnemius (gas-trahk-NEE-mee-us)

gastroesophageal (gas-troh-e-sah-fuh-GEE-ul)

glenoid (GLEN-oyd)

glomerulus (gloh-MAIR-yoo-lus)

glossopharyngeal (glah-soh-fair-IN-jee-ul)

gluteal (GLOO-tee-ul)

gluteus (GLOO-tee-us)

Golgi (GOHL-jee)

gonads (GOH-nadz)

gracilis (grah-SIH-lis)

granulocytes (GRAN-yoo-loh-sytz)

granulosum (gran-yoo-LOH-sum)

gyri (JY-ree)

hemoglobin (HEE-moh-gloh-bin)

hemolysis (hee-MAH-lih-sis)

hepatopancreatic ampulla (hep-at-oh-pank-ree-A-tik
    am-PYOO-luh)

hilum (HY-lum)

humerus (HYOO-mur-us)

hyaline (HY-uh-lin)

hyoid (HY-oyd)

hypertonic (hy-per-TAHN-ik)

hypoglossal (hy-poh-GLAH-sul)

hypothalamus (hy-poh-THAL-uh-mus)

hypotonic (hy-poh-TAHN-ik)

iliac (il-EE-ak)

ileocecal (il-ee-oh-SEE-kul)

iliopsoas (il-ee-oh-SOH-us)

ilium (IL-ee-um)

incus (INK-us)

infundibulum (in-fun-DIB-yoo-lum)

inguinal (IN-gwen-ul)

integumentary (in-TEG-yoo-MEN-tuh-ree)

intercalated (in-TUR-kuh-lay-tid)

interstitial (in-tur-STISH-ul)

ischium (ISS-kee-um)

isotonic (eye-soh-TAHN-ik)

jejunum (je-JOO-num)

keratinocytes (KAIR-ah-tin-oh-sytz)

lacrimal (LAK-rim-ul)

lacunae (la-KOO-nee)

lamellae (lah-MEL-ee)

laryngopharynx (lair-ING-oh-fair-inx)

larynx (LAIR-inx)

latissimus dorsi (lah-TIS-ih-mus DOHR-sye)

leukocytes (LOO-koh-sytz)

lipase (LY-payz)

lucidum (LOO-sid-um)

lumbar (LUHM-bahr)

luteinizing (LOO-tee-nye-zing)

lymph (limf)

lymphocytes (LIMF-oh-sytz)

lysosomes (LY-soh-somz)

macula lutea (MAK-yoo-luh LOO-tee-uh)

malleolus (mal-ee-OH-lus)

malleus (MAL-ee-us)

mammary (MAM-uh-ree)

manubrium (man-OO-bree-um)

masseter (MAS-e-tur)

mastication (mas-tih-KAY-shun)

maxillae (max-IL-ee)

mediastinum (mee-dee-uh-STYN-um)

medulla oblongata (med-OO-luh ahb-lahn-GAH-tuh)

meiosis (my-OH-sis)

melanin (MEL-uh-nin)

melatonin (mel-uh-TOH-nin)

meninges (men-IN-jeez)

menisci (men-IH-sky)

mental (MEN-tul)

mesentery (MES-en-tair-ee)

metacarpals (met-uh-KAR-pulz)

metatarsals (met-uh-TAHR-sulz)

micelles (my-SELZ)

microvilli (my-kroh-VIL-eye)

micturition (mik-chur-ISH-un)

mitochondria (my-toh-KAHN-dree-uh)

mitosis (my-TOH-sis)

mitral (MY-trul)

monocytes (MAH-noh-sytz)

musculocutaneous (mus-kyoo-loh-kyoo-TAY-nee-us)

myelin (MY-e-lin)

myocardium (my-oh-KAR-dee-um)

myofibrils (my-oh-FY-brilz)

nasal (NAY-zul)

nasopharynx (NAYZ-oh-fair-inx)

nephrons (NEF-rahnz)

neurilemma (noor-ih-LEM-uh)

neuroglial (noor-oh-GLEE-ul)

neurons (NOOR-ahnz)

neutrophils (NOO-troh-filz)

nuclei (NOO-klee-eye)

nucleolus (noo-klee-OH-lus)

nucleus (NOO-klee-us)

obturator (AHB-tur-ay-tur)

occipital (ahk-SIP-ih-tul)

oculomotor (ahk-yoo-loh-MOH-tohr)

olecranon (oh-LEK-ruh-nahn)

omentum (oh-MEN-tum)

oocytes (OH-oh-sytz)

oral (OH-rul)

orbicularis oculi (ohr-bik-yoo-LAIR-is AHK-yoo-lye)

orbital (OHR-bit-ul)

organelles (ohr-gan-ELZ)

oropharynx (OHR-oh-fair-inx)

osmosis (ahz-MOH-sis)

osseous (AH-see-us)

osteons (AHS-tee-ahnz)

otic (OH-tik)

palatine (PAL-uh-teen)

palmar (PAHL-mur)

palpebrae (pal-PEE-bray)

pancreas (PAYN-kree-us)

papillae (pa-PIL-ee)

parafollicular (PAIR-uh-fah-LIK-yoo-lur)

parotid (pair-AH-tid)

parietal (puh-RY-ih-tul)

patella (puh-TEL-uh)

patellar (puh-TEL-ur)

pectoral (PEK-tohr-ul)

pectoralis (pek-tohr-AL-is)

pelvic (PEL-vik)

pericardial (pair-ih-KAR-dee-ul)

pericardium (pair-ih-KAR-dee-um)

perimysium (pair-ih-MY-see-um)

peristalsis (pair-ih-STAHL-sis)

periosteum (pair-ee-AHS-tee-um)

peritoneal (pair-ih-toh-NEE-ul)

phalanges (fuh-LAN-jeez)

pharyngotympanic (fair-in-go-tim-PAN-ik)

pharynx (FAIR-inx)

phrenic (FREN-ik)

pia mater (PEE-uh MAH-tur)

pineal (pih-NEE-ul)

pituitary (pih-TOO-ih-tair-ee)

pleural (PLOO-rul)

pneumothorax (noo-muh-THOHR-ax)

podocytes (POH-doh-sytz)

popliteal (pahp-lih-TEE-ul)

prostate (PRAHS-tayt)

pseudostratified (soo-doh-STRAT-ih-fyed)

pterygoid (TAIR-ih-goyd)

pubic (PYOO-bik)

pubis (PYOO-bis)

pylorus (py-LOHR-us)

quadriceps femoris (QWAH-drih-seps fem-OHR-is)

radius (RAY-dee-us)

rami (RAY-mee)

Ranvier (rahn-vee-AY)

rectus abdominis (REK-tus ab-DAHM-in-us)

renal (REE-nul)

rete testis (REET TES-tis)

ribosomes (RY-boh-zohmz)

rugae (ROO-gee)

saccule (SAK-yool)

sacroiliac (say-kroh-IL-ee-ak)

sacrum (SAY-krum)

sagittal (SAJ-ih-tul)

saphenous (SAF-in-us)

sarcolemma (sahr-koh-LEM-uh)

sarcomere (SAR-koh-meer)

sarcoplasm (SAHR-koh-plazm)

sartorius (sahr-TOHR-ee-us)

scapula (SKAP-yoo-luh)

scapular (SKAP-yoo-lur)

sciatic (SY-a-tik)

sclera (SKLAIR-uh)

sebaceous (se-BAY-shus)

sella turcica (SEL-uh TUR-sih-kuh)

semimembranosus (sem-eye-mem-bray-NOH-sus)

semitendinosus (sem-eye-ten-din-OH-sus)

serous (SEER-us)

soleus (SOH-lee-us)

sphenoid (SFEE-noyd)

sphygmomanometer (sfig-mah-man-AHM-et-ur)

spinae (SPY-nee)

spinosum (spin-OH-sum)

spirometer (spy-RAH-met-ur)

squamous (SQWAY-mus)

stapes (STAY-peez)

sternal (STUR-nul)

sternocleidomastoid (stur-noh-kly-doh-MAS-toyd)

subclavian (sub-KLAY-vee-un)

sublingual (sub-LING-wul)

sulci (SUL-kee)

sutures (SOO-churz)

symphysis (SIM-fih-sis)

synovial (sin-OH-vee-ul)

systolic (sis-TAH-lik)

tarsals (TAHR-sulz)

telodendria (tel-oh-DEN-dree-uh)

temporalis (tem-pohr-AL-is)

temporomandibular (tem-pohr-oh-man-DIB-yoo-lur)

testes (TES-teez)

thalamus (THAL-uh-mus)

thoracic (thoh-RAS-ik)

thyroxine (thy-ROX-in)

tibia (TIH-bee-uh)

tibialis (tih-bee-AL-us)

tonicity (toh-NIH-sih-tee)

trabeculae (tra-BEK-you-lee)

trachea (TRAY-kee-uh)

transversus (tranz-VUR-sus)

trapezius (tra-PEE-zee-us)

triceps brachii (TRY-seps BRAY-kee-eye)

trigone (TRY-gohn)

triiodothyronine (try-eye-oh-doh-THY-roh-neen)

trochanter (troh-KAN-tur)

trochlea (TROH-klee-uh)

trochlear (TROH-klee-ur)

trophoblast (TROH-foh-blast)

ulna (UL-nuh)

umbilical (um-BIL-ih-kul)

ureters (YOO-re-turz)

uterine (YOO-tur-in)

utricle (YOO-trih-kul)

uvea (YOO-vee-uh)

vagus (VAY-gus)

vasa recta (VAY-zah REK-tah)

vena cava (VEE-nah KAY-vuh)

vertebral (vur-TEE-brul)

vestibulocochlear (ves-tib-yoo-loh-KOHK-lee-ur)

visceral (VIS-ur-ul)

xiphoid (ZY-foyd)

zygomatic (zy-goh-MAT-ik)

zygomaticus (zy-goh-MAT-ih-kus)

zygote (ZY-goht)

Contents

Introduction to Anatomy and Physiology

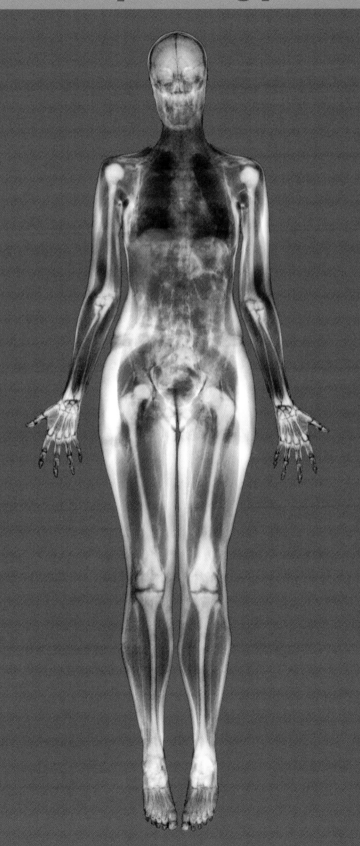

OBJECTIVES

Once you have completed this unit, you should be able to:

1. Demonstrate and describe anatomical position.

2. Apply directional terms to descriptions of anatomical parts.

3. Use regional terms to describe anatomical locations.

4. Locate and describe the divisions of the major body cavities and the membranes lining each cavity.

5. Demonstrate and describe anatomical planes of section.

6. Identify the organ systems, their functions, and the major organs in each system.

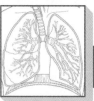

1

PRE-LAB EXERCISES

Complete the following exercises prior to coming to lab, using your textbook and lab manual for reference.

Pre-Lab Exercise **1-1**

✎ Key Terms

You should be familiar with the following terms before coming to lab.

Term	Definition

Directional Terms

Anterior (ventral) _____

Posterior (dorsal) _____

Superior _____

Inferior _____

Proximal _____

Distal _____

Medial _____

Lateral _____

Superficial _____

Deep _____

Body Cavities and Membranes

Dorsal body cavity _____

_____

Ventral body cavity _____

_____

Serous membrane _____

_____

Planes of Section

Sagittal plane _____

_____

Frontal (coronal) plane _____

_____

Transverse plane _____

_____

Pre-Lab Exercise 1-2

Organ Systems

The body has 11 organ systems, each of which contains certain organs, and each with a specific subset of functions. Note that some organs are part of more than one system.

In this exercise you will identify the 11 organ systems, their major organ(s), and the basic function(s) of each system (Table 1.1). Use your textbook and Exercise 1-4 from this unit for reference.

TABLE **1.1** Organ Systems

Organ System	Major Organs	Organ System Functions
Integumentary system		
Skeletal system		
Muscular system		
Nervous system		
Endocrine system		

(continues)

TABLE **1.1** Organ Systems *(cont.)*

1

Organ System	Major Organs	Organ System Functions
Cardiovascular system		
Lymphatic system		
Respiratory system		
Digestive system		
Urinary system		
Reproductive systems		

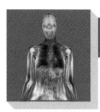

EXERCISES

The bullet entered the right posterior scapular region, 3 centimeters lateral to the vertebral region, 4 centimeters inferior to the cervical region, and penetrated deep to the muscle and bone, but superficial to the parietal pleura . . .

Would you believe that by the end of this unit, you will be able to translate the above sentence and also locate the hypothetical wound? Unit 1 will introduce you to the world of anatomy and physiology. We will begin with an introduction to the unique language of anatomy and physiology. Like learning any new language, this may seem overwhelming at first. The key to success is repetition and application: The more you use the terms, the easier it will be for them to become part of your normal vocabulary.

From the terminology we will move on to the organization of the body into body cavities and organ systems. After you have completed this unit, return to the above sentence, and challenge yourself to locate the precise position of the bullet wound on an anatomical model.

Exercise **1-1**

Anatomical Terms

MATERIALS
- ❏ Laminated outline of the human body
- ❏ Water-soluble marking pens

Accurate communication among scientists in the fields of anatomy and physiology is critical, which means we must describe body parts, wounds, procedures, and more in a specific, standardized way. The first way in which we standardize communication is in the presentation of specimens in anatomical position. As you can see in Figure 1.1, in anatomical position the specimen is presented facing forward, with the toes pointing forward, the feet shoulder-width apart, and the palms facing forward.

Another method that makes communication easier and less prone to errors is to use certain terms to define the location of body parts and body markings (Figure 1.2). For example, when describing a wound on the chest, we could say:

- ▮ The wound is near the middle and top of the chest; or
- ▮ The wound is on the right *anterior* thoracic region, 4 centimeters *lateral* to the sternum and 3 centimeters *inferior* to the acromial region.

The second option is precise and allows the reader to locate the wound exactly. Note that these descriptions are referring to a figure in anatomical position.

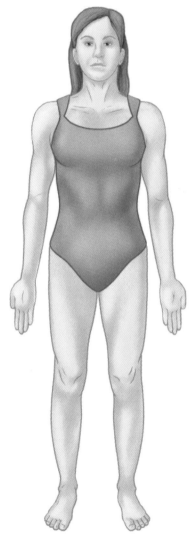

FIGURE **1.1** Anatomical position

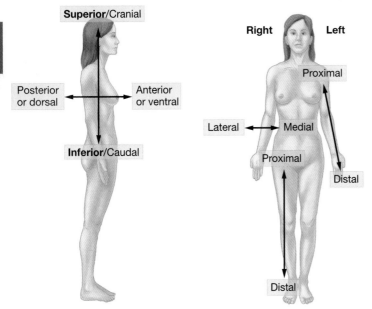

FIGURE **1.2** Directional terms

You may have noticed that in the examples in the previous paragraph, we used the anatomical terms *thoracic region* and *acromial region* instead of using generic terms such as "chest" and "shoulder." This is the third way we standardize communication. For example, "shoulder" could consist of quite a large anatomical area, whereas the "acromial region" refers to one specific location on the shoulder.

The following regional terms, illustrated in Figure 1.3, are among the more common terms you will encounter in your study of anatomy and physiology. Note that most of these terms are adjectives rather than nouns. This means the term is not complete unless it is paired with the term "region." For example, we cannot say, "The wound is in the antebrachial"; instead we must say, "The wound is in the antebrachial *region*."

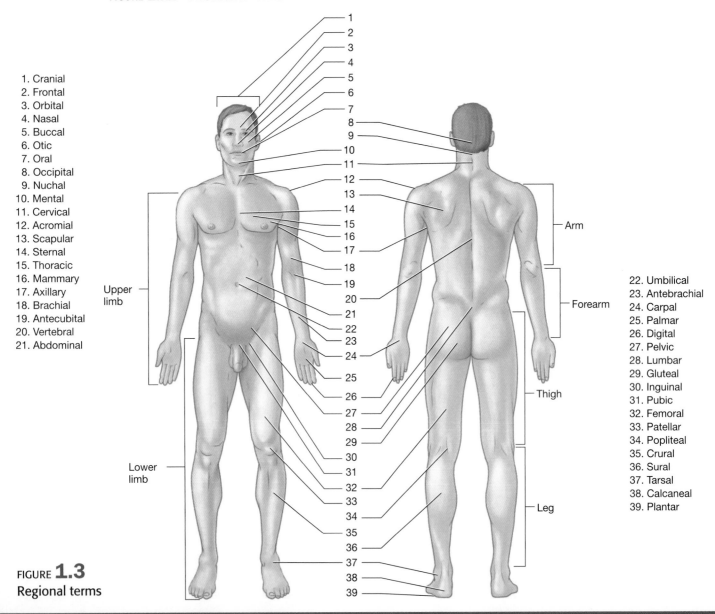

1. Cranial
2. Frontal
3. Orbital
4. Nasal
5. Buccal
6. Otic
7. Oral
8. Occipital
9. Nuchal
10. Mental
11. Cervical
12. Acromial
13. Scapular
14. Sternal
15. Thoracic
16. Mammary
17. Axillary
18. Brachial
19. Antecubital
20. Vertebral
21. Abdominal

22. Umbilical
23. Antebrachial
24. Carpal
25. Palmar
26. Digital
27. Pelvic
28. Lumbar
29. Gluteal
30. Inguinal
31. Pubic
32. Femoral
33. Patellar
34. Popliteal
35. Crural
36. Sural
37. Tarsal
38. Calcaneal
39. Plantar

FIGURE **1.3**
Regional terms

Procedure 1 Demonstrating Anatomical Position

Have your lab partner stand in a normal, relaxed way, then adjust his or her position so it matches anatomical position.

Procedure 2 Directional Terms

Fill in the correct directional term for each of the following items. Note that in some cases, more than one directional term may apply.

The elbow is _____ to the wrist.

The chin is _____ to the nose.

The shoulder is _____ to the sternum (breastbone).

The forehead is _____ to the mouth.

The skin is _____ to the muscle.

The spine is _____ to the esophagus.

The nose is _____ to the cheek.

The spine is on the _____ side of the body.

The arm is _____ to the torso.

The knee is _____ to the hip.

Procedure 3 Labeling Body Regions

Use water-soluble markers to locate and label each of the following regions on laminated outlines of the human body. If outlines are unavailable, label the regions on Figure 1.4. The following list may look daunting, but you are probably familiar with several of the terms already. For example, you likely know the locations of the "oral," "nasal," and "abdominal" regions. Watch for other terms you may know.

Adjectives

❏ Abdominal (**ab-DAH-min-ul**)
❏ Acromial (**ah-KROH-mee-ul**)
❏ Antebrachial (**an-tee-BRAY-kee-ul**)
❏ Axillary (**AX-il-air-ee**)
❏ Brachial (**BRAY-kee-ul**)
❏ Buccal (**BYOO-kul**)
❏ Calcaneal (**kal-KAY-nee-ul**)
❏ Carpal (**KAR-pul**)
❏ Cephalic (**sef-AL-ik**)
❏ Cervical (**SUR-vih-kul**)
❏ Cranial (**KRAY-nee-ul**)
❏ Crural (**KROO-rul**)

❏ Digital (**DIJ-it-ul**)
❏ Femoral (**FEM-oh-rul**)
❏ Frontal (**FRUHN-tul**)
❏ Gluteal (**GLOO-tee-ul**)
❏ Inguinal (**IN-gwen-ul**)
❏ Lumbar (**LUHM-bahr**)
❏ Mammary (**MAM-uh-ree**)
❏ Mental (**MEN-tul**)
❏ Nasal (**NAY-zul**)
❏ Occipital (**ahk-SIP-it-ul**)
❏ Oral (**OH-rul**)
❏ Orbital (**OHR-bit-ul**)

❏ Otic (**OH-tik**)
❏ Palmar (**PAHL-mur**)
❏ Patellar (**puh-TEL-ur**)
❏ Pelvic (**PEL-vik**)
❏ Popliteal (**pahp-lih-TEE-ul**)
❏ Pubic (**PYOO-bik**)
❏ Scapular (**SKAP-yoo-lur**)
❏ Sternal (**STUR-nul**)
❏ Tarsal (**TAR-sul**)
❏ Thoracic (**thoh-RAS-ik**)
❏ Umbilical (**um-BIL-ih-kul**)
❏ Vertebral (**vur-TEE-brul**)

Nouns

❏ Arm
❏ Forearm

❏ Leg
❏ Lower limb

❏ Thigh
❏ Upper limb

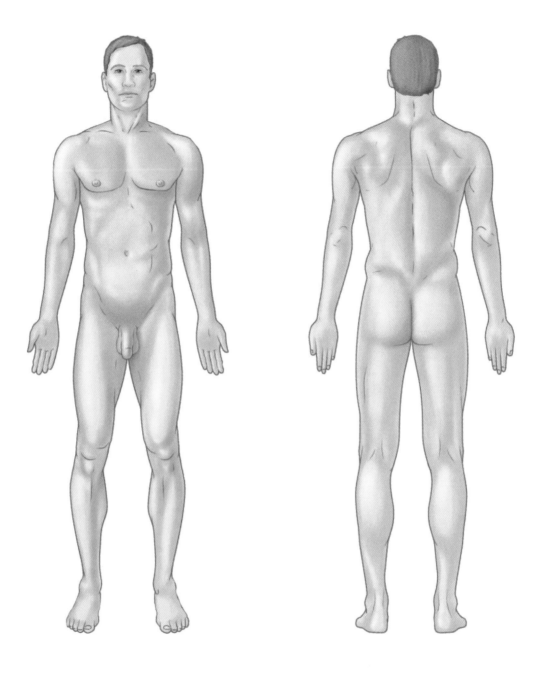

FIGURE **1.4** Anterior and posterior views of the human body in anatomical position

Exercise 1-2

Body Cavities and Membranes

MATERIALS

- ❑ Human torso models
- ❑ Fetal pigs (or other preserved small mammals)
- ❑ Dissection kits/dissection trays

The body is divided into several fluid-filled cavities, each of which contains specific organs. In this exercise you will identify the body cavities and the organs contained within each cavity.

As you can see in **Figure 1.5**, there are two major body cavities, each of which is subdivided into smaller cavities, as follows:

1. **Dorsal (posterior) cavity.** As implied by its name, the dorsal body cavity is largely on the posterior, or dorsal, side of the body. It contains two smaller cavities:

   a. **Cranial cavity.** The cranial cavity is the area encased by the skull. It contains the brain and the special sense organs, such as the eyes and the organs for hearing.

   b. **Vertebral (or spinal) cavity.** The vertebral cavity is the area encased by the vertebrae. It contains the spinal cord.

2. **Ventral (anterior) cavity.** The ventral body cavity is largely on the anterior, or ventral, side of the body. It has two main divisions: the **thoracic cavity,** superior to the diaphragm, and the **abdominopelvic cavity,** inferior to the diaphragm. Within the thoracic and abdominopelvic cavities are smaller subcavities formed by thin sheets of tissue called **serous (SEER-us) membranes.** Cells of these membranes produce a thin, watery fluid called **serous fluid** that lubricates organs so they move with a minimum of friction. Serous membranes are composed of two

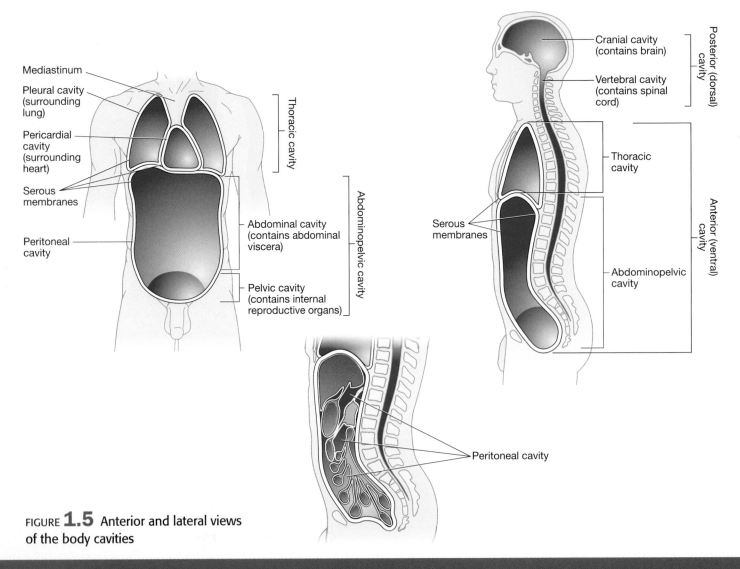

FIGURE **1.5** Anterior and lateral views of the body cavities

layers: an outer **parietal** (puh-RY-ih-tul) **layer** attached to the surrounding structures, and an inner **visceral** (VIS-ur-ul) **layer** attached to the organ or organs of the ventral cavity. Between the parietal and visceral layers is a thin potential space that contains serous fluid. This potential space is also referred to as a cavity. The following are the divisions of the ventral cavity:

a. **Thoracic cavity.** The thoracic cavity is superior to the diaphragm and encompasses the area encased by the ribs. We find the following smaller cavities within the thoracic cavity:

(1) **Pleural cavities.** Each pleural (PLOO-rul) cavity surrounds one of the lungs. The pleural cavities are located between two serous membranes called the **pleural membranes.** The **parietal pleura** is attached to the body wall, and the **visceral pleura** is attached to the surface of the lung.

(2) **Mediastinum.** The area between the pleural cavities, called the mediastinum (mee-dee-uh-STYN-um), contains the great vessels, the esophagus, the trachea and bronchi, and other structures. It houses another set of serous membranes that form the **pericardial** (pair-ih-KAR-dee-ul) **cavity**, which surrounds the heart. The pericardial cavity is between the **pericardial membranes**; the **parietal pericardium** is attached to surrounding structures, and the inner **visceral pericardium** is attached to the heart muscle.

b. **Abdominopelvic cavity.** The abdominopelvic cavity encompasses the area inferior to the diaphragm and extends into the bony pelvis. It contains the **peritoneal** (pair-ih-toh-NEE-ul) **membranes**; the **parietal peritoneum** is attached to the body wall and surrounding structures, and the inner **visceral peritoneum** is attached to the surface of many of the organs in the cavity. Between these two layers of peritoneal membranes we find the **peritoneal cavity.** The abdominopelvic cavity is divided into two smaller cavities:

(1) **Abdominal cavity.** The area superior to the bony pelvis, called the abdominal cavity, houses many of the organs of the digestive, lymphatic, and urinary systems.

(2) **Pelvic cavity.** The cavity housed within the bony pelvis, the pelvic cavity, contains certain organs of the reproductive system as well as certain organs of the digestive and urinary systems.

We often divide the abdominopelvic cavity into four quadrants: the right upper, right lower, left upper, and left lower quadrants. We can also divide the abdominopelvic cavity into nine regions based on a series of lines drawn over the surface of the abdomen. The regions are listed and labeled in Figure 1.6.

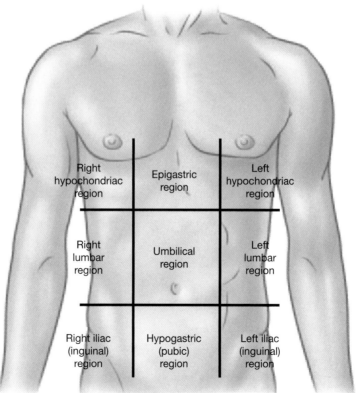

FIGURE **1.6** Regions of the abdominopelvic cavity

Procedure 1 Body Cavities

In this procedure you will use a human torso model or a preserved small mammal such as a cat, fetal pig, or rat to examine the body cavities. If you are using a preserved small mammal, you may use the following procedure to open the body cavities. Note that you will not open the animal fully in this procedure in order to preserve structures for future dissections.

1 Place the animal on a dissecting tray with its dorsal (back) side facing you. Use your scalpel to make a shallow, cross-shaped incision. Make the first incision through the skin along the nape of the neck. Make the second incision from the anterior part of the skull down along the animal's midline to about 4 inches inferior to the first incision. Ensure your incisions are shallow so you do not damage structures deep to the skin. List in Table 1.2 the organs you are able to see.

2 Gently peel back the skin using a blunt dissection probe, and note the appearance of the skin and the exposed muscles, bones, and joints. If your instructor wants you to expose the brain and spinal cord, use either a scalpel or a saw to carefully cut through the skull and a section of the vertebral column.

3 When you have finished your examination of the animal's dorsal side, close the skin, and wrap the area with wet towels soaked with a preservative solution.

4 Flip the animal over, and place it in the dissecting tray with its ventral side facing you. Use a scalpel to make a shallow incision along the animal's midline from the superior neck down to its groin. Make a second incision across the animal's chest and a third incision across the animal's abdomen.

5 Using a blunt dissection probe, peel back the skin of the abdomen carefully to expose the abdominopelvic cavity, and examine its contents.

6 Gently peel back the skin of the chest and neck incisions. Use scissors or a scalpel to carefully cut through the sternum, expose the thoracic cavity, and examine its contents.

When you have opened your preserved small mammal or examined the human torso model, locate and identify each cavity, and do the following:

1 List in Table 1.2 the organs you are able to see. See Figures 1.7 and 1.8 for reference.

2 Mark each region of the abdominopelvic cavity with a pin or marking tape (if working with a torso model). Note which organs are visible in each region.

TABLE **1.2** Body Cavities and Regions of the Abdominopelvic Cavity

Cavity	Organ(s)
Dorsal Cavity	
1. Cranial cavity	
2. Vertebral cavity	
Ventral Cavity	
1. Thoracic cavity	
a. Pleural cavities	
b. Mediastinum	
(1) Pericardial cavity	
2. Abdominopelvic cavity	
a. Abdominal cavity	
b. Pelvic cavity	

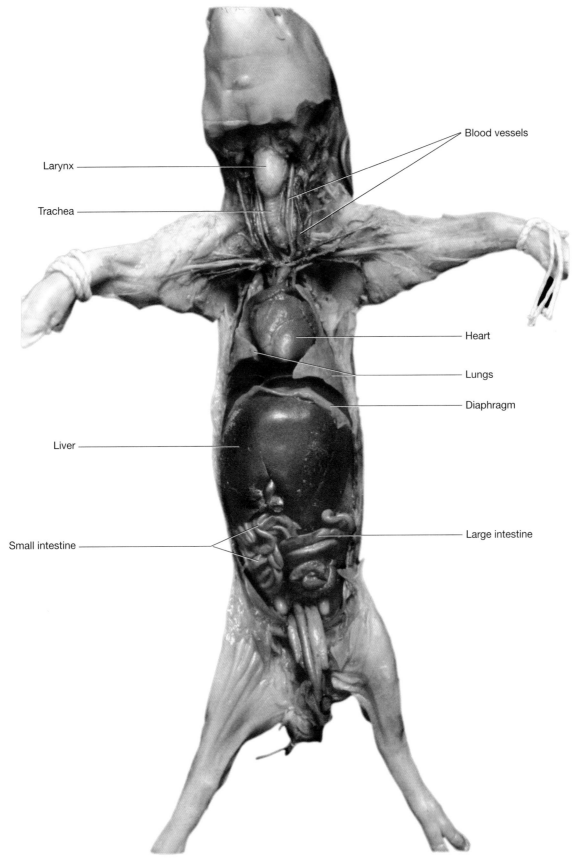

Larynx

Trachea

Blood vessels

Heart

Lungs

Diaphragm

Liver

Small intestine

Large intestine

FIGURE **1.7** Ventral view of the fetal pig

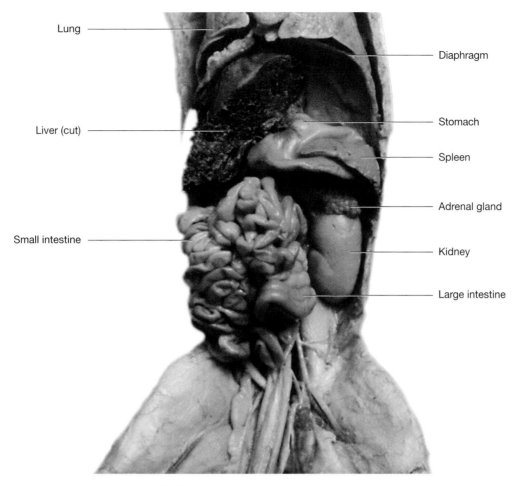

Lung

Liver (cut)

Small intestine

Diaphragm

Stomach

Spleen

Adrenal gland

Kidney

Large intestine

FIGURE **1.8** Abdominopelvic cavity of the fetal pig

Procedure 2 Serous Membranes

Part 1

Serous membranes are best examined on a preserved specimen, such as a fetal pig or a cat, because their structure is difficult to appreciate on a model. As you dissect the fetal pig or cat, look for the serous membranes listed in Table 1.3. Take care not to tear the fragile membranes, which consist of just a few layers of cells. As you identify each membrane, record in the table where you found the membrane and the structure to which the membrane is attached (the lungs, heart, abdominal wall, etc.).

TABLE **1.3** Serous Membranes

Membrane	Cavity	Structure
Parietal pleura		
Visceral pleura		
Parietal pericardium		
Visceral pericardium		
Parietal peritoneum		
Visceral peritoneum		

Part 2

Draw in the body cavities on your laminated outlines of the human body or Figure 1.9. Label the serous membranes surrounding the cavity where applicable.

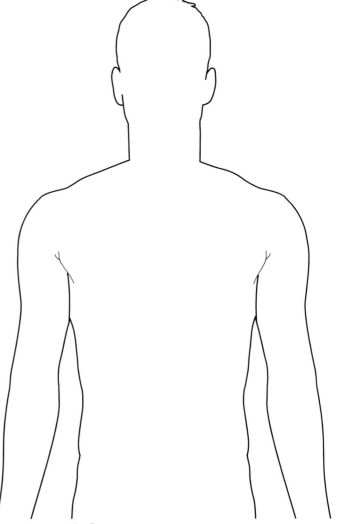

FIGURE **1.9** Anterior view of the human torso

Procedure 3 Applications of Terms to Cavities and Membranes

Assume you are acting as coroner, and you have a victim with three gunshot wounds. In this scenario your "victim" will be your fetal pig or a human (torso model) your instructor has "shot." For each "bullet wound," state in Table 1.4 the anatomical region and/or body cavity in which the "bullet" was found and any serous membranes involved, and describe the location of the wound using at least three directional terms. As coroner, you have to be as specific as possible, and keep your patient in anatomical position!

TABLE **1.4** Location of Gunshot Wounds

Shot **1**	
Shot **2**	
Shot **3**	

Exercise **1-3**

Planes of Section

MATERIALS
❑ Modeling clay
❑ Knife or scalpel

Often in science and in the medical field, it is necessary to obtain different views of the internal anatomy of an organ or a body cavity. These views are obtained by making an anatomical section along a specific plane. The commonly used planes of section, shown in Figures 1.10 and 1.11, are as follows:

1. **Sagittal plane**. A section along the sagittal (SAJ-ih-tul) plane is parallel to the body's longitudinal axis and divides the body part into right and left parts. The sagittal section has two variations:

   a. **Midsagittal sections** divide the body part into equal right and left halves.

   b. **Parasagittal sections** divide the body part into unequal right and left parts.

2. **Frontal plane**. The frontal plane, also known as the **coronal (koh-ROH-nul) plane**, is also parallel to the body's longitudinal axis. It divides the body part into an anterior (front) part and a posterior (back) part.

3. **Transverse plane**. The transverse plane, also known as a **cross section** or the **horizontal plane**, is perpendicular to the body's longitudinal axis. It divides the body part into a superior (or proximal) part and an inferior (or distal) part.

Note that although there is only a single midsagittal plane, there are a near infinite number of possible parasagittal, frontal, and transverse planes. In your study of anatomy and physiology, you will see many different examples of these planes of section.

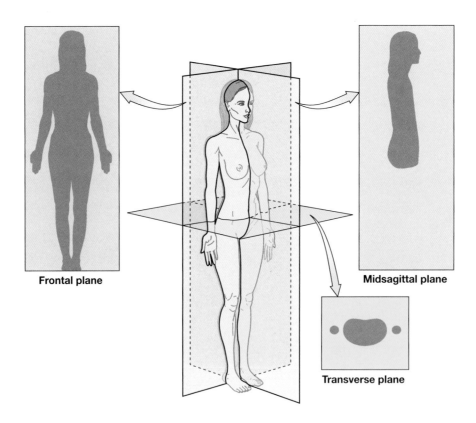

Frontal plane

Midsagittal plane

Transverse plane

FIGURE **1.10** Anatomical planes of section

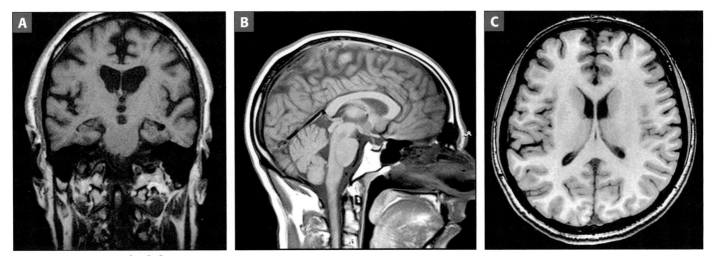

FIGURE **1.11** Planes of anatomical section visible on computed tomography scans of the brain: **(A)** frontal section; **(B)** midsagittal section; **(C)** transverse section

Procedure **1** Sectioning along Anatomical Planes

Use a scalpel to cut a ball of modeling clay in each of following anatomical planes. Before you make your cuts, you may wish to mold your clay into the shape of a head and to draw eyes on the head to denote anterior and posterior sides. Use Figures 1.10 and 1.11 for reference.

1. Sagittal
   a. Midsagittal
   b. Parasagittal
2. Frontal
3. Transverse

Exercise 1-4

Organs and Organ Systems

MATERIALS

- ❏ Human torso models
- ❏ Fetal pigs (or other preserved small mammals)
- ❏ Dissection kits/dissection trays

The human body has 11 organ systems, each with specific organs and functions (Figure 1.12). In this exercise you will examine the organ systems and identify their major organs.

Procedure 1 Identifying Organs and Organ Systems

Identify the following organs on your preserved mammal specimen or human torso models. Check off each organ as you identify it, and record the organ system to which it belongs in Table 1.5. Remember some organs may function in more than one system.

- ❏ Blood vessels
- ❏ Bones
- ❏ Brain
- ❏ Esophagus
- ❏ Gallbladder
- ❏ Heart
- ❏ Intestines

- ❏ Joints
- ❏ Kidneys
- ❏ Liver
- ❏ Lungs
- ❏ Muscles
- ❏ Pancreas
- ❏ Skin

- ❏ Spinal cord
- ❏ Spleen
- ❏ Stomach
- ❏ Testes (male) or ovaries (female)
- ❏ Thyroid gland
- ❏ Trachea
- ❏ Urinary bladder

TABLE **1.5** Organs and Organ Systems

Organ System	Major Organ(s)
Integumentary system	
Skeletal system	
Muscular system	
Nervous system	
Endocrine system	
Cardiovascular system	
Lymphatic system	
Respiratory system	
Digestive system	
Urinary system	
Reproductive systems	

Procedure 2 Organ Systems

The body's organ systems are illustrated in Figure 1.12. Fill in the blanks next to each organ system to identify the major organs shown and principal functions of each system.

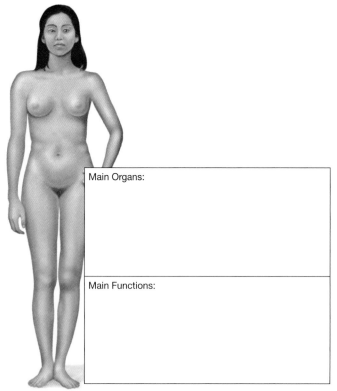

Main Organs:

Main Functions:

Integumentary System

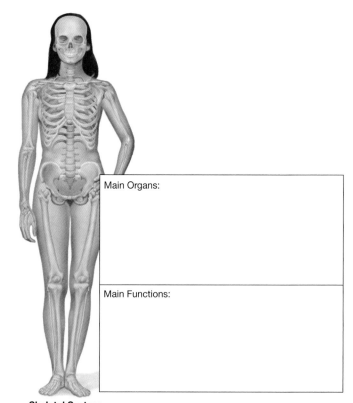

Main Organs:

Main Functions:

Skeletal System

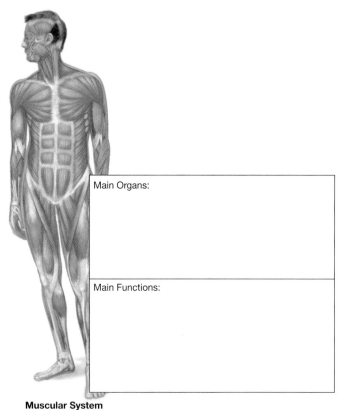

Main Organs:

Main Functions:

Muscular System

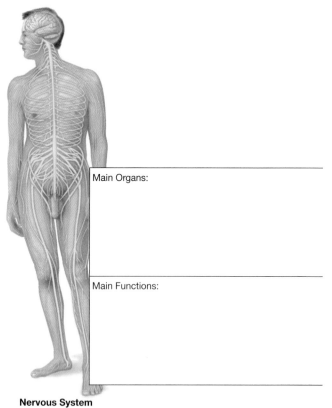

Main Organs:

Main Functions:

Nervous System

FIGURE **1.12** Organ systems of the body *(continues)*

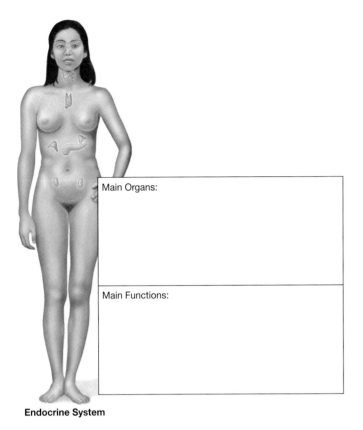

Main Organs:

Main Functions:

Endocrine System

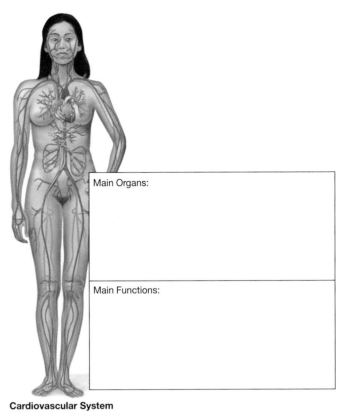

Main Organs:

Main Functions:

Cardiovascular System

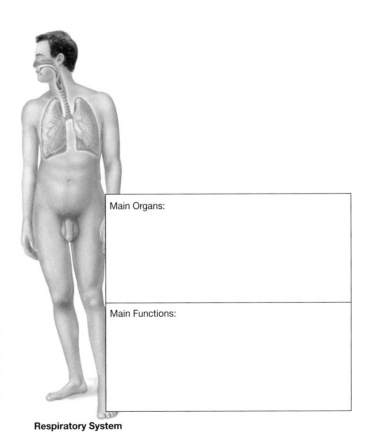

Main Organs:

Main Functions:

Lymphatic System

Main Organs:

Main Functions:

Respiratory System

FIGURE **1.12** *(cont.)* **Organ systems of the body** *(continues)*

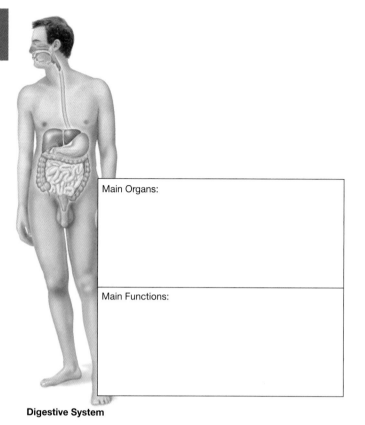

Main Organs:

Main Functions:

Digestive System

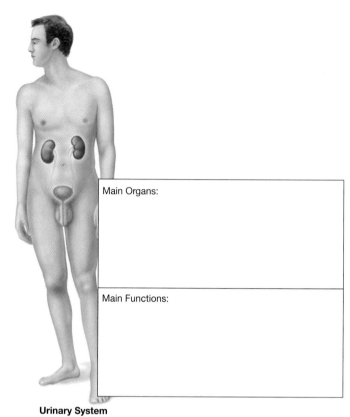

Main Organs:

Main Functions:

Urinary System

Main Organs:

Main Functions:

Male Reproductive System

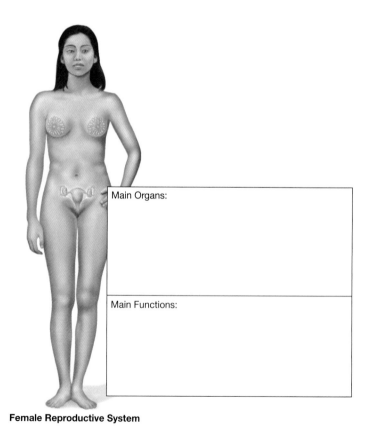

Main Organs:

Main Functions:

Female Reproductive System

FIGURE **1.12** *(cont.)* **Organ systems of the body**

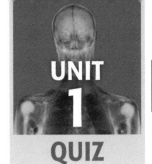

1 Which of the following best describes anatomical position?

a. Body facing forward, toes pointing forward, palms facing backward

b. Body, toes, and palms facing backward

c. Body facing forward, arms at the sides, palms facing forward

d. Body facing backward and palms facing outward

2 Match the directional term with its correct definition.

_____ Distal

_____ Lateral

_____ Anterior

_____ Proximal

_____ Inferior

_____ Deep

_____ Superficial

_____ Posterior

_____ Medial

_____ Superior

A. Away from the surface/toward the body's interior

B. Toward the back of the body

C. Closer to the point of origin (e.g., of a limb)

D. Away from the body's midline

E. Toward the head

F. Farther from the point of origin (e.g., of a limb)

G. Toward the body's midline

H. Away from the head/toward the tail

I. Toward the front of the body

J. Toward the surface/skin

3 Which of the following is an incorrect use of a directional term?

a. The ankle is inferior to the knee.

b. The sternum is superior to the abdomen.

c. The bone is deep to the muscle.

d. The mouth is medial to the ears.

4 Label the following anatomical regions on Figure 1.13:

- ❏ Brachial region
- ❏ Carpal region
- ❏ Cervical region
- ❏ Digital region
- ❏ Forearm
- ❏ Inguinal region
- ❏ Leg
- ❏ Lumbar region
- ❏ Orbital region
- ❏ Otic region
- ❏ Sternal region
- ❏ Upper limb

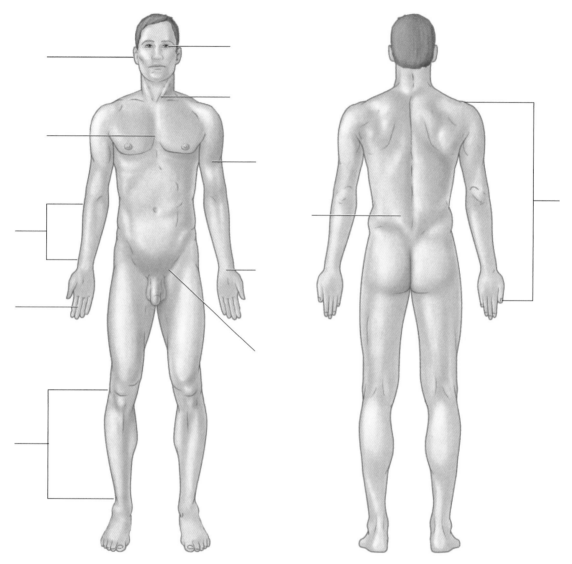

FIGURE **1.13** Anterior and posterior views of the body

5 Anatomical position and specific directional and regional terms are used in anatomy and physiology to:

a. standardize units of measure.

b. provide a standard that facilitates communication and decreases the chances for errors.

c. provide a standard used to develop drug delivery systems.

d. make students' lives difficult.

6 Label the following body cavities on Figure 1.14.

- ❏ Abdominopelvic cavity
- ❏ Cranial cavity
- ❏ Mediastinum
- ❏ Pericardial cavity
- ❏ Pleural cavity
- ❏ Vertebral cavity

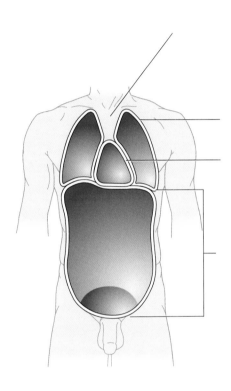
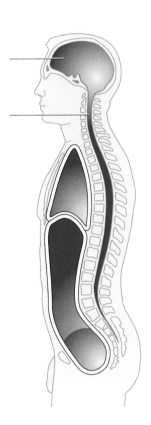

FIGURE **1.14** Anterior and lateral views of the body cavities

7 *Fill in the blanks:* A serous membrane secretes _____, which _____ the organs in certain _____ body cavities.

8 Define the following planes of section:

a Midsagittal plane _____

b Parasagittal plane _____

c Frontal plane _____

d Transverse plane _____

9 The following organs belong to the _____ system: esophagus, gallbladder, liver.
   a. integumentary
   b. reproductive
   c. lymphatic
   d. digestive

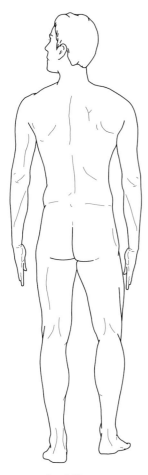

FIGURE **1.15** Figure not in anatomical position

10 Figure 1.15 is not in anatomical position. List all of the deviations from anatomical position.

_____

_____

_____

_____

_____

_____

11 Locate the following wounds, and mark them on the body in Figure 1.16.

a The wound is located in the left inferior, posterior lumbar region. It is 5 centimeters superior to the gluteal region and 3 centimeters lateral to the vertebral region.

b The wound is located on the right anterior, medial crural region, 10 centimeters proximal to the tarsal region.

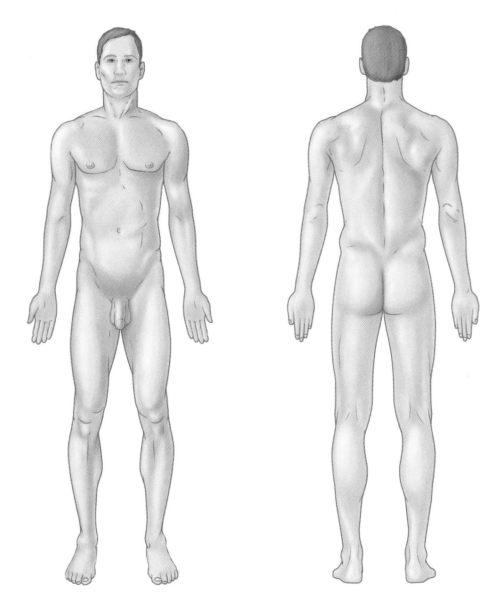

FIGURE **1.16** Anterior and posterior views of the body

12 You are reading a surgeon's operative report. During the course of the surgery, she made several incisions. Your job is to read her operative report and determine where the incisions were made. Draw and label the incisions on Figure 1.17.

a The first incision was made in the right anterior cervical region, 3 centimeters lateral to the trachea. The cut extended vertically, 2 centimeters inferior to the mental region to 3 centimeters superior to the thoracic region.

b The second incision was made in the left anterior axillary region and extended medially to the sternal region. At the sternal region the cut turned inferiorly to 4 centimeters superior to the umbilical region.

c The third incision was made in the left posterior scapular region. The cut was extended medially to 2 centimeters lateral to the vertebral region, where it turned superiorly and progressed to 1 centimeter inferior to the cervical region.

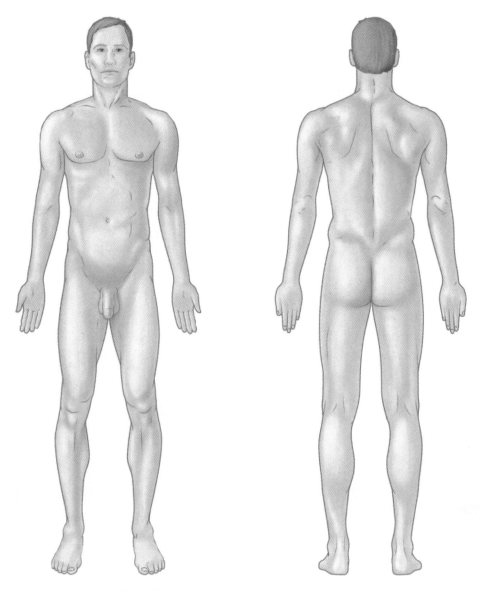

FIGURE **1.17** Anterior and posterior views of the body

The Chemical Level of Organization

2

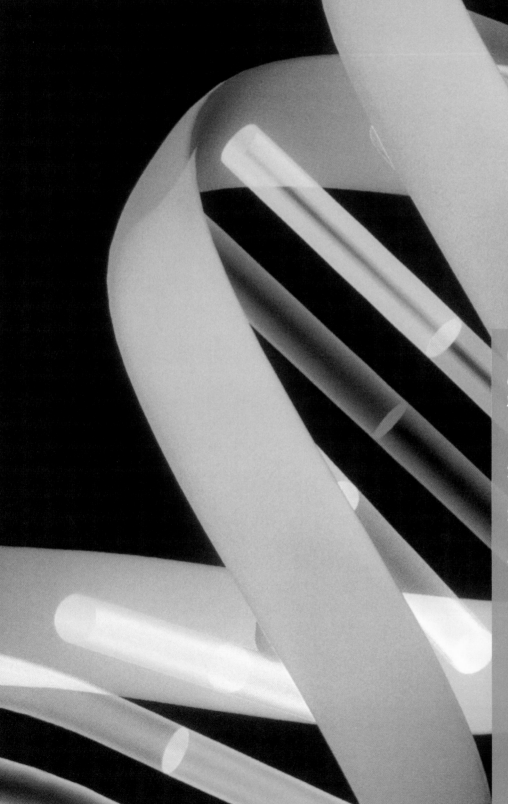

OBJECTIVES

*Once you have completed this unit,
you should be able to:*

1. Demonstrate the proper
interpretation of pH paper.

2. Describe and apply the pH
scale.

3. Describe the purpose and
effects of a buffer.

4. Explain the purpose of
an enzyme.

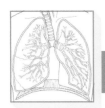

Name _____ Section _____ Date _____

Complete the following exercises prior to coming to lab, using your textbook and lab manual for reference.

Pre-Lab Exercise **2-1**

 Key Terms

You should be familiar with the following terms before coming to lab.

Term	Definition
pH	
Acid	
Base	
Buffer	
Chemical reaction	
Enzyme	

Pre-Lab Exercise 2-2

The pH Scale and –logarithms

The **pH scale** is a numerical scale from 0 to 14 that represents the hydrogen ion concentration of a solution. Solutions with a pH of 0 have the highest hydrogen ion concentration, and solutions with a pH of 14 have the lowest hydrogen ion concentration. This is because the pH isn't the actual hydrogen ion concentration; instead, it is a negative logarithm of a solution's hydrogen ion concentration. This actually isn't as difficult as it sounds. Grab your calculator and enter the following:

–log(0.01)   = _____

–log(0.001)   = _____

–log(0.0001) = _____

–log(0.00001) = _____

Notice the general trend here: *As the number gets smaller, its negative log gets bigger.*

Here's a quick example using hydrogen ions: Solution X has a hydrogen ion concentration of 0.05 M. Solution Y has a hydrogen ion concentration of 0.0002 M.

▌ Which solution has more hydrogen ions? (*Hint:* It's just the solution with the bigger number.) _____

▌ What is the –log of solution X? _____

▌ What is the –log of solution Y? _____

As you can see, the solution with the *higher* hydrogen ion concentration has the *lower* –log. This means that:

▌ Solution X is the more _____ (acidic/basic) solution and has a _____ (lower/higher) pH.

▌ Solution Y is the more _____ (acidic/basic) solution and has a _____ (lower/higher) pH.

Including a chemistry unit with an anatomy and physiology course may seem odd, but consider for a moment the simplest level of organization—the chemical level. Our cells, tissues, and organs, as well as our extracellular environments, are all composed of chemicals that undergo countless chemical reactions every second. So, to be able to understand our anatomy and physiology, we first must understand the most basic structures in our bodies—chemicals. The following exercises introduce you to the world of chemistry with procedures pertaining to the pH scale, buffers, and enzymes.

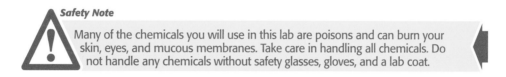

Safety Note

Many of the chemicals you will use in this lab are poisons and can burn your skin, eyes, and mucous membranes. Take care in handling all chemicals. Do not handle any chemicals without safety glasses, gloves, and a lab coat.

Exercise **2-1**

pH, Acids, and Bases

MATERIALS
- ❏ 3 glass test tubes
- ❏ Test-tube rack
- ❏ Graduated cylinder
- ❏ Dropping pipette
- ❏ pH paper
- ❏ Samples of various acids and bases
- ❏ 0.1M hydrochloric acid
- ❏ Samples of various antacid tablets

The **pH** is a measure of the concentration of hydrogen ions present in a solution. As the hydrogen ion concentration increases, the solution becomes more **acidic**. As the hydrogen ion concentration decreases, the solution becomes more **alkaline**, or **basic**. Notice that

the **pH scale**, shown in Figure 2.1, ranges from 0 (the most acidic) to 14 (the most basic). As you learned in the Pre-Lab Exercises, the reason for this is that the pH is actually a negative logarithm, so the lower the pH, the higher the hydrogen ion concentration. A pH of 7 is considered **neutral**, which is neither acidic nor basic, because the number of hydrogen ions equals the number of base ions in the solution.

Acids and bases are some of the most important chemicals in the human body: They are found in the stomach, in the blood and other extracellular body fluids, in the cytosol, and in the urine, and are released by cells of the immune system. The normal pH for the blood is about 7.35–7.45. The body regulates this pH tightly because swings of even 0.2 points in either direction can cause serious disruptions to our homeostasis.

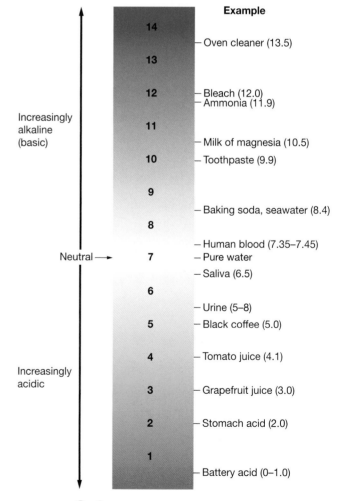

Increasingly alkaline (basic)

14

13

12 — Bleach (12.0) / Ammonia (11.9)

11

10

9

8

Neutral → 7

6

Increasingly acidic

5

4

3

2

1

Oven cleaner (13.5)

Milk of magnesia (10.5)

Toothpaste (9.9)

Baking soda, seawater (8.4)

Human blood (7.35–7.45)
Pure water

Saliva (6.5)

Urine (5–8)

Black coffee (5.0)

Tomato juice (4.1)

Grapefruit juice (3.0)

Stomach acid (2.0)

Battery acid (0–1.0)

Example

FIGURE **2.1** pH scale and examples of solutions with different pH values

Procedure 1 Reading the pH

A simple way to measure pH is to use pH paper (Figure 2.2). To test the pH with pH paper, drop one or two drops of the sample solution on the paper with a dropping pipette, and compare the color change with the colors on the side of the pH paper container. The pH is read as the number that corresponds to the color the paper turned.

Safety Note

⚠ Safety glasses and gloves are required!

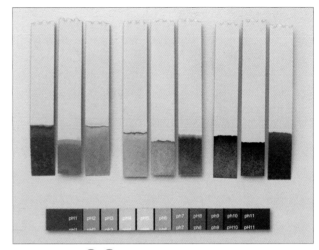

FIGURE 2.2 pH paper and indicator strip

1 Obtain two samples each of known acids and bases, and record their molecular formulae in Table 2.1 (the molecular formula should be on the side of each bottle).

2 Measure the pH of each acid and base using pH paper and a dropping pipette, and record its pH values in Table 2.1.

3 Obtain two randomly selected unknown samples, and measure their pH using pH paper and a dropping pipette.

4 Record the pH values in Table 2.1, and determine if this substance is an acid, a base, or is neutral.

TABLE 2.1 Samples of Acids and Bases

Samples	Molecular Formula	pH
Acid #1		
Acid #2		
Base #1		
Base #2		
Unknown Samples	pH	Acid, Base, or Neutral?
Unknown #1		
Unknown #2		

Procedure 2 pH Applications

Now let's apply the pH scale to physiological systems. The stomach contains concentrated hydrochloric acid (HCl), and the pH of the stomach contents ranges between 1 and 3. **Antacids** are medications that neutralize stomach acid to treat a variety of conditions, including *gastroesophageal reflux*, commonly known as *heartburn*. In this activity you will compare the effectiveness of three widely available antacids in neutralizing concentrated hydrochloric acid.

1 Obtain three glass test tubes, and label them 1, 2, and 3.

2 Obtain a bottle of 0.1M hydrochloric acid (HCl), use a dropping pipette to put a few drops on pH paper, and record its pH in the blank.

Safety Note
Safety glasses and gloves are required!

pH of 0.1M HCl: _____

3 In each tube, place 2 ml of the 0.1M HCl.

4 Add about one-fourth of one crushed Tums® tablet to tube 1.

5 Add about one-fourth of one crushed Rolaids® tablet to tube 2.

6 Add about one-fourth of one crushed Alka-Seltzer® tablet to tube 3.

7 Allow the tubes to sit undisturbed for three minutes.

8 Measure the pH of the contents of each tube using pH paper and a dropping pipette, and record the values in Table 2.2.

9 What effect did the antacids have on the acid? _____

TABLE **2.2** Effectiveness of Three Antacids

Antacid	Active Ingredient	pH
Tums®		
Rolaids®		
Alka-Seltzer®		

10 Based upon your observations, which antacid is most effective at neutralizing the acid?

Exercise 2-2

Buffers

MATERIALS

❏ Well plates

❏ Stirring rods

❏ Dropping pipettes

❏ 0.1M hydrochloric acid

❏ Buffered solution

❏ Distilled water

❏ 0.1M NaOH

❏ pH paper

A **buffer** is a chemical that resists large or dramatic changes in pH; a solution to which a buffer has been added is called a **buffered solution**. When acid is added to a buffered solution, the buffer binds the added hydrogen ions and removes them from the solution. Similarly, when a base is added to a buffered solution, the buffer releases hydrogen ions into the solution. Both effects minimize pH changes that otherwise would occur in the solution if the buffer were not present.

Procedure 1 Testing Buffered Solutions

In this experiment you will examine the effects of adding an acid or a base to buffered solutions and nonbuffered solutions. You will use distilled water as your nonbuffered solution, and your instructor will choose an appropriate buffered solution for you to use.

Safety Note

Safety glasses and gloves are required!

1 Obtain a well plate, and number four wells 1, 2, 3, and 4.

2 Fill wells 1 and 2 about half-full of distilled water. Measure the pH of the distilled water, and record that value in Table 2.3 ("pH of Initial Solution").

3 Fill wells 3 and 4 about half-full of buffered solution. Measure the pH of the buffered solution, and record that value in Table 2.3 ("pH of Initial Solution").

4 Add two drops of 0.1M HCl to wells 1 and 3. Stir the solutions with a stirring rod (or a toothpick), and measure the pH of each well. Record the pH in Table 2.3 ("pH after").

5 Add two drops of 0.1M NaOH (a base) to wells 2 and 4. Stir the solutions, and measure the pH of each well. Record the pH in Table 2.3 ("pH after").

TABLE **2.3** Buffered and Nonbuffered Solutions

Well	Contents	pH of Initial Solution	pH after Adding Acid or Base
1	Water and HCl		
2	Water and NaOH		
3	Buffer and HCl		
4	Buffer and NaOH		

6 Interpret your results. What effect did the buffer have on the pH changes you saw? _____

Exercise 2-3

Enzymes and Chemical Reactions

MATERIALS
- ❑ 9 glass test tubes
- ❑ Test-tube rack
- ❑ Lipase
- ❑ Boiled lipase
- ❑ Bile salts
- ❑ Vegetable oil
- ❑ 0.1M NaOH
- ❑ Ice-water bath
- ❑ Warm-water bath (set to 37°C)
- ❑ Distilled water
- ❑ Phenol red

Often when atoms or molecules interact, chemical bonds are formed, broken, or rearranged, or electrons are transferred between molecules. These interactions are called **chemical reactions**. Most chemical reactions can proceed spontaneously, but they often take an extremely long time.

One factor that can alter the rate at which a reaction takes place is *temperature*. Generally, when temperature increases (up to a point), molecules move faster, and they collide and react at a faster rate. The opposite happens when temperature decreases.

Another factor that can affect reaction rate is a substance called a **catalyst** added to a reaction to increase its rate. Catalysts are not consumed in the reaction and may be reused after the reaction has completed.

In the body, biological catalysts called **enzymes** speed up essentially all of our chemical reactions. Nearly all enzymes in the body are proteins that work by binding specifically to the reacting components and by reducing the amount of energy required for a reaction to proceed (called the *activation energy*). Note here that an enzyme must bind to the reactants for it to work. This means if the enzyme is damaged and loses its shape, it will not be able to function. Enzymes may be damaged by the same processes that damage all proteins, including extreme heat and extreme pH swings. An enzyme that has lost its shape as a result of such damage is said to be **denatured**.

Procedure 1 Testing Enzymatic Activity

In the following procedure, you will be comparing the ability of three solutions—lipase, boiled lipase, and water—to digest vegetable oil at three different temperatures. **Lipase** is an enzyme found in the human digestive tract that speeds up the digestion of dietary fats. Note that you also must add another component, called **bile**, to your mixture. Bile is not an enzyme itself, but it does increase the ability of lipase to facilitate fat digestion.

You will check for the presence of digestion using an indicator called **phenol red**. Phenol red appears pink at an alkaline (basic) pH, changes to an orange-red color at a neutral pH, and changes to a yellow color when the pH becomes acidic.

If fat has been digested, fatty acids will be released that will decrease the pH of the contents of your tube and turn them orange-red or yellow. You may interpret your results in the following way (Figure 2.3):

- ▌ Yellow color = the pH is acidic, and significant fat digestion occurred

- ▌ Red-orange color = the pH is neutral, and some fat digestion occurred

- ▌ Pink color = the pH is basic, and no (or limited) fat digestion occurred

1 Obtain nine glass test tubes and label them 1 through 9 with a marker.

Safety Note

Safety glasses and gloves are required!

2 Add 3 ml of vegetable oil to each test tube.

3 Add 8–10 drops of the pH indicator phenol red to each test tube. The oil now should appear pink. If it does not, add drops of 0.1M NaOH (a base) to each tube until the indicator turns pink.

FIGURE **2.3** Possible results from the lipid digestion experiment

4 Add the following ingredients to each test tube:

  ▌ Tubes 1, 4, and 7: 1 ml lipase, 1 ml bile

  ▌ Tubes 2, 5, and 8: 1 ml boiled lipase, 1 ml bile

  ▌ Tubes 3, 6, and 9: 2 ml water

5 Place tubes 1, 2, and 3 in an ice-water bath, and incubate them for 30 minutes.

6 Leave tubes 4, 5, and 6 in your test-tube rack to incubate at room temperature for 30 minutes.

7 Place tubes 7, 8, and 9 in a warm-water bath set to 37°C, and incubate them for 30 minutes.

8 After 30 minutes have passed, remove the tubes from the ice-water bath and warm-water bath, and place them in your test-tube rack.

9 Record the color of each tube in Table 2.4, and interpret your results.

TABLE **2.4** Enzymatic Activity of Lipase

Tube Number	Color	pH (Acidic, Neutral, or Alkaline)	Amount of Digestion That Occurred
1			
2			
3			
4			
5			
6			
7			
8			
9			

10 Answer the following questions about your results:

  a What effect does temperature have on enzyme activity?

  b Were your results with the boiled lipase different from the results with nonboiled lipase? Why?

  c Predict what color change you would see in tubes 3, 6, and 9 if you were to leave them in a warm-water bath for several days.

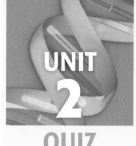

Name _____

Section _____ Date _____

1 *Fill in the blanks:* A solution with a pH less than 7 is considered _____ , a solution with a pH of 7

is considered _____ , and a solution with a pH greater than 7 is considered _____ .

2 The pH is a measure of a solution's _____ .
   a. hydrogen concentration
   b. oxygen concentration
   c. cation concentration
   d. hydrogen ion concentration

3 What is the pH detected by the pH paper in Figure 2.4?

_____

FIGURE 2.4 pH paper and indicator strip

4 A buffer is a chemical that
   a. keeps the pH of a solution neutral.
   b. resists a large or dramatic change in pH.
   c. adds hydrogen ions to a solution when the pH decreases.
   d. removes hydrogen ions from a solution when the pH increases.

5 A chemical reaction takes place when:
   a. chemical bonds are formed.
   b. chemical bonds are broken.
   c. chemical bonds are rearranged.
   d. electrons are transferred between molecules.
   e. All of the above.

6 *Fill in the blanks:* Increasing the temperature generally _____ the rate of reactions, and decreasing the temperature generally _____ the rate of reactions.

7 Which of the following is *not* a property of enzymes?
   a. They increase the rate of a reaction.
   b. They are not consumed in the reaction.
   c. They change the products of a reaction.
   d. They are biological catalysts.

8 An enzyme that has lost its shape
   a. is denatured and no longer functional.
   b. is denatured but still functional.
   c. is not different from a regular enzyme because shape is not important.
   d. can be restored by extreme temperatures or pH swings.

9 Your lab partner argues with you that if you add acid to a solution, the hydrogen ion concentration should increase and, therefore, the pH should increase. Is he correct? What do you tell him?

_____

_____

_____

_____

10 A hypothetical drug binds all of the buffer molecules in the blood, effectively removing them from circulation. Predict what will happen to the pH of the blood if hydrogen ions are added to it.

_____

_____

_____

_____

Introduction to the Cell and the Microscope

3

OBJECTIVES

Once you have completed this unit, you should be able to:

1. Identify the major parts of the microscope and demonstrate its proper use.

2. Define the magnification of high, medium, and low power and depth of focus.

3. Identify parts of the cell and organelles.

4. Describe the process of diffusion.

5. Describe the effects of hypotonic, isotonic, and hypertonic environments on cells.

6. Identify the stages of the cell cycle and mitosis.

PRE-LAB EXERCISES

Complete the following exercises prior to coming to lab, using your textbook and lab manual for reference.

Pre-Lab Exercise 3-1

3

✎ Key Terms

You should be familiar with the following terms before coming to lab.

Term	Definition

Cell Structures and Organelles

Plasma membrane _____

_____

Cytoplasm _____

_____

Nucleus _____

_____

Mitochondrion _____

_____

Ribosome _____

_____

Peroxisome _____

_____

Smooth endoplasmic reticulum (SER) _____

_____

Rough endoplasmic reticulum (RER) _____

_____

Golgi complex (or apparatus) _____

_____

Lysosome _____

_____

Centrosome _____

_____

Cilia _____

_____

Flagella _____

_____

Membrane Transport

Diffusion _____

_____

Osmosis _____

_____

Tonicity _____

_____

Cell Cycle and Mitosis

Cell cycle _____

_____

Interphase _____

_____

Mitosis _____

_____

Pre-Lab Exercise 3-2

The Parts of the Cell

Label and color the parts of the cell depicted in Figure 3.1 with the following terms. Use your text and Exercise 3-1 in this unit for reference.

❑ Plasma membrane

❑ Nucleus

    ❑ Nuclear membrane

    ❑ Nuclear pores

    ❑ Chromatin

    ❑ Nucleolus

❑ Cytoplasm

❑ Ribosome

❑ Smooth endoplasmic reticulum (SER)

❑ Rough endoplasmic reticulum (RER)

❑ Golgi complex

❑ Lysosome

❑ Mitochondrion

❑ Centrioles

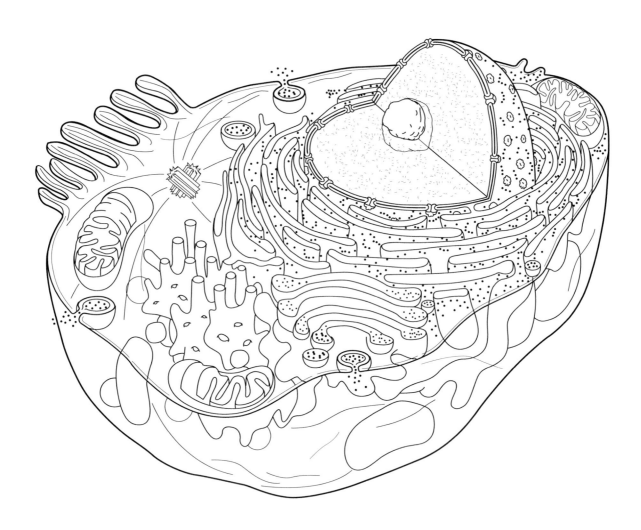

FIGURE 3.1 Generalized cell

EXERCISES

A basic principle we will revisit repeatedly in our study of anatomy and physiology is:

Form follows function.

This principle may be stated in a variety of ways and is alternatively called the "principle of complementarity of structure and function." Essentially, this means the structure's anatomy (the *form*) is always suited for its physiology (the *function*). This is obvious at the organ level: Imagine if the heart were solid rather than composed of hollow chambers, or if the femur were pencil-thin rather than the thickest bone in the body. These organs wouldn't be able to carry out their functions of pumping blood and supporting the weight of the body very well, would they? But this principle is applicable even at the chemical and cellular level, which we will see in this unit.

We begin with an examination of the instrument we use to examine the cell: the microscope. We then turn our attention to the cell, its structures, and two critical processes that occur at the cellular level: *diffusion* and *osmosis*. In the final exercise we explore the *cell cycle* and the process of cell division.

Note that this is the first lab in which you will use a *Model Inventory*—something you will use throughout this lab manual. In this inventory you will list the anatomical models or diagrams you use in lab (if the model is not named, make up a descriptive name for it), and record in a table the structures you are able to locate on each model. This is particularly helpful for study purposes because it allows you to return to the proper models to locate specific structures.

Exercise 3-1

Introduction to the Microscope

MATERIALS

❏ Light microscopes with three objective lenses

❏ Introductory slides (letter "e" and three colored threads)

Working with the microscope and slides seems one of the least favorite tasks of anatomy and physiology students. But with a bit of help, a fair amount of patience, and a lot of practice, the use of microscopes becomes progressively easier.

The microscopes you will use in this lab are called **light microscopes** (Figure 3.2). This type of microscope shines light through the specimens to illuminate them, and the light is refracted through objective lenses to magnify the image. Light microscopes have the following components:

▌ **Ocular lens.** The ocular lens is the lens through which you look to examine the slide. The microscope may have one ocular lens (a **monocular** microscope) or two ocular lenses (a **binocular** microscope). Many ocular lenses have pointers that can be moved by rotating the black **eyepiece.** The area of the slide visible when you look into the ocular is known as the **field of view.**

▌ **Objective lenses.** The objective lenses are lenses with various powers of magnification. Most microscopes have low- ($4\times$), medium- ($10\times$), and high-power ($40\times$) objective lenses. Note that sometimes the $4\times$ objective is referred to as the *scan objective.* On such microscopes, the $10\times$ objective is actually called the *low*-power objective. The objective lenses are attached to the **nosepiece,** which allows the operator to switch between objectives. Certain microscopes have a higher-power objective ($100\times$) called the **oil-immersion lens** that requires a drop of oil to be placed between the slide and objective lens. Your instructor may have an oil-immersion microscope set up for demonstration purposes.

▌ **Stage.** The stage is the surface on which the slide sits. It typically has stage clips to hold the slide in place. The stage on many microscopes is movable using the mechanical stage-adjustment knob. Others require you to move the slide manually.

▌ **Arm.** The arm supports the body of the microscope and typically houses the adjustment knobs.

▌ **Coarse-adjustment knob.** The large coarse-adjustment knob on the side of the arm moves the stage up and down to change the distance of the stage from the objective lenses. It allows gross focusing of the image.

▌ **Fine-adjustment knob.** The smaller fine-adjustment knob allows fine-tuning of the image's focus.

- **Lamp.** The lamp, also called the *illuminator*, provides the light source. It rests on the *base* of the microscope.
- **Iris diaphragm.** The iris diaphragm, an adjustable wheel on the underside of the stage, controls the amount of light allowed to pass through the slide.

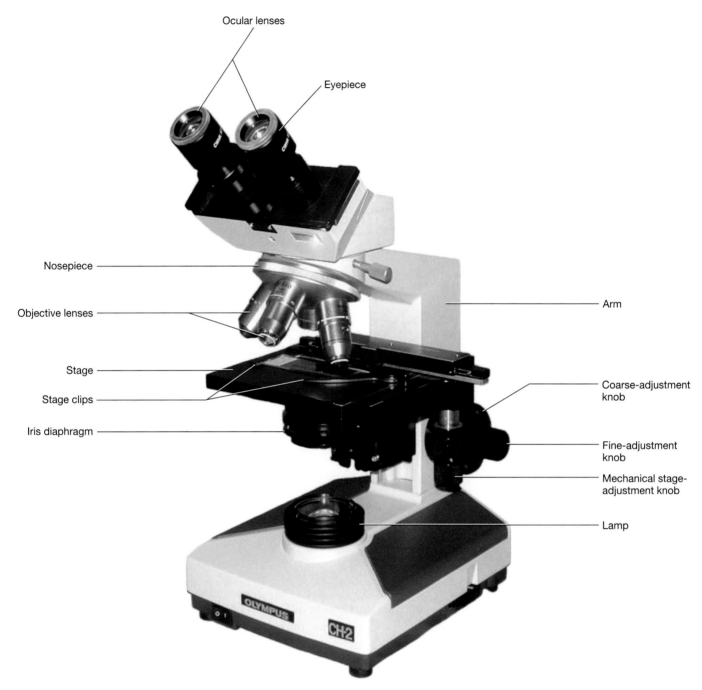

FIGURE **3.2** Compound light microscope

Procedure 1 Magnification

Light is refracted through two lenses to obtain magnification—the ocular lens and the objective lens. Magnification of the ocular lens is usually $10\times$ (magnified 10 times). Magnification of the objectives lens varies, but typically is $4\times$ for low power, $10\times$ for medium power, and $40\times$ for high power. (To verify this is the case for your microscope, look at the side of the objective lens, which usually is labeled with its magnification.) Remember that oil immersion provides even greater magnification at $100\times$. The total magnification is obtained by multiplying the power of the ocular lens by the power of the objective lens. Fill in Table 3.1 to determine total magnification at each power.

TABLE **3.1** Total Magnification at Each Power

Magnification of Ocular Lens	Power	Magnification of Objective Lens	Total Magnification
	Low		
	Medium		
	High		
	Oil immersion		

As I'm certain your instructor will point out, microscopes are expensive! Care must be taken to ensure the microscopes stay in good working condition. Taking proper care of microscopes makes the histology sections of your labs run more smoothly, and also ensures you stay on your lab instructor's good side! Bearing that in mind, following are some general guidelines for handling the microscopes:

- Use two hands to support the microscope when carrying it—one hand to hold the arm and the other hand to support the base.
- Gather up the cord so it does not dangle off the lab table after you have plugged in the microscope. This will help prevent people from tripping over loose cords.
- Clean the lenses with lens paper only. Do not use paper towels or cloth to clean a lens, because this will scratch its surface.
- Make sure the lowest-power objective is in place before you begin.
- Get the image in focus on low power, then switch to higher power and adjust with the fine-adjustment knob. Be careful not to use the coarse-adjustment knob with the high-power objective in place, because you could break the slide and damage the lens.
- When you are finished with the microscope, turn the nosepiece to the lowest-power objective, and remove the slide. Be sure to clean off the objective if you used oil, because oil left on the objective tends to harden. Turn off the power to the microscope, and unplug it. This will decrease the chances of a blown bulb or fuse next time the microscope is used. Before putting the microscope away, wrap the electrical cord around the base, and cover it with a dust cover.

If you follow these general guidelines, you can rest assured the microscopes (and your grade) will not suffer any harm.

Procedure 2 Focusing the Microscope

Now that we know how to handle the microscope properly, let's practice using it.

1 Obtain a slide of the letter "e."

2 Examine the letter "e" slide macroscopically before placing it on the stage. How is the "e" oriented on the slide? Is it right side up, upside down, backward, etc.?

_____

3 Ensure the nosepiece is switched to low power, place the slide on the stage, and secure it with the stage clips. Move the slide using the stage-adjustment knob until the "e" is in your field of view.

4 Use the coarse-adjustment knob to bring the slide into focus slowly. After it is grossly in focus, use the fine-adjustment knob to sharpen the focus. How is the "e" oriented in the field of view? Is it different from the way it was when you examined it in step 2?

_____

5 Move the nosepiece to medium power. You should only have to adjust the focus with the fine-adjustment knob; no adjustment of the coarse focus should be necessary.

6 After you have examined the slide on medium power, move the nosepiece to high power. Again, focus only with the fine-adjustment knob. Wasn't that easy?

Procedure 3 Depth of Focus

At times you will look at a slide and see something brown or black and kind of neat-looking with interesting swirls and specks. What is this fascinating discovery you've made? It's dirt on top of the slide. This happens because people tend to focus the objective on the first thing they can make out, which usually is the top of the coverslip on the slide, which has a tendency to be dirty.

These "dirt discoveries" can be avoided by appreciating what is known as **depth of focus**. Also called the _depth of field_, the depth of focus is the thickness of a specimen in sharp focus. Thicker specimens will require you to focus up and down to look at all levels of the specimen. This takes practice and skill. Let's get some practice doing this.

1 Obtain a slide with three colored threads. The threads are located on the slide at varying depths, and you will have to focus on each thread individually.

2 Examine the slide macroscopically prior to putting it on the stage.

3 Ensure the nosepiece is switched to low power, place the slide on the stage, and secure it with the stage clips. Move the slide using the stage-adjustment knob until the threads are in your field of view.

4 Use the coarse-adjustment knob to get the slide into focus on low power.

5 Switch to medium power, and use the fine-adjustment knob to sharpen the focus. Which thread(s) is (are) in focus?

6 Move the objective up and down slowly with the coarse-adjustment knob, focusing on each individual thread. Figure out which color thread is on the bottom, in the middle, and on the top, and write the color below:

Bottom _____

Middle _____

Top _____

How to Approach Microscopy

Okay, so you can focus on newsprint and threads, but what about cellular structures and tissue sections? Well, those certainly are more difficult, but if you keep the following hints in mind, the task becomes much simpler:

- **Always start on low power.** You are *supposed* to start on low power anyway, to avoid damaging the objective lenses. Sometimes, though, students forget, and jump straight to medium or high power. This risks damaging the lenses and also makes it harder on you. Bear in mind that most slides will have more than one histological or cellular structure on them. Starting on low power allows you to scroll through a large area of the slide, and then focus in on the desired part of the section.

- **Beware of too much light.** It is easy to wash out the specimen with too much light. If you are having difficulty making out details, first adjust the focus with the fine-adjustment knob. If this doesn't help, use the iris diaphragm to reduce the amount of light illuminating the specimen. This will increase the contrast and allow you to observe more details. It also helps to reduce headaches and eyestrain.

- **Keep both eyes open.** It is tempting to close one eye when looking through a monocular microscope. Admittedly, keeping both eyes open isn't easy at first, but it also helps reduce eyestrain and headaches.

- **Compare your specimen with the photos in your lab manual.** Although the slides you are examining will not necessarily be identical to the photos in this book, they should be similar in appearance. Generally speaking, if you are looking at something vastly different from what is in this book, you probably should move the slide around a bit or change to a different power objective to find the correct tissue or cell type on the slide. Other good sources for micrographs include atlases, your textbook, and images on the Internet.

- **Remember that the slides aren't perfect.** Not all slides will clearly demonstrate what you need to see. Some aren't stained adequately or properly. Some are sectioned at a funny angle. Some don't contain all of the tissue or cell types you need to see. What should you do about this? See the next hint for the answer.

- **Look at more than one slide of each specimen.** This will help you in the face of subpar slides and also will assist you overall in gaining a better understanding of the specimens you are examining.

- **Draw what you see.** Students tend to resist drawing, often claiming artistic incompetence as an excuse. But even the most basic picture is helpful for two reasons. First, it allows you to engage more parts of your brain in the learning process. The more areas of your brain engaged, the better are the chances you will retain the information. Second, drawing is helpful in that you actually have to look at the specimen long enough to draw it!

- **Have patience!** It really does get easier. Don't get frustrated, and don't give up. By the end of the semester, you may come to appreciate the microscope and the fascinating world it reveals!

Exercise 3-2

Organelles and Cell Structures

MATERIALS
❑ Cell models and diagrams
❑ Light microscope
❑ Cell slides (with red blood cells, skeletal muscle, and sperm cells)
❑ Colored pencils

Most cells in the body are composed of three basic parts—the plasma membrane, the cytoplasm, and the nucleus.

1. **Plasma membrane.** The plasma membrane is the outer boundary of the cell. It is composed of a **phospholipid bilayer** with multiple components interspersed throughout, including **proteins, cholesterol,** and **carbohydrates.** It is a dynamic, fluid structure that acts as a selectively permeable barrier. In parts of the body where rapid absorption is necessary, the plasma membrane is folded into projections called **microvilli** (my-kroh-VIL-eye) that increase its surface area.

2. **Cytoplasm.** The cytoplasm (SY-toh-plaz-m) is the material inside the cell. It consists of three parts: **cytosol** (SY-toh-sahl), the **cytoskeleton,** and **organelles** (ohr-gan-ELZ; Figure 3.3). Cytosol is the fluid portion of the cytoplasm and contains water, solutes, enzymes, and other proteins. The cytoskeleton is a collection of protein filaments that together support the cell, function in cell movement, and move substances within the cell.

   In addition, components of the cytoskeleton called *microtubules* form the core of motile extensions from the cell known as **cilia** (SIL-ee-uh) and **flagella** (fla-JEL-uh). Cilia are small, hairlike extensions that beat rhythmically together to propel substances past the cell. Flagella are single extensions that propel the cell itself (sperm cells are the only flagellated cells in the human body).

   Organelles are specialized cellular compartments that carry out a variety of functions. The organelles we cover in this unit include the following:

   a. **Ribosomes.** The small, granular ribosomes (RY-boh-zohmz) are not surrounded by a membrane and are composed of two subunits. Some ribosomes float freely in the cytosol, whereas others are bound to the membrane of another organelle or the nucleus. Ribosomes are the sites of protein synthesis in the cell.

   b. **Mitochondria.** The bean-shaped mitochondria (my-toh-KAHN-dree-uh) are double-membrane-bounded organelles that produce the bulk of the cell's ATP (energy).

   c. **Endoplasmic reticulum.** The series of membrane-enclosed sacs known as the endoplasmic reticulum (en-doh-PLAZ-mik re-TIK-yoo-lum) may be of two types: **rough endoplasmic reticulum (RER),** which has ribosomes on its surface, and **smooth endoplasmic reticulum (SER),** which lacks ribosomes. RER functions in protein synthesis and modifies proteins the ribosomes have made. SER has multiple functions, including lipid synthesis and detoxification reactions.

   d. **Golgi complex.** The Golgi (GOHL-jee) complex or apparatus is a stack of flattened sacs near the RER. Its membrane-enclosed sacs receive vesicles from the RER and other places in the cell and process, modify, and sort the products within the vesicles.

   e. **Lysosomes.** Lysosomes (LY-soh-somz) are sacs filled with digestive enzymes that digest particles brought into the cell, old and worn-out organelles, and even the cell itself.

   f. **Centrioles.** Centrioles (SEN-tree-ohlz) are paired organelles composed primarily of microtubules that appear to be microtubule organizing centers and are important in facilitating the assembly and disassembly of microtubules.

3. **Nucleus.** The third component in nearly all cells is a specialized organelle called the nucleus (NOO-klee-us). The nucleus is the cell's biosynthetic center, which directs the synthesis of all of the body's proteins as well as certain nucleic acids. The nucleus is surrounded by a double membrane called the **nuclear envelope.** Within the nucleus we find **chromatin,** a ball-like mass of tightly coiled DNA and proteins; RNA; and a dark-staining region called the **nucleolus** (noo-klee-OH-lus).

Note that the cell shown in Figure 3.3 is a **generalized cell** that contains each organelle. Most cells in the body don't look like this and instead are specialized so their forms follow their functions. For example, the cells of the liver contain a large amount of smooth endoplasmic reticulum, and immune cells (phagocytes) house a large number of lysosomes.

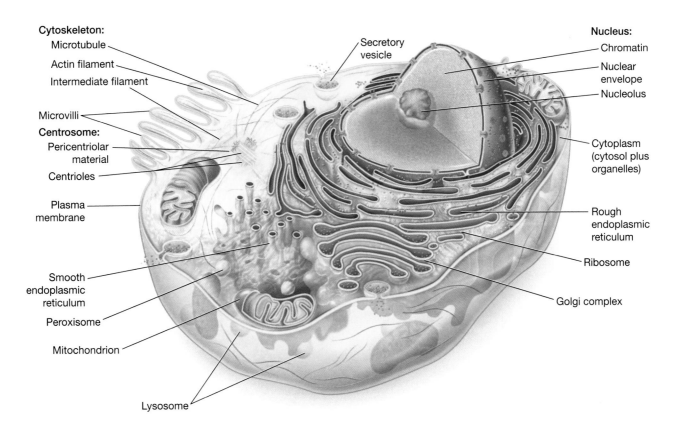

Cytoskeleton:
- Microtubule
- Actin filament
- Intermediate filament

Microvilli

Centrosome:
- Pericentriolar material
- Centrioles

Plasma membrane

Smooth endoplasmic reticulum

Peroxisome

Mitochondrion

Lysosome

Secretory vesicle

Nucleus:
- Chromatin
- Nuclear envelope
- Nucleolus

Cytoplasm (cytosol plus organelles)

Rough endoplasmic reticulum

Ribosome

Golgi complex

FIGURE **3.3** Generalized cell: sectional view

Procedure 1 Model Inventory for the Cell

Identify the following structures of the cell on models and diagrams, using your textbook and this unit for reference. As you examine the anatomical models and diagrams, record on the model inventory in Table 3.2 the name of the model and the structures you were able to identify.

1. Plasma membrane
2. Nucleus
   a. Nuclear membrane
   b. Nuclear pores
   c. Chromatin
   d. Nucleolus
3. Cytoplasm
4. Ribosomes
5. Smooth endoplasmic reticulum (SER)
6. Rough endoplasmic reticulum (RER)
7. Golgi complex
8. Lysosomes
9. Mitochondria
10. Centrioles
11. Cilia
12. Flagella

TABLE **3.2** Cellular Structures Model Inventory

Model/Diagram	Structures Identified

Procedure 2 Examining Cellular Diversity with Microscopy

The structure of different cell types can vary drastically. Cells differ not only in size and shape but also in the types and prevalence of organelles in the cell. In this activity you will examine prepared microscope slides of red blood cells, sperm cells, and skeletal muscle cells. Use the techniques you learned in Exercise 3-1: Begin your observation on low power, and advance to high power for each slide. Note that sperm cells can be difficult to find, so an oil-immersion lens is helpful to find the tiny cells. Draw, color, and label the cellular structures and organelles you see on each slide. You may wish to look at Figures 4.3I (p. 82) for red blood cells, 4.4A (p. 87) for skeletal muscle cells, and 16.12 (p. 417) for sperm cells.

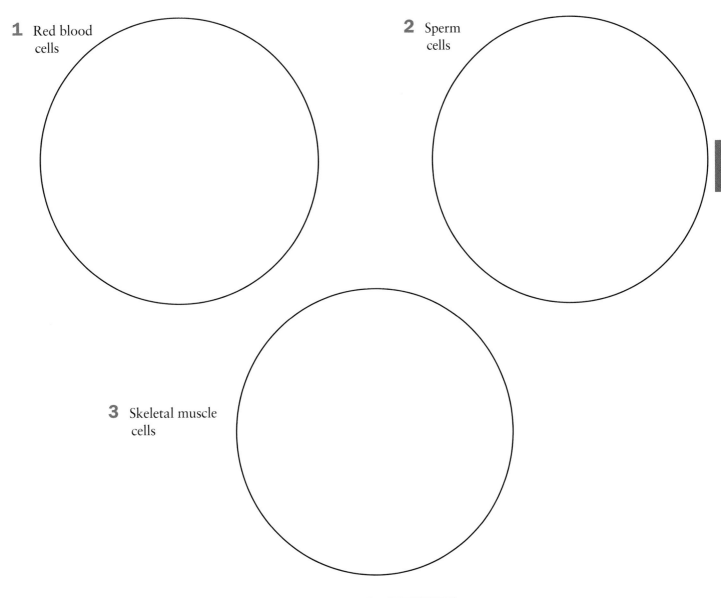

1 Red blood cells

2 Sperm cells

3 Skeletal muscle cells

➤ HINTS & TIPS

How to Draw Useful Micrograph Diagrams

You don't need to be a great artist to draw useful micrograph diagrams. Following are some tips for producing effective drawings that can help you learn the material and study for practical exams.

ⓘ First look at a diagram of the cell or tissue in question in this book or your textbook to get oriented and get an idea of what you should look for in the field of view.

ⓘ Make note of the image's magnification. As always, start on low power, then advance to higher-powered objectives as needed. You should aim for a magnification about the same as the magnification in the diagram.

ⓘ Reproduce as closely as possible what you see in the field of view using a pencil. This doesn't have to be a work of art, but you should take care to draw the shape of the cells, the way the cells are organized, and the components of the extracellular matrix. You may draw in the circles in this manual or on a piece of white paper for larger diagrams.

ⓘ Add color to your drawing with colored pencils using the slide as a guide. Color is a critical component, particularly for study purposes. Some slides will have uniquely colored stains or staining patterns, and studying the colored images can prove quite helpful. In addition, the slides your lab uses might have different stains than the images in your book. In these cases, it is useful to have a drawing with those specific stain colors.

ⓘ The final step is to label your drawing. Use your lab manual, textbook, and other resources as a guide to ensure your labels are accurate.

Exercise 3-3

Diffusion

MATERIALS

- ❑ 2 beakers (100 ml)
- ❑ Food coloring
- ❑ Hot water
- ❑ Ice water
- ❑ Ruler

Diffusion is defined as the movement of solute from a high concentration to a low concentration (Figure 3.4). Diffusion is a **passive process**—one that requires no net input of energy by a cell—because the energy for diffusion comes from a **concentration gradient**. A concentration gradient is defined as a substance present in different concentrations at two different points. A concentration gradient is illustrated in Figure 3.4 in the panels "Time 1" and "Time 2."

The rate at which diffusion takes place depends upon several factors, including the steepness of the concentration gradient, the temperature, and the size of the particles. Generally, smaller particle size, a steeper concentration gradient, and/or a higher temperature will increase the rate of diffusion. Diffusion will continue until the concentration of the substance is distributed evenly, a condition known as **equilibrium**. At this point, net diffusion ceases.

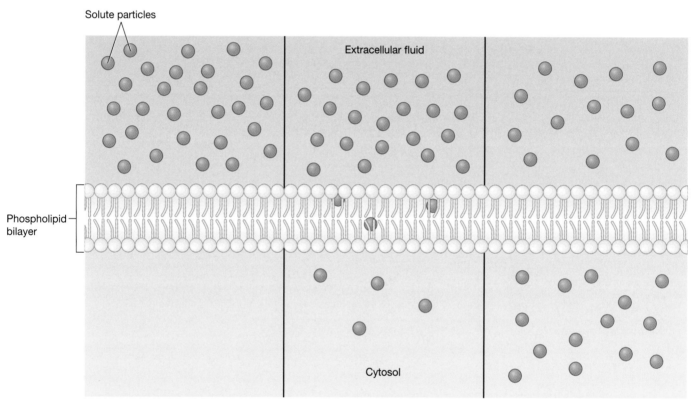

Solute particles

Extracellular fluid

Phospholipid bilayer

Cytosol

Time 1: Steep concentration gradient

Time 2: Diffusion begins

Time 3: Equilibrium

FIGURE **3.4** Diffusion across a plasma membrane

Procedure 1 Measuring Rates of Diffusion

Diffusion is a process that occurs all around us and therefore is easy to witness in action (Figure 3.5). In this experiment you will examine the effects of temperature on the rate of diffusion by placing food coloring in water.

1 Obtain two 100 ml glass beakers. Label one beaker "cold" and the other "hot." Fill the "cold" beaker with ice water (take care not to get ice in the beaker, though), and fill the "hot" beaker with heated water.

2 Add two drops of food coloring to each beaker.

3 Observe the beakers from the side, and measure with a ruler the distance the food coloring spreads every minute for five minutes. Record your results in Table 3.3.

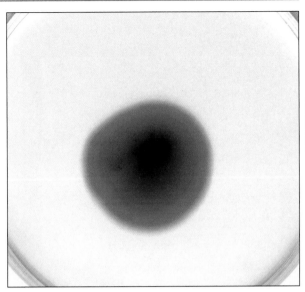

FIGURE 3.5 Example of diffusion as seen with potassium permanganate dye in agar. The dye diffuses outward over time from a high concentration to a low concentration.

TABLE 3.3 Diffusion Results for Food Coloring in Water

Time	Distance of Diffusion: Cold Water	Distance of Diffusion: Hot Water
1 minute		
2 minutes		
3 minutes		
4 minutes		
5 minutes		

4 Interpret your results. What effect does temperature have on the rate of diffusion?

Exercise 3-4

Osmosis and Tonicity

MATERIALS

- ❏ Animal or human blood cells
- ❏ 3 glass slides (blank)
- ❏ Coverslips
- ❏ Dropper
- ❏ Wooden applicator stick
- ❏ 5% dextrose in water solution
- ❏ Deionized water
- ❏ 25% NaCl in water solution
- ❏ Lens paper/paper towel
- ❏ Light microscope with 40X objective

Whereas diffusion refers to the movement of solute, a separate passive process called **osmosis** (ahs-MOH-sis) refers to the movement of *solvent* (**Figure 3.6**). Specifically, osmosis is the movement of solvent (usually water) from a solution with a lower solute concentration to a solution with a higher solute concentration through a selectively permeable membrane. Notice in **Figure 3.6** that the solvent (water) moves to the more concentrated solution and dilutes it until the concentrations are approximately equal on each side, because the solute particles cannot pass through the membrane.

In discussing biological solutions, it is useful to describe the concentration of a solution outside a cell compared with the concentration of the cytosol. This is called **tonicity** (toh-NIH-sih-tee), and it determines how water crosses the plasma membrane. The three variations of tonicity are:

▌ **Hypotonic.** A **hypotonic** (hy-poh-TAHN-ik) **solution** has a lower solute concentration than the cytosol. A cell placed in a hypotonic solution will gain water by osmosis and may swell and burst.

▌ **Isotonic.** An **isotonic** (eye-soh-TAHN-ik) **solution** has the same solute concentration as the cytosol. There is no concentration gradient to drive osmosis, so there is no net movement of water into or out of a cell in an isotonic solution.

▌ **Hypertonic.** A **hypertonic** (hy-per-TAHN-ik) **solution** has a higher solute concentration than the cytosol. A cell in a hypertonic environment will lose water by osmosis and shrivel, or **crenate**, because water will be drawn toward the more concentrated solution.

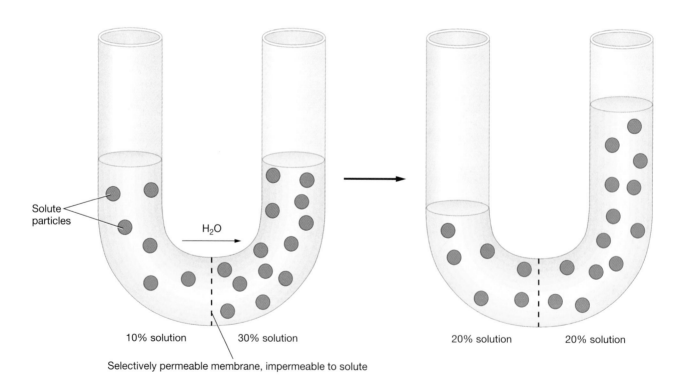

FIGURE **3.6** Osmosis

Procedure 1 Watching Osmosis in Action

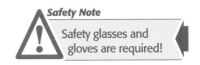

The following experiment will allow you to watch osmosis in action by placing cells—in this case, red blood cells—in solutions of different tonicity.

1 Obtain three blank slides, and number them 1, 2, and 3.

2 Place one small drop of animal blood on each slide with a dropper. Take care to keep your droplet fairly small; otherwise you won't be able to see individual cells.

3 Gently spread the droplet around the center of the slide with a wooden applicator stick, and place a coverslip on it.

4 On slide 1, place a drop of 5% dextrose solution on one side of the coverslip. On the other side of the coverslip, hold a piece of lens paper or a paper towel. The lens paper will draw the fluid under the coverslip.

5 Observe the cells under the microscope on high power.

6 Repeat the procedure by placing 25% NaCl solution on slide 2 and distilled water on slide 3.

7 Draw and describe what you see on each slide.

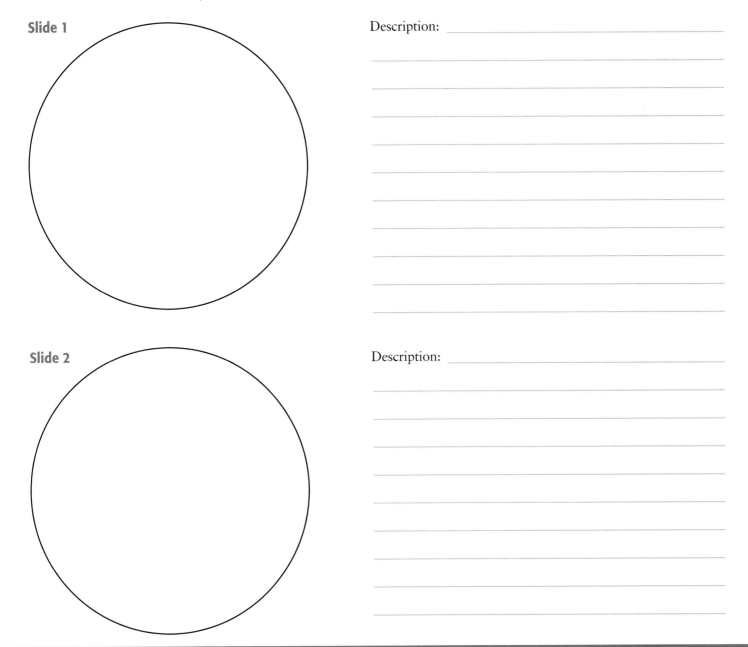

Slide 1

Description: _____

_____

_____

_____

_____

_____

_____

_____

_____

_____

Slide 2

Description: _____

_____

_____

_____

_____

_____

_____

_____

_____

_____

Description: _____

_____

_____

_____

_____

_____

_____

_____

_____

_____

_____

_____

8 Interpret your results:

a Which solution was hypotonic? Explain your reasoning. _____

_____

_____

_____

b Which solution was isotonic? Explain your reasoning.

_____

_____

_____

c Which solution was hypertonic? Explain your reasoning.

_____

_____

_____

Exercise 3-5

Mitosis and the Cell Cycle

MATERIALS

- ❏ Cell models or diagrams
- ❏ Mitosis models
- ❏ Mitosis slides
- ❏ Light microscope
- ❏ Colored pencils

Most cells go through a continual cycle of growth and replication called the **cell cycle**. The cell cycle consists of four phases:

1. **G1**, or the initial growth phase,
2. **S phase**, during which the DNA is replicated,
3. **G2**, the second growth phase, and
4. **M phase** or **mitosis** (my-TOH-sis), during which the cell divides its organelles, cytosol, and replicated DNA among two identical **daughter cells**.

Each daughter cell has the identical genetic and structural characteristics as the original cell. The portions of the cycle from G1–G2, when the cell is not dividing, are collectively called **interphase**. Mitosis proceeds in the four general stages shown in Figure 3.7.

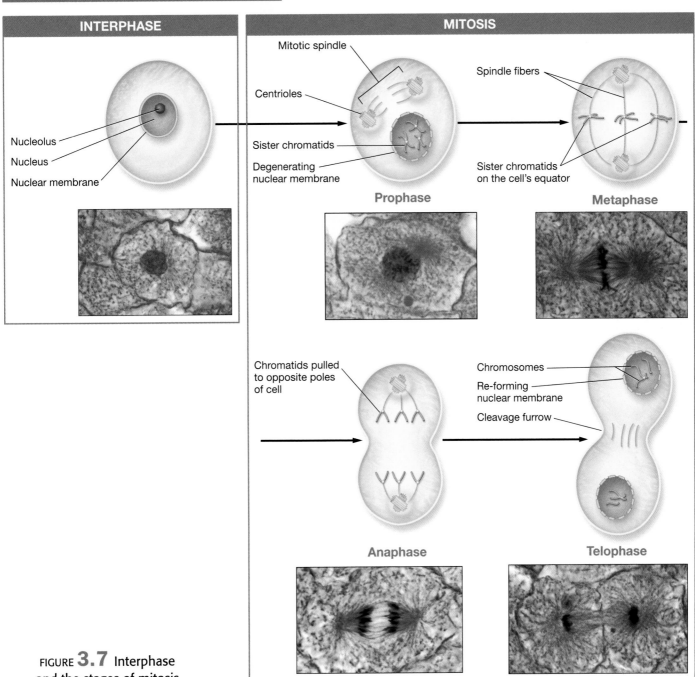

FIGURE **3.7** Interphase and the stages of mitosis

1. **Prophase.** During prophase, the nuclear membrane starts to degenerate, and the DNA condenses so individual **chromosomes** (KROH-moh-somz) are visible. Also during this stage, we see the formation of a structure called the **mitotic spindle.**

2. **Metaphase.** In metaphase we see the chromosomes line up along the central portion of the cell. Microtubules called **spindle fibers** emanate from the mitotic spindle and attach to the center of each pair of chromosomes.

3. **Anaphase.** During anaphase we see the chromosomes start to move toward opposite poles of the cell as the spindle fibers shorten. In addition, a process called **cytokinesis** (SY-toh-kin-EE-sis) begins, during which the cytoplasm is divided up among the two cells.

4. **Telophase.** In the final phase of mitosis, a divot forms between the two cells, called a **cleavage furrow**, that will pinch the cell into two identical daughter cells. In addition, during this stage the nuclear membranes begin to reassemble, the mitotic spindle becomes less visible, and cytokinesis is completed.

Procedure 1 Model Mitosis

Arrange models of the cell cycle and mitosis in the proper order. As an alternative, build a set of cell cycle models with modeling clay, and arrange them in the proper order of the cycle.

1. Interphase

2. Mitosis
   a. Prophase
   b. Metaphase
   c. Anaphase
   d. Telophase

Procedure 2 Microscopy of the Cell Cycle

Examine the five phases of the cell cycle on prepared whitefish mitosis slides using the highest-power objective. Note that every stage of the cell cycle may not be visible on one single slide, so you may have to use more than one slide. Note also that most of the cells you see will be in interphase.

Draw what the cell looks like during each phase of the cell cycle, and label your drawing with as many of the structures of cell division (see p. 61) as you can see in each cell. Then, describe in Table 3.4 what you see in each phase. Use Figure 3.7 for reference.

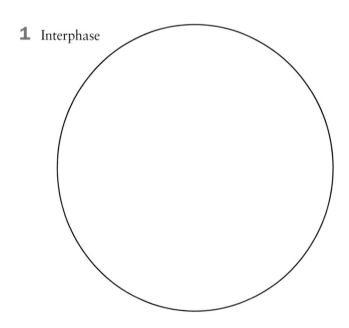

1 Interphase

2 Mitosis

a Prophase

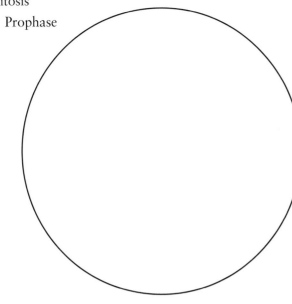

b Metaphase

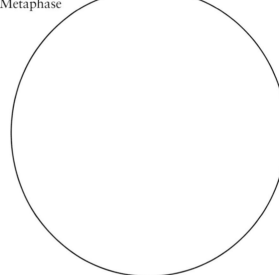

c Anaphase

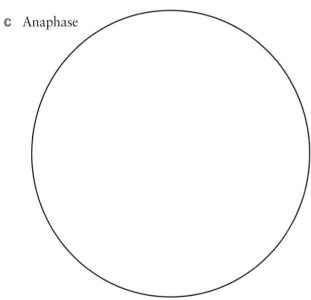

d Telophase

TABLE **3.4** Stages of the Cell Cycle

Stage of the Cell Cycle	Events Taking Place in the Cell	Cell Appearance
Interphase		
Prophase		
Metaphase		
Anaphase		
Telophase		

1 Label the following parts of the cell on Figure 3.8.
- ❏ Golgi complex
- ❏ Mitochondrion
- ❏ Nuclear envelope
- ❏ Nucleolus
- ❏ Plasma membrane
- ❏ Rough endoplasmic reticulum
- ❏ Smooth endoplasmic reticulum

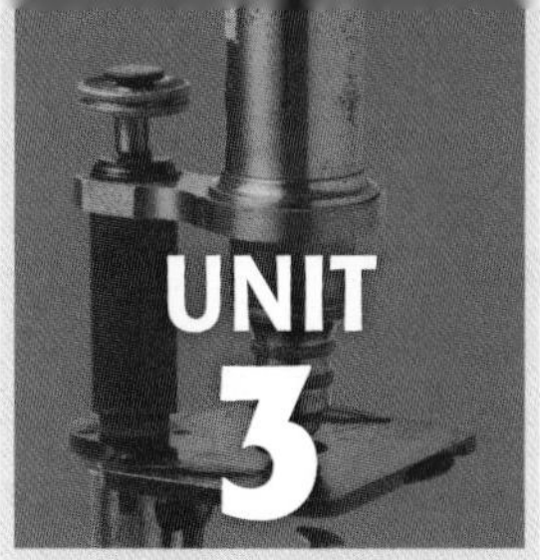

2 Which of the following is not a basic component of most cells?
a. Microvilli
b. Plasma membrane
c. Nucleus
d. Cytoplasm

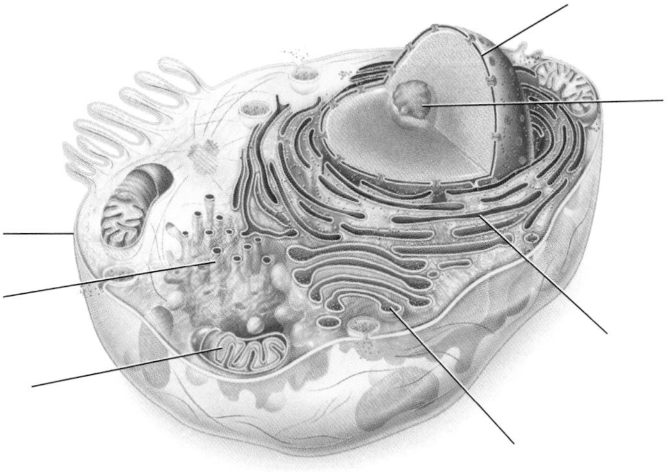

FIGURE **3.8** Generalized cell

3 *Matching:* Match the following organelles and cell structures with the correct definitions.

_____ Plasma membrane
_____ Smooth ER
_____ Mitochondria
_____ Ribosomes
_____ Rough ER
_____ Nucleus
_____ Lysosome
_____ Golgi complex

A. Biosynthetic center of the cell; houses the cell's DNA
B. Produce(s) the bulk of the cell's ATP
C. Contain(s) digestive enzymes
D. Stack of flattened sacs that modify and sort proteins
E. Barrier around the cell; composed of a phospholipid bilayer
F. Membrane-enclosed sacs with ribosomes on the surface
G. Membrane-enclosed sacs that detoxify substances and synthesize lipids
H. Granular organelles that are the sites of protein synthesis

4 *Fill in the blanks:* Diffusion is a _____ process where a solute moves from a _____

concentration to a _____ concentration.

5 Which of the following factors influence the rate at which diffusion takes place?
a. Size of the particles
b. Temperature
c. Steepness of the concentration gradient
d. All of the above

6 *Fill in the blanks:* Osmosis is the movement of _____ from a solution with a _____ solute concentration to a solution with a _____ solute concentration.

7 How do isotonic, hypertonic, and hypotonic solutions differ?

_____

_____

_____

8 Label the stages of mitosis and the cell cycle on Figure 3.9.

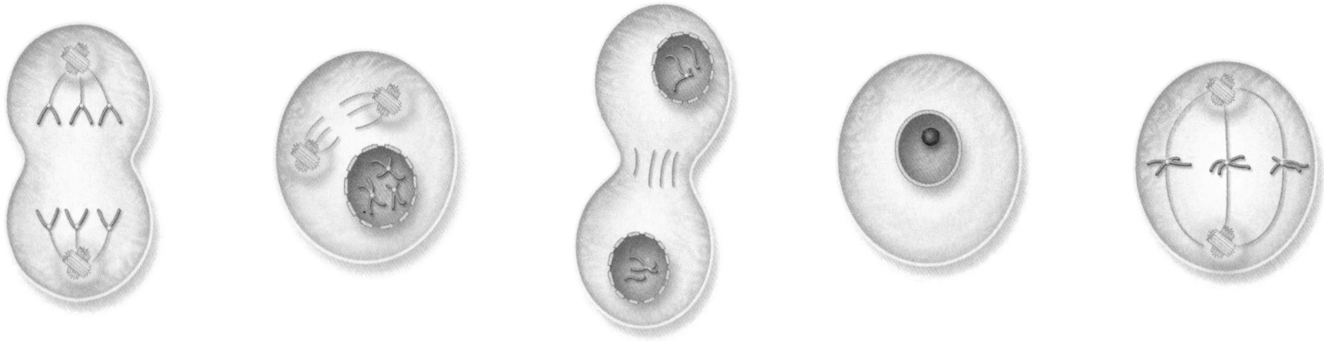

_____ _____ _____ _____ _____

FIGURE **3.9** Stages of the cell cycle and mitosis

9 Which of the following is *not* a phase of mitosis?
  a. Prophase
  b. Telophase
  c. Interphase
  d. Anaphase

10 Which type of cell you observed lacks a nucleus? What functions would this cell be unable to carry out?

_____

_____

_____

11 Isotonic saline and 5% dextrose in water are solutions considered isotonic to human blood. What effect on red blood cells would you expect if a patient were given these fluids intravenously? A solution of 10% dextrose in water is hypertonic to human blood. What would happen if you were to infuse your patient with this solution?

_____

_____

_____

12 Many anticancer drugs inhibit the formation of the mitotic spindle. What impact will this have on cell division? Why?

_____

_____

_____

Histology: The Tissue Level of Organization

4

OBJECTIVES

Once you have completed this unit, you should be able to:

1. Relate tissue structure to tissue function, and describe how organs are formed from two or more tissue types.

2. Identify epithelial tissues by number of layers, cell shape, and specializations.

3. Identify and describe connective tissues.

4. Identify and describe muscle and nervous tissues.

PRE-LAB EXERCISES

Complete the following exercises prior to coming to lab, using your textbook and lab manual for reference.

Pre-Lab Exercise **4-1**

✎ Key Terms

You should be familiar with the following terms before coming to lab.

Term	Definition
Epithelial Tissue	
Simple epithelial tissue	
Stratified epithelial tissue	
Squamous cell	
Cuboidal cell	
Columnar cell	
Connective Tissue	
Extracellular matrix	
Loose connective tissue	
Dense connective tissue	
Cartilage	
Bone	
Blood	

Muscle Tissue

Striated _____

_____

Skeletal muscle tissue _____

_____

Cardiac muscle tissue _____

_____

Smooth muscle tissue _____

_____

Nervous Tissue

Neuron _____

_____

Neuroglial cell _____

_____

EXERCISES

The histology labs can be some of the more intimidating and frustrating labs for beginning anatomy and physiology students. The subjects are somewhat abstract and unfamiliar and require use of a complicated tool—the microscope. The best way to approach this subject is to be systematic, and let your lab manual walk you through it step by step. If you get confused, don't despair. With the help of this book, your lab instructor, and a little patience, you can do it! Before you begin, you may wish to review the "Hints and Tips" box on p. 51.

The exercises in this unit introduce you to the four basic types of tissue: **epithelial tissue**, **connective tissue**, **muscle tissue**, and **nervous tissue** (Figure 4.1). All four of these tissue types have two main components:

1. cells, unique for each tissue type, and

2. the **extracellular matrix (ECM)**, produced largely by the tissue's cells.

ECM consists of two components: ground substance and protein fibers. **Ground substance** is a gelatinous material that contains water, ions, nutrients, large polysaccharides, and glycoproteins. It enables the tissue to resist compression. **Protein fibers** are found within the ground substance and give the tissue distensibility (ability to stretch) and tension resistance. Let's now begin our exploration of this fascinating level of biological organization.

4

Epithelial Tissue

Epithelial tissue covers the outside of the body and lines all body cavities. Its primary function is to provide protection.

Simple squamous epithelium

Simple cuboidal epithelium

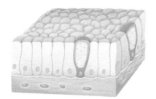

Simple columnar epithelium

Connective Tissue

Connective tissue functions as a binding and supportive tissue for all other tissues in the body.

Dense regular connective tissue

Adipose tissue

Bone tissue

Muscle Tissue

Muscle tissue is a tissue adapted to contract.

Skeletal muscle

Cardiac muscle

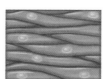

Smooth muscle

Nervous Tissue

Nervous tissue functions to receive stimuli and transmit signals from one part of the body to another.

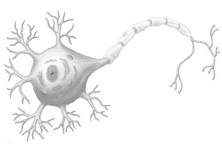

Neuron

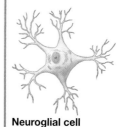

Neuroglial cell

FIGURE **4.1** The four different types of tissue

Exercise 4-1

Epithelial Tissue

MATERIALS

❑ Epithelial tissue slides

❑ Light microscope

❑ Colored pencils

4

Epithelial (ep-ih-THEE-lee-ul) tissues are our covering and lining tissues. They are found covering body surfaces, lining body passageways and body cavities, and forming glands. Epithelia predominantly contain cells called **epithelial cells**, and their ECM is limited mostly to the space underneath the cells in a layer called the **basal lamina (BAY-zul LAM-in-uh)**. The basal lamina adheres to another layer of ECM produced by the connective tissues deep to the epithelium, and together, these two structures are called the **basement membrane.**

Epithelial tissues have no blood vessels to supply them directly and rely on oxygen and nutrients diffusing up from deeper tissues. For this reason, epithelial tissues can be only a certain number of cell layers in thickness. If they are too thick, oxygen and nutrients will not reach the more superficial cells, and they will die.

The many types of epithelia are classified according to the number of cell layers and the shape of the epithelial cells. The classes include the following (Figure 4.2):

1. **Simple epithelia** have only one layer of cells and include:

    a. **Simple squamous epithelium.** This type of epithelium, shown in Figure 4.2A, consists of a single layer of flat cells also known as **squamous (SQWAY-mus) cells** with a flattened nucleus. We often find simple squamous epithelium in places where substances have to cross the epithelium quickly, such as the air sacs of the lungs.

    b. **Simple cuboidal epithelium.** Note in Figure 4.2B that the **cuboidal cells** of this type of epithelium are about as wide as they are tall, with a round, central nucleus. Simple cuboidal epithelium is found lining glands, such as the thyroid gland, certain respiratory passages, and in the kidneys.

    c. **Simple columnar epithelium.** The **columnar cells** of this type of epithelium, shown in Figure 4.2C, are taller than they are wide, with round nuclei located near the base of the cell. These cells line certain respiratory passages, much of the digestive tract, and the genitourinary tract. The plasma membranes of simple columnar epithelial cells often contain cilia or are folded into microvilli.

2. **Stratified epithelia** have two or more layers of cells and include the following:

    a. **Stratified squamous epithelium.** This type of epithelium, shown in Figure 4.2D, consists of many layers of flattened cells. It is located in places subject to high degrees of mechanical stress, such as the skin, the oral cavity, the pharynx (throat), the anus, and the vagina. Some stratified squamous epithelium, such as that of the skin, contains the hard protein **keratin** (Figure 4.2E). Cells filled with keratin are referred to as *keratinized*.

    b. **Stratified cuboidal epithelium** and **stratified columnar epithelium.** Both of these types of epithelium are rare in the human body (they are not included in Figure 4.2) and are found lining the ducts of certain glands.

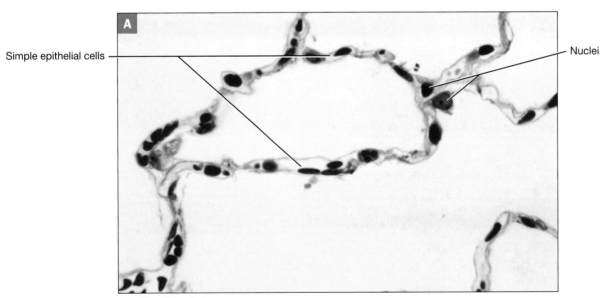

FIGURE **4.2** Epithelial tissues: (**A**) simple squamous epithelium from the lungs *(continues)*

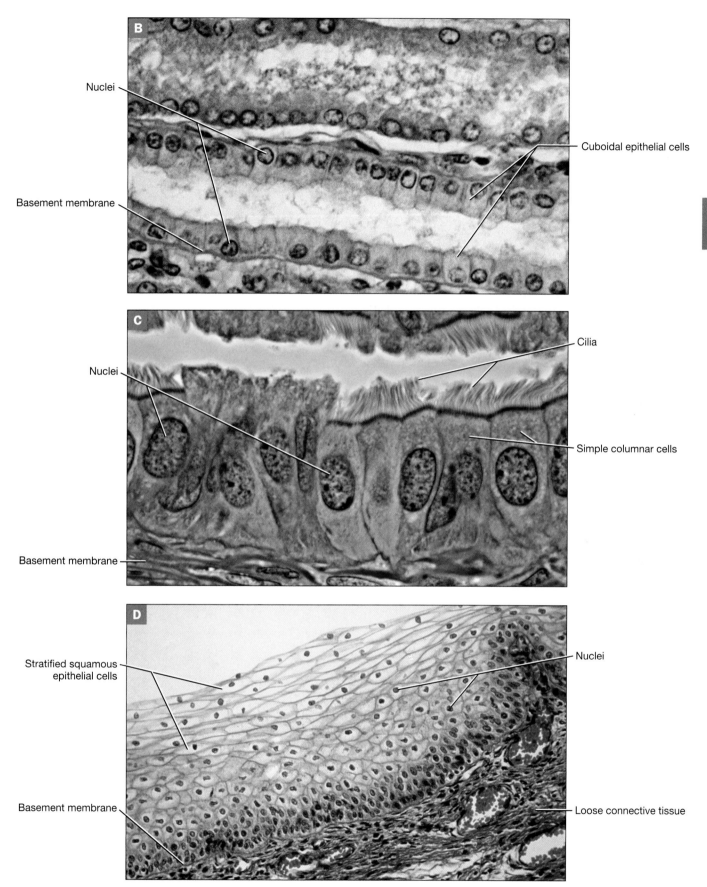

FIGURE 4.2 Epithelial tissues *(cont.)*: (**B**) simple cuboidal epithelium from the kidney; (**C**) simple ciliated columnar epithelium from the uterine tube; (**D**) stratified squamous nonkeratinized epithelium from the vagina *(continues)*

Not all epithelial tissues fit this classification scheme. One such epithelial tissue is called **transitional epithelium** (**Figure 4.2F**), also called *urinary epithelium*. This type of epithelial tissue is stratified but is not classified by its shape because its cells can change shape. Typically, the surface cells are dome-shaped, but when the tissue is stretched, they flatten and are squamous in appearance. Transitional epithelium is found lining the urinary bladder and ureters.

Another type of epithelial tissue that does not fit neatly into this classification system is **pseudostratified** (soo-doh-STRAT-ih-fyed; *pseudo* = false) **ciliated columnar epithelium**. This epithelium has the appearance of having many layers but actually has only one layer of cells (**Figure 4.2G**). Note that this type of epithelium usually has cilia, and the cell shape is always columnar. It is found lining the nasal cavity and much of the respiratory tract.

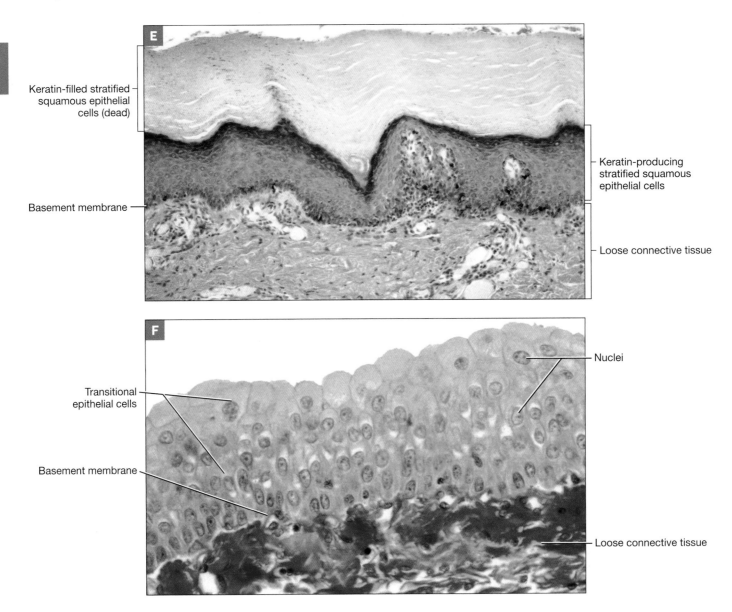

FIGURE **4.2** Epithelial tissues *(cont.)*: (**E**) stratified squamous keratinized epithelium from the skin; (**F**) transitional epithelium from the urinary bladder *(continues)*

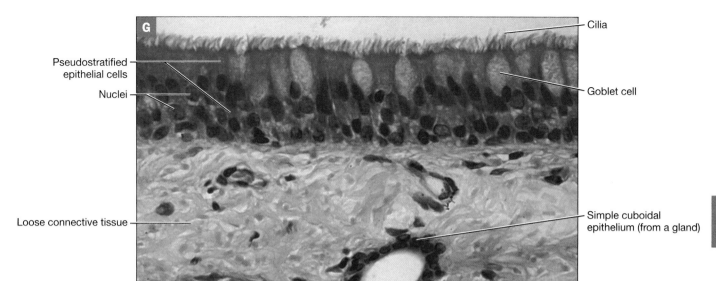

Labels on figure:
- Cilia
- Pseudostratified epithelial cells
- Nuclei
- Goblet cell
- Loose connective tissue
- Simple cuboidal epithelium (from a gland)
- G

FIGURE **4.2** Epithelial tissues *(cont.)*: (**G**) pseudostratified ciliated columnar epithelium from the trachea

HINTS & TIPS

How to Approach Epithelium

Before you start, remember how to approach any slide: First examine the slide with the naked eye, then begin on low power and scan the slide, and advance progressively to higher power to see details. Use Figure 4.2 as a guide—if your slide looks nothing like the tissue in Figure 4.2, scroll around the slide, and keep looking. But do not rely completely on Figure 4.2, because the slides your lab uses may be prepared with different stains or from different tissues. A few simple things will help you distinguish epithelial tissues from other tissues, including:

ⓘ Epithelial tissues lack blood vessels, so you won't see any in epithelium.

ⓘ Epithelial tissues are often on the outer edge of the slide. Keep in mind that most slides have several tissues in each section. To find the epithelial tissue, scroll to one end of the slide or the other.

ⓘ Epithelial tissues consist mostly of cells. If you aren't sure if something is a cell, look for a nucleus. If you can see a nucleus, you typically will be able to see the plasma membrane surrounding the cell as well, which will help you define borders between cells.

Examine prepared slides of the following epithelial tissues. Use colored pencils to draw what you see under the microscope, and label your drawings with the terms from Figure 4.2. Then (**a**) describe what you see, and (**b**) give examples of locations in the body where this tissue is found.

1 Simple squamous epithelium

a _____

_____

b _____

_____

2 Simple cuboidal epithelium

a _____

_____

b _____

_____

3 Simple columnar epithelium

a _____

_____

b _____

_____

4 Stratified squamous nonkeratinized epithelium

a _____

_____

b _____

_____

5 Transitional epithelium

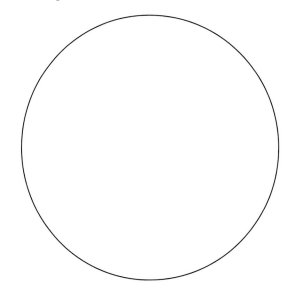

a _____

_____

b _____

_____

6 Pseudostratified ciliated columnar epithelium

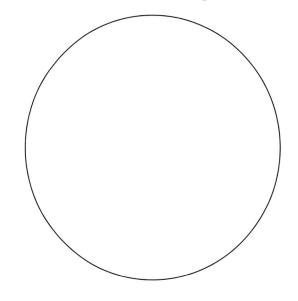

a _____

_____

b _____

_____

4

Exercise 4-2

Connective Tissue

MATERIALS

- ❏ Connective tissue slides
- ❏ Light microscope
- ❏ Colored pencils

Connective tissues (CT) are found throughout the body. They have a variety of functions, most of which serve to *connect*, as their name implies (blood is an exception). Connective tissues are distinguished easily from epithelial tissues by the prominence of their extracellular matrices. Typically, connective tissues contain few cells and have an extensive ECM consisting of ground substance and three main types of protein fibers:

1. **collagen fibers**, which give a tissue tensile strength,
2. **elastic fibers**, which make a tissue distensible, and
3. thin **reticular fibers** that interweave to form networks that support blood vessels, nerves, and other structures.

The four general types of connective tissue (CT) are as follows (Figure 4.3):

1. **Connective tissue proper.** Connective tissue proper, the most widely distributed class of connective tissue in the body, consists of scattered cells called **fibroblasts** (FY-broh-blastz) that secrete an extensive ECM filled with many types of protein fibers. This tissue is highly vascular with an extensive blood supply. The subclasses of CT proper include the following:

   a. **Loose (areolar) CT.** You can see in Figure 4.3A that the primary element in loose CT is ground substance, which gives it a "loose" appearance on a slide. All three types of protein fibers are scattered in loose CT ground substance. Loose CT is found as part of the basement membrane and in the walls of hollow organs.

   b. **Reticular CT.** As you can guess by the name, reticular CT consists of many reticular fibers produced by cells called **reticular cells** (Figure 4.3B). It is located in the spleen and lymph nodes, where the fine reticular fibers interweave to form "nets" that trap pathogens and foreign cells. Reticular CT also is located around blood vessels and nerves, where it forms supportive networks.

   c. **Adipose tissue.** Notice in Figure 4.3C that adipose tissue (fat tissue) has a much different appearance than the other types of CT proper. It consists mostly of cells, with little visible ECM, and the huge cells are called **adipocytes** (AD-ih-poh-sytz). Each adipocyte contains a large lipid droplet that occupies most of its cytoplasm. The nucleus and other organelles are barely visible, because they are pushed to the periphery of the cell against the plasma membrane. Adipose tissue is distributed widely throughout the body under the skin and around organs.

   d. **Dense CT.** The difference between loose and dense CT is obvious in Figure 4.3D—dense consists primarily of protein fibers, and loose is mostly ground substance. The protein fibers may be arranged in parallel bundles or in an irregular, haphazard fashion without a consistent pattern. This tissue is quite strong and is located in places that require a great deal of tensile strength, such as the dermis of the skin, tendons, and joint and organ capsules.

2. **Cartilage.** Cartilage is a tough but flexible tissue resistant to tension, twisting, and compressive forces. It consists of cells called **chondrocytes** (KAHN-droh-sytz) located in cavities embedded in the ECM. Cartilage is notable among the connective tissues for lacking blood vessels. Each of the three types of cartilage has a different ECM composition.

   a. **Hyaline cartilage.** Notice in Figure 4.3E that hyaline (HY-uh-lin) cartilage contains mostly chondrocytes scattered in ground substance with few visible protein fibers. This lack of protein fibers gives hyaline cartilage a smooth, glassy appearance and makes it an ideal tissue to cover the ends of bones where they form joints with another bone. The smooth texture of hyaline cartilage provides a nearly frictionless surface on which bones can articulate. Hyaline cartilage also is found in the nose, connecting the ribs to the sternum, and forming the framework for certain respiratory passages.

   b. **Fibrocartilage.** As you can see in Figure 4.3F, fibrocartilage is named appropriately, because it is full of protein fibers (mostly collagen). This makes fibrocartilage tough and extremely strong but not at all smooth (think of the surface of fibrocartilage like a flannel sheet, with the cotton fibers representing the protein fibers). For this reason, fibrocartilage does not cover the ends of bones, but it does reinforce ligaments and form *articular discs*, tough structures that improve the fit of two bones. In addition, fibrocartilage is found in joints where hyaline cartilage has been damaged.

c. **Elastic cartilage.** The final type of cartilage, elastic cartilage, is shown in Figure 4.3G. It is filled with elastic fibers that allow it to stretch and recoil. Elastic cartilage is found in the ear and in the epiglottis.

3. **Bone.** Bone tissue, also called **osseous (AH-see-us) tissue**, consists of bone cells called **osteocytes** encased in an ECM that contains collagen fibers and calcium crystals. Note in Figure 4.3H that the ECM is arranged in concentric layers called **lamellae (lah-MEL-ee)**, with the osteocytes sandwiched between them. This structure makes bone the hardest tissue in the body and the most resistant to mechanical stresses.

4. **Blood.** Blood (Figure 4.3I) is unique in that it is the only connective tissue that doesn't actually connect anything physically. It consists of cells called red blood cells and white blood cells, cellular fragments called platelets, and an ECM called **plasma**.

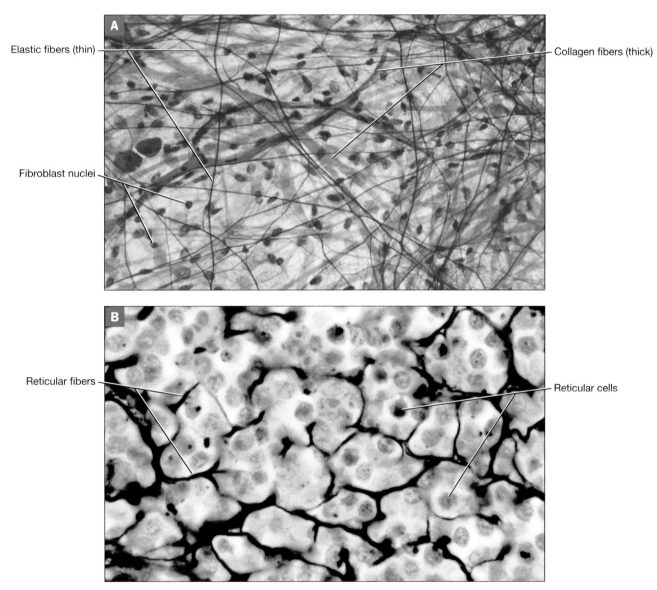

FIGURE **4.3** Connective tissues: (**A**) loose (areolar) CT; (**B**) reticular CT from the spleen *(continues)*

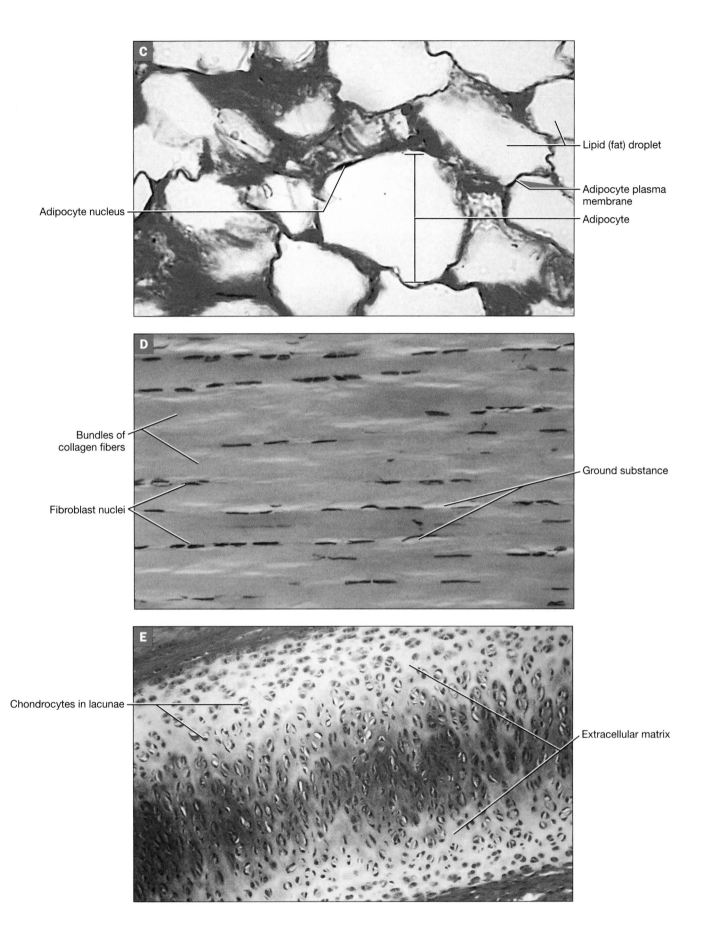

FIGURE **4.3** Connective tissues *(cont.)*: (**C**) adipose tissue; (**D**) dense collagenous CT from a tendon; (**E**) hyaline cartilage from a joint *(continues)*

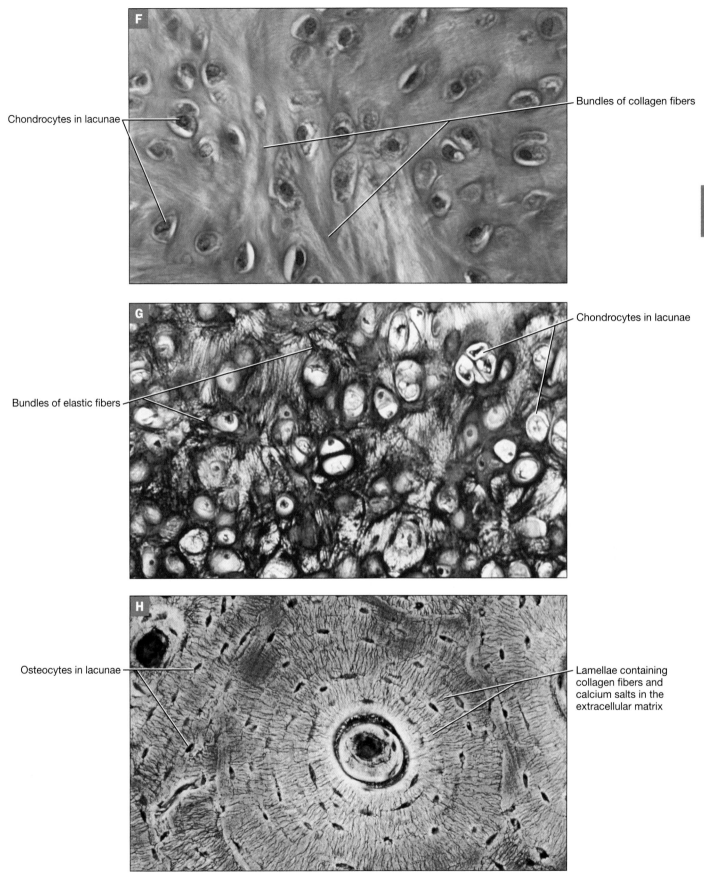

Chondrocytes in lacunae

Bundles of collagen fibers

Bundles of elastic fibers

Chondrocytes in lacunae

Osteocytes in lacunae

Lamellae containing collagen fibers and calcium salts in the extracellular matrix

FIGURE 4.3 Connective tissues *(cont.)*: (F) fibrocartilage from an articular disc; (G) elastic cartilage from the ear; (H) bone tissue; *(continues)*

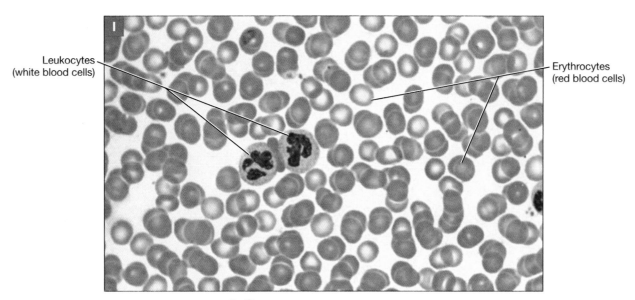

Leukocytes
(white blood cells)

Erythrocytes
(red blood cells)

FIGURE **4.3** Connective tissues *(cont.)*: (**I**) blood

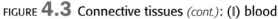

HINTS & TIPS

How to Approach Connective Tissue

Students typically find connective tissue the most difficult tissue to identify. Don't let this scare you away. Simply take care to approach these slides systematically in the same manner you do the epithelial slides, and use Figure 4.3 as a guide. The following points will help you identify the various connective tissues and differentiate them from other tissue types:

ⓘ The cells typically are not densely packed together, and you usually will see a large amount of space between connective tissue cells. Remember to look for the nucleus and plasma membrane to discern the borders of a cell.

ⓘ Generally connective tissue, particularly connective tissue proper, contains a lot of ground substance and protein fibers in the extracellular matrix. One exception is adipose tissue, which consists of densely packed adipocytes filled with a large lipid droplet.

ⓘ Many types of CT can be distinguished by the types of fibers they contain:

1. Reticular fibers are the thinnest fibers, which typically stain brown or black. Look for reticular fibers in loose and reticular CT.

2. Collagen fibers are thick fibers that often stain pink. Look for collagen fibers in fibrocartilage, dense CT, and loose CT.

3. Elastic fibers are fairly thick and may have a wavy appearance. They are thinner than collagen fibers. Their color ranges from purple-black to blue, depending on the stain used. Look for them in elastic cartilage and loose CT.

ⓘ Cartilage is easy to discern from CT proper by looking at the shape of the cells. Fibroblasts are generally small and flat, whereas chondrocytes are much larger and round. In addition, chondrocytes sit in cavities.

ⓘ Blood and bone are perhaps the two easiest tissues you will examine in this lab. They should look much like they do in Figure 4.3, and no other tissues resemble them.

Procedure 1 Microscopy of Connective Tissue Proper

View prepared slides of each type of connective tissue proper. Use colored pencils to draw pictures of what you see under the microscope, and label your drawings with the terms from Figure 4.3. Then (**a**) describe what you see, and (**b**) give examples of locations in the body where this tissue is found.

1 Loose (areolar) CT

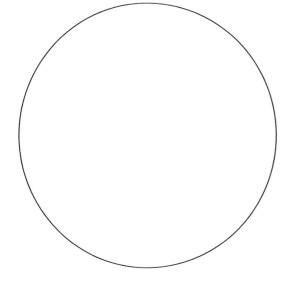

a _____

_____

b _____

_____

2 Reticular CT

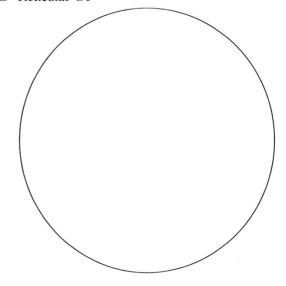

a _____

_____

b _____

_____

3 Adipose tissue

a _____

_____

b _____

_____

4 Dense CT

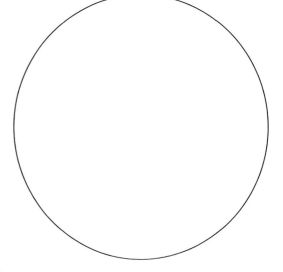

a _____

_____

b _____

_____

Procedure 2 Microscopy of Cartilage

View prepared slides of the three types of cartilage. Use colored pencils to draw pictures of what you see under the microscope, and label your drawings with the terms from Figure 4.3. Then (**a**) describe what you see, and (**b**) give examples of locations in the body where this tissue is found.

1 Hyaline cartilage

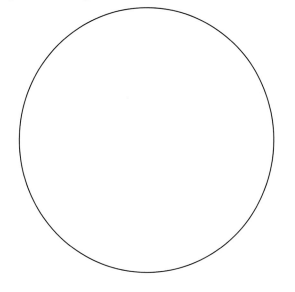

a _____

_____

b _____

_____

2 Fibrocartilage

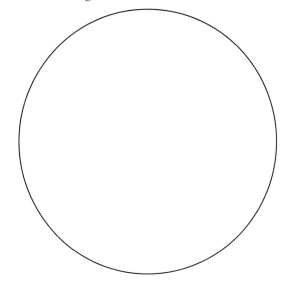

a _____

_____

b _____

_____

3 Elastic cartilage

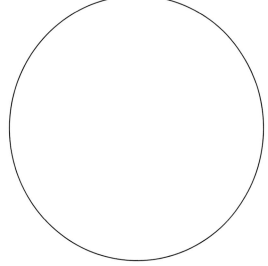

a _____

_____

b _____

_____

Procedure 3 Microscopy of Bone and Blood

View prepared slides of bone and blood. Use colored pencils to draw pictures of what you see under the microscope, and label your drawings with the terms in Figure 4.3. Then (**a**) describe what you see, and (**b**) give examples of locations in the body where this tissue is found.

1 Bone

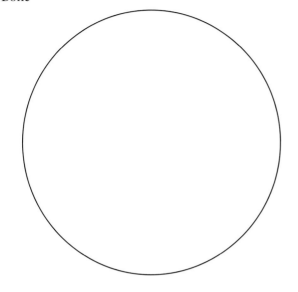

a _____

_____

b _____

_____

2 Blood

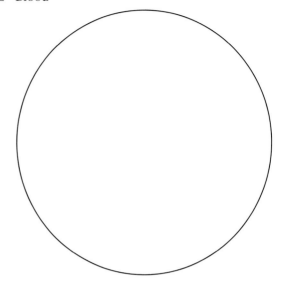

a _____

_____

b _____

_____

Exercise 4-3

Muscle Tissue

MATERIALS
❏ Muscle tissue slides
❏ Light microscope
❏ Colored pencils

Muscle tissue is located in skeletal muscles, in the walls of hollow organs, in the heart, and in other locations, such as the iris of the eye. It consists of muscle cells, sometimes called **muscle fibers**, and a small amount of ECM called the **endomysium** (en-doh-MY-see-um). Notice in Figures 4.4A–C that muscle fibers aren't shaped like the cells you are accustomed to seeing. For this reason, muscle tissue is easy to discern from the other tissue types.

There are three types of muscle tissue:

1. **Skeletal muscle tissue.** The muscle fibers of skeletal muscle tissue are long, tubular, and **striated** (striped) in appearance with multiple nuclei (Figure 4.4A). The striations result from the arrangement of proteins within the muscle fiber.

2. **Cardiac muscle tissue.** The cells of cardiac (KAR-dee-ak) muscle tissue, located in the heart, are short, fat, striated, and tend to be branching (Figure 4.4B). Adjacent myocytes are linked by specialized junctions called **intercalated** (in-TUR-kuh-lay-tid) **discs.** Cardiac myocytes typically have only one nucleus, but some may have two or more.

3. **Smooth muscle tissue.** The cells of smooth muscle tissue are flat with one nucleus in the center of the cell (Figures 4.4C and 4.4D). The arrangement of proteins within smooth muscle fibers differs from that of skeletal and cardiac muscle fibers, and as a result, these cells lack noticeable striations (hence the name *smooth* muscle). It lines all hollow organs and is found in the skin, the eyes, and surrounding many glands.

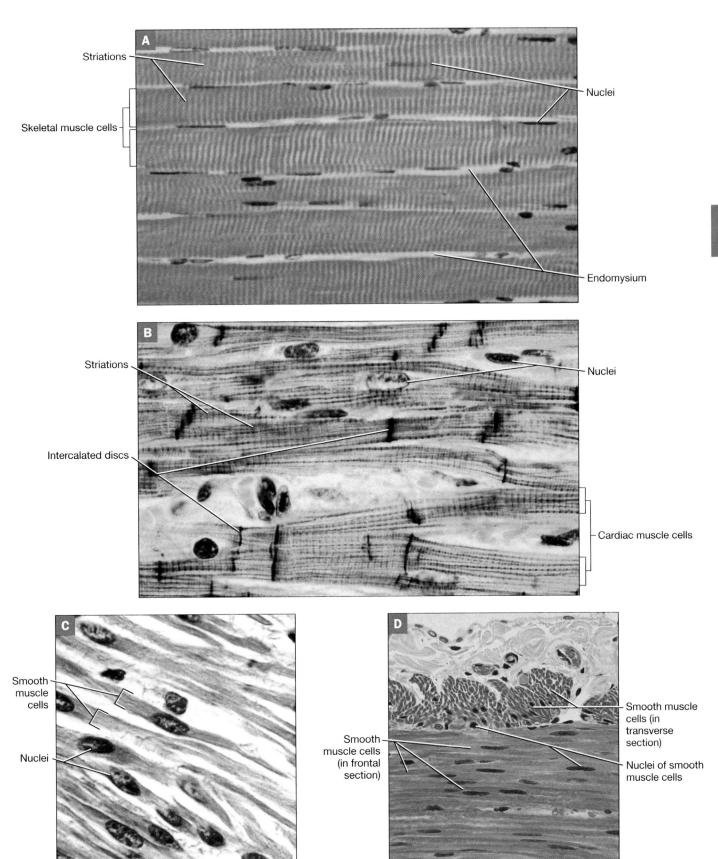

FIGURE **4.4** Muscle tissue: (**A**) skeletal muscle tissue; (**B**) cardiac muscle tissue; (**C**) teased muscle cells; (**D**) smooth muscle cells in tissue

Procedure 1 Microscopy of Muscle Tissue

View prepared slides of skeletal, smooth, and cardiac muscle tissue. Use colored pencils to draw what you see under the microscope, and label your drawing with the terms from Figure 4.4. Record your observations of each slide in Table 4.1.

1 Skeletal muscle

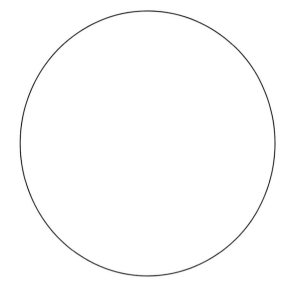

a _____

_____

b _____

_____

2 Cardiac muscle

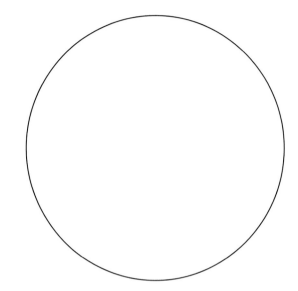

a _____

_____

b _____

_____

3 Smooth muscle

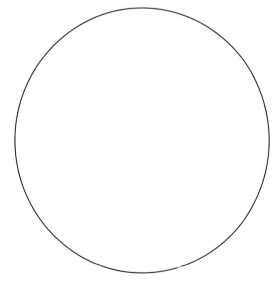

a _____

_____

b _____

_____

TABLE **4.1** Characteristics of Muscle Tissues

Muscle Tissue Type	Striated or Nonstriated	One or Multiple Nuclei	Size and Shape of Cells	Special Features
Cardiac muscle				
Skeletal muscle				
Smooth muscle				

Exercise 4-4

Nervous Tissue

MATERIALS
❑ Nervous tissue slides
❑ Light microscope
❑ Colored pencils

Nervous tissue (Figure 4.5) is the primary component of the brain, the spinal cord, and the peripheral nerves. It consists of a unique ECM and two main cell types:

1. **Neurons.** The neurons (NOOR-ahns) are responsible for sending and receiving messages within the nervous system. On your slide they are the larger of the two cell types. The large, central portion of the neuron is called the **cell body**. Within the cell body we find the nucleus and most of the neuron's organelles. Most neurons contain two types of long armlike processes extending from the cell body—the **dendrites** (DEN-drytz), which receive messages from other neurons, and the **axon** (AX-ahn), which sends messages to other neurons, muscle cells, or gland cells.

2. **Neuroglial cells.** The smaller and more numerous cells around the neurons are the neuroglial (noor-oh-GLEE-ul) cells. The six different types of neuroglial cells vary significantly in shape and appearance. Neuroglial cells in general perform functions that support the neurons in some way.

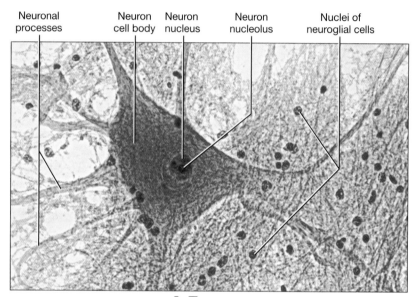

FIGURE **4.5** Nervous tissue

Neuronal processes | Neuron cell body | Neuron nucleus | Neuron nucleolus | Nuclei of neuroglial cells

Procedure 1 Microscopy of Nervous Tissue

View a prepared slide of nervous tissue (the slide might be called a "motor neuron smear"). Use colored pencils to draw a picture of what you see under the microscope, and label your drawing with the terms from Figure 4.5. Then (**a**) describe what you see, and (**b**) give examples of locations in the body where this tissue is found.

Nervous tissue

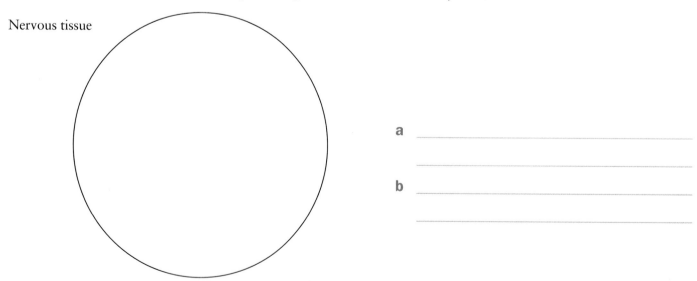

a _____

b _____

Name _____

Section _____ Date _____

1 Identify each of the following tissues in Figure 4.6.

a _____   c _____

b _____   d _____

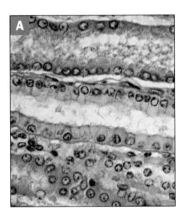 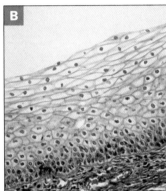 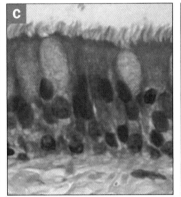 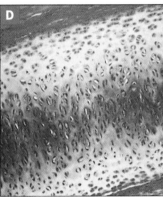

FIGURE **4.6** Unknown tissues for question 1

2 List the four basic tissue types:

_____   _____

_____   _____

3 *Fill in the blanks:* All tissues consist of two main components: _____ and _____ .

4 Which of the following statements about epithelial tissues is *false*?
a. Epithelial tissues lack blood vessels.
b. Epithelial tissues consist of few cells and an extensive ECM.
c. The ECM of epithelial tissues is located in the basal lamina.
d. Epithelial tissues are our covering and lining tissues.

5 How do simple and stratified epithelial tissues differ?

_____

_____

_____

6 Which of the following statements about connective tissue is *false*?
a. All connective tissues stem from a common embryonic tissue.
b. Connective tissues may contain three types of protein fibers: collagen, elastic, and reticular fibers.
c. Most connective tissues are highly vascular, with the exception of cartilage.
d. Most connective tissues consist largely of cells with little ECM.

7 How do loose and dense connective tissues differ?

_____

_____

_____

8 Which of the following statements about muscle tissue is *true*?
   a. Skeletal muscle and cardiac muscle tissues have no striations.
   b. Smooth muscle tissue is found in the heart.
   c. The cells of skeletal muscle tissue are long, tubular, and multinucleated.
   d. Smooth muscle cells are joined by intercalated discs.

9 *Fill in the blanks:* Nervous tissue is composed of _____ and _____.

10 The formation of fibrocartilage is a common response to injury of hyaline cartilage. Do you think fibrocartilage would provide an articular surface (i.e., the cartilage in joints) as smooth as the original hyaline cartilage? Why or why not?

_____

_____

_____

_____

11 Explain how the structure of each of the following tissues follows its function:

   a Simple squamous epithelium

_____

_____

   b Hyaline cartilage

_____

_____

   c Bone

_____

_____

12 When muscle tissue dies, it usually is replaced with dense irregular collagenous connective tissue. How do these tissues differ in structure? Will the muscle be able to function normally? Why or why not?

_____

_____

_____

_____

Integumentary System

OBJECTIVES

Once you have completed this unit, you should be able to:

1. Identify structures of the integumentary system.

2. Describe the gross and microscopic structure of thick and thin skin.

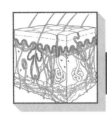

Name _____ Section _____ Date _____

PRE-LAB EXERCISES

Complete the following exercises prior to coming to lab, using your textbook and lab manual for reference.

Pre-Lab Exercise **5-1**

✎ Key Terms

You should be familiar with the following terms before coming to lab.

Term	Definition

Epidermal Structures

Epidermis _____

_____

Keratinocyte _____

_____

Melanocyte _____

_____

Structures of the Dermis

Dermis _____

_____

Dermal papillae _____

_____

Lamellated (Pacinian) corpuscle _____

_____

Tactile (Meissner's) corpuscle _____

_____

Other Structures

Hypodermis _____

_____

Sweat gland _____

_____

Sebaceous gland _____

_____

Hair follicle _____

_____

Nails 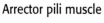 _____

_____

Arrector pili muscle _____

_____

Pre-Lab Exercise **5-2**
Skin Anatomy

5

Label and color the structures of the skin depicted in Figure 5.1 with the following terms from Exercise 5-1. Use your text and Exercise 5-1 in this unit for reference.

❏ Epidermis
❏ Dermis
  ❏ Papillary layer
  ❏ Reticular layer
❏ Dermal papillae
❏ Blood vessels
❏ Sweat gland
  ❏ Sweat duct
  ❏ Sweat pore
❏ Sebaceous gland
❏ Hypodermis

Nerves

❏ Lamellated (Pacinian) corpuscle
❏ Tactile (Meissner's) corpuscles

Hair

❏ Hair follicle
❏ Hair shaft
❏ Arrector pili muscle
❏ Hair root

Nail

❏ Nail matrix
❏ Nail fold (proximal and lateral)
❏ Nail plate

A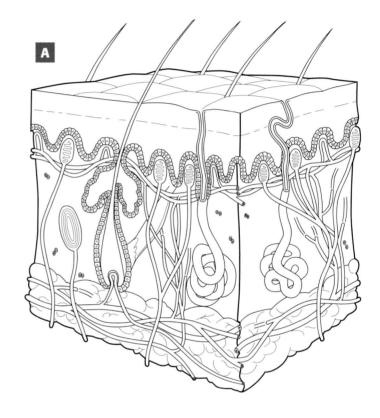

B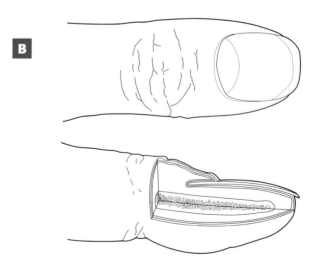

FIGURE **5.1** Structures of the integument: (**A**) skin section; (**B**) nail anatomy

EXERCISES

Although the skin is the largest organ in the body, most people don't realize it is actually an organ. Like all organs, the skin is composed of several tissue types, including several layers of epithelial tissue, connective tissue, muscle tissue, and nervous tissue. In the following exercises you will examine the tissues of this organ, along with the other structures of the integumentary system.

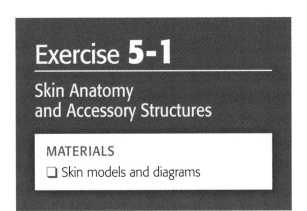

Exercise 5-1

Skin Anatomy and Accessory Structures

MATERIALS
❑ Skin models and diagrams

The **integumentary (in-TEG-yoo-MEN-tuh-ree) system** is composed of the skin (the **integument**) and its **accessory structures**: the **hair**, **glands**, and **nails**. The skin is composed of two layers, the **epidermis** and the **dermis** (Figure 5.2). The tissue beneath the dermis, sometimes called the **hypodermis** or the *subcutaneous tissue*, connects the skin to the underlying tissues and is not considered part of the integument.

The epidermis contains layers (or *strata*) of stratified squamous keratinized epithelium. From superficial to deep, the layers are as follows:

1. **Stratum corneum (KOHR-nee-um).** This superficial layer is composed of dead cells called **keratinocytes (KAIR-ah-tin-oh-sytz).** Under microscopic examination, the cells of the stratum corneum bear little resemblance to living cells and have a dry, flaky appearance. These cells contain a hard protein called **keratin** that protects the underlying layers of cells.

2. **Stratum lucidum (LOO-sid-um).** This is a single layer of translucent, dead cells found only in the skin of the palms and the soles of the feet.

3. **Stratum granulosum (gran-yoo-LOH-sum).** The superficial cells of the stratum granulosum are dead, but the deeper cells are alive. This layer is named for the cells' cytoplasmic granules, which contain the protein keratin and an oily waterproofing substance.

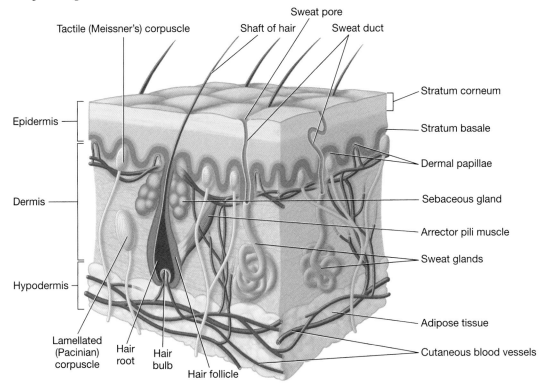

FIGURE **5.2** Skin section

4. **Stratum spinosum** (spin-OH-sum). The first actively metabolizing cells are encountered in the stratum spinosum. The pigment **melanin** (MEL-uh-nin) is found in this layer, which provides protection from UV light. It also decreases production of vitamin D so the body does not overproduce it.

5. **Stratum basale** (bay-ZAY-lee). The stratum basale is the deepest layer and contains a single row of actively dividing cells.

Why does the epidermis have so many dead cells? Recall that the epidermis is composed of epithelial tissue, and epithelial tissue lacks blood vessels. All epithelial tissues require oxygen and nutrients to diffuse up from the deeper tissues. In the case of the epidermis, this deeper tissue is the dermis. Only the cells of the deeper parts of the stratum granulosum, the stratum spinosum, and the stratum basale are close enough to the blood supply in the dermis to get adequate oxygen and nutrients for survival. As the cells migrate farther away from the blood supply, they begin to die.

Immediately deep to the stratum basale of the epidermis is the dermis. The dermis is composed of highly vascular connective tissue and contains two layers:

1. **Papillary layer.** The superficial papillary layer is composed of loose connective tissue. It contains fingerlike projections called the **dermal papillae** (pa-PIL-ee) that project into the epidermis. These dermal papillae contain touch receptors called **tactile** (or *Meissner's*) **corpuscles** and capillary loops that provide blood to the epidermis.

2. **Reticular layer.** The thick reticular layer is composed of dense irregular collagenous connective tissue. It houses structures such as **glands**, blood vessels, and pressure receptors called **lamellated corpuscles** (also known as *Pacinian corpuscles*).

Both hair and nails are considered accessory structures of the integumentary system (Figure 5.3). A hair consists of two basic parts: (1) the long, slender **shaft** composed of dead keratinized cells, which projects from the skin's surface, and (2) the hair **root** or **bulb** embedded in the dermis (Figure 5.3A). The structure surrounding the hair bulb is an epithelial tissue–lined sheath known as the **hair follicle**. Small bands of smooth muscle called **arrector pili** (ar-EK-tur PEE-lee) **muscles** attach to hair follicles and function to pull the hairs into an upright position.

Like hairs, nails are composed primarily of dead, keratinized cells (Figure 5.3B). A nail consists of a **nail plate** surrounded by folds of skin on all three sides, known as **nail folds**. The nail plate is formed by a group of dividing cells proximal to the nail fold called the **nail matrix**.

Other accessory structures of the integumentary system are its **sebaceous** (se-BAY-shus) **glands** and the **sweat glands**, both exocrine glands that secrete their products onto the skin's surface. Sebaceous glands secrete sebum (oil) into a hair follicle, and sweat glands secrete sweat through a small pore.

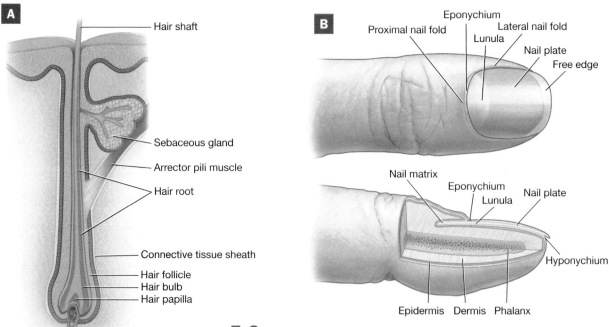

FIGURE **5.3** **(A)** Hair structure; **(B)** nail anatomy

Procedure 1 Model Inventory for the Integumentary System

Identify the following structures of the integumentary system on models and diagrams, using your textbook and this unit for reference. As you examine the anatomical models and diagrams, record on the model inventory in Table 5.1 the name of the model and the structures you were able to identify.

Structures of the Skin

1. Epidermal layers
   a. Stratum corneum
   b. Stratum lucidum
   c. Stratum granulosum
   d. Stratum spinosum
   e. Stratum basale
2. Dermal layers
   a. Papillary layer
   b. Reticular layer
3. Dermal papillae
4. Blood vessels
5. Nerves:
   a. Lamellated (Pacinian) corpuscle
   b. Tactile (Meissner's) corpuscles

Other Structures

1. Sweat gland
   a. Sweat duct
   b. Sweat pore
2. Hair
   a. Hair follicle
   b. Hair shaft
   c. Arrector pili muscle
   d. Hair root
3. Nail
   a. Nail matrix
   b. Nail fold (proximal and lateral)
   c. Nail plate
4. Sebaceous gland
5. Hypodermis

TABLE **5.1** Model Inventory for the Integumentary System

Model/Diagram	Structures Identified

Exercise 5-2

Histology of Integument

MATERIALS

❑ Slide of thick skin
❑ Slide of thin skin
❑ Light microscope
❑ Colored pencils

In this exercise we will examine prepared slides of skin from different regions of the body so we can compare and contrast two types of skin: (1) **thick skin**, found on the palms and soles of the feet, and (2) **thin skin**, found everywhere else (Figure 5.4).

Before moving on, you may wish to review the basics of microscopy from Unit 3. Remember to follow a step-by-step approach when examining the slides: Look at the slide with the naked eye first, then begin your examination on low power, and advance to higher power to see more details.

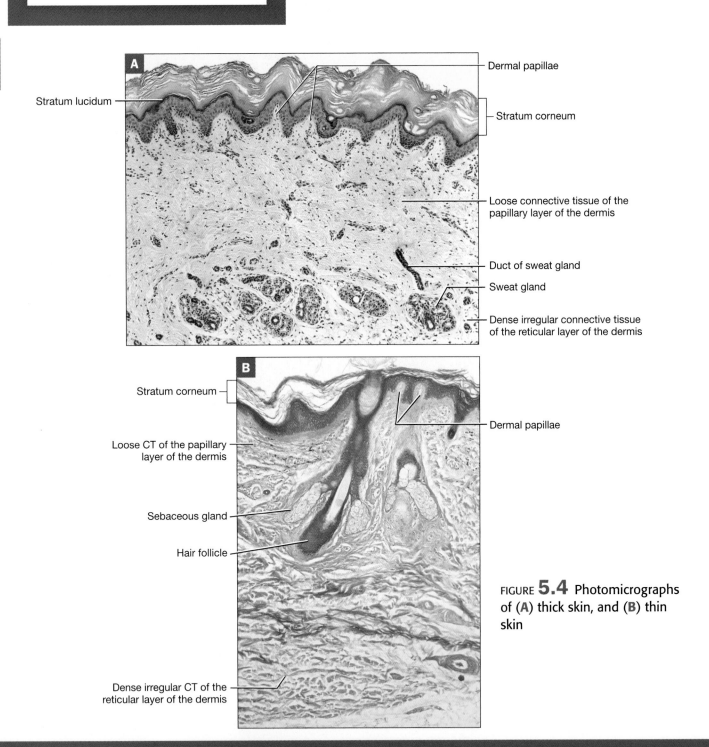

A
Stratum lucidum
Dermal papillae
Stratum corneum
Loose connective tissue of the papillary layer of the dermis
Duct of sweat gland
Sweat gland
Dense irregular connective tissue of the reticular layer of the dermis

B
Stratum corneum
Loose CT of the papillary layer of the dermis
Sebaceous gland
Hair follicle
Dermal papillae
Dense irregular CT of the reticular layer of the dermis

FIGURE **5.4** Photomicrographs of (**A**) thick skin, and (**B**) thin skin

Procedure 1 Microscopy of Thick Skin

Obtain a prepared slide of thick skin (which may be labeled "palmar skin"), and examine it with the naked eye to get oriented. After you are oriented, place the slide on the stage of the microscope, and scan it on low power. You should be able to see the epidermis with its superficial layers of dead cells and the dermis with its pink clusters of collagen bundles that make up the dense irregular collagenous connective tissue. Advance to higher power to see the cells and associated structures in greater detail.

Use your colored pencils to draw what you see in the field of view (you will be able to see the most structures on low power). Label your drawing with the following terms, using Figure 5.4 for reference. When you have completed your drawing, fill in Table 5.2.

1. Epidermis
   a. Stratum corneum
   b. Stratum lucidum
   c. Stratum granulosum
   d. Stratum spinosum
   e. Stratum basale

2. Dermis
   a. Dermal papillae
   b. Collagen bundles
   c. Sweat gland

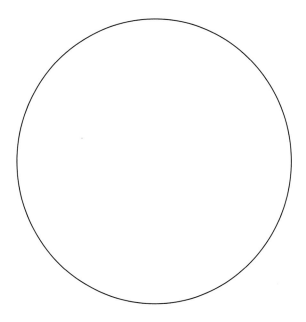

5

Procedure 2 Microscopy of Thin Skin

Obtain a prepared slide of thin skin (which may be called "scalp skin"). As before, examine the slide with the naked eye, then scan the slide on low power, advancing to higher power as needed to see the structures more clearly.

Use your colored pencils to draw what you see in the field of view (you will be able to see the most structures on low power). Label your drawing using the following terms, using **Figure 5.4** for reference. When you have completed your drawing, fill in the remainder of **Table 5.2**.

1. Epidermis
   a. Stratum corneum
   b. Stratum granulosum
   c. Stratum spinosum
   d. Stratum basale
2. Dermis
   a. Dermal papillae
   b. Collagen bundles
3. Hair follicle
4. Sebaceous gland
5. Sweat gland
6. Arrector pili muscle

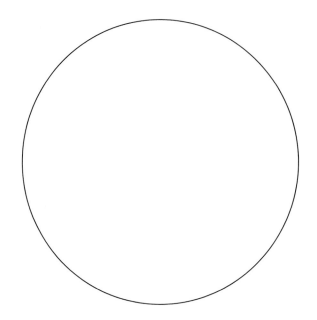

TABLE **5.2** Characteristics of Thick and Thin Skin

Characteristic	Thick Skin	Thin Skin
Thickness of stratum corneum		
Hair follicles present?		
Sebaceous glands present?		
Stratum lucidum present?		
Arrector pili muscles present?		

Name _____

Section _____ Date _____

1 Label the following parts of the skin on Figure 5.5.

- ❑ Arrector pili muscle
- ❑ Dermal papillae
- ❑ Dermis
- ❑ Epidermis
- ❑ Hair follicle
- ❑ Hair shaft
- ❑ Hypodermis
- ❑ Sebaceous gland
- ❑ Sweat gland

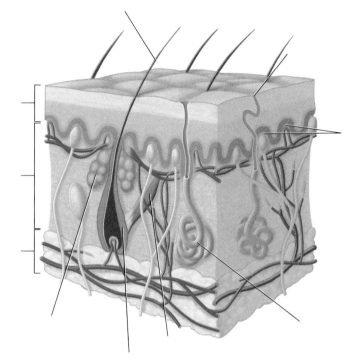

FIGURE **5.5** Skin section

2 The main cell type in skin is the

a. melanocyte.

b. reticulocyte.

c. monocyte.

d. keratinocyte.

3 Number the layers of the epidermis, with 1 being the most superficial layer and 5 being the deepest layer.

_____ Stratum lucidum

_____ Stratum basale

_____ Stratum corneum

_____ Stratum spinosum

_____ Stratum granulosum

4 Which layers of the epidermis contain living cells?

a. Stratum granulosum only

b. Stratum corneum, stratum granulosum, stratum lucidum

c. Stratum basale, stratum spinosum, stratum granulosum

d. All of the layers of the epidermis contain living cells.

e. None of the layers of the epidermis contain living cells.

5 From where do the cells of the epidermis obtain oxygen and nutrients?

   a. From blood vessels in the epidermis

   b. Diffusion from blood vessels in the dermis

   c. Diffusion from the air

   d. From blood vessels in other epithelial tissues

6 Oily secretions are produced by _____ glands.

   a. Sweat glands

   b. Mucus glands

   c. Serous glands

   d. Sebaceous glands

7 Which of the following are characteristics of thick skin? (*Circle all that apply.*)

   a. Located over the palms and the soles of the feet

   b. Contains hair and arrector pili muscles

   c. Contains sweat glands

   d. Very thick stratum corneum

   e. Contains sebaceous glands

   f. Contains a stratum lucidum

8 The dividing cells of a nail are located in the

   a. nail fold.

   b. nail plate.

   c. nail bed.

   d. nail matrix.

9 Explain why a superficial skin scrape (such as a paper cut) doesn't bleed. Why don't you bleed when a hair is pulled out?

10 Shampoos and hair conditioners often claim to have nutrients and vitamins your hair must have to grow and be healthy. Taking into account the composition of hair, do you think these vitamins and nutrients will be beneficial? Why or why not?

11 The disease *bullous pemphigoid* results in the destruction of proteins within the basement membrane that hold the epidermis and dermis together. How would this likely affect the epidermis?

Skeletal System: Bone Tissue, Bones, and Joints

6

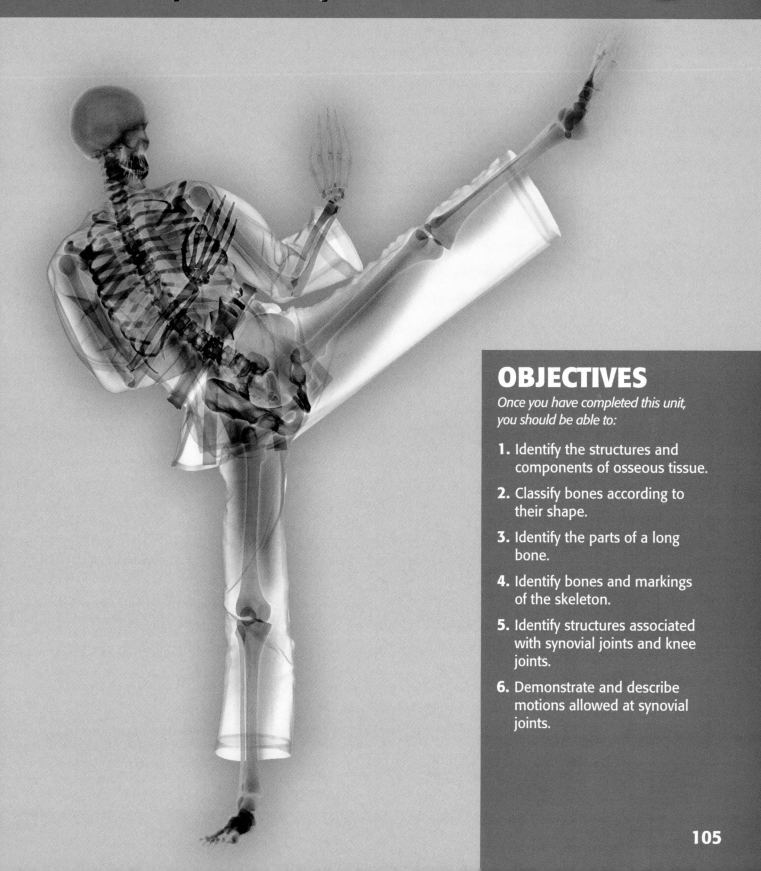

OBJECTIVES

Once you have completed this unit, you should be able to:

1. Identify the structures and components of osseous tissue.

2. Classify bones according to their shape.

3. Identify the parts of a long bone.

4. Identify bones and markings of the skeleton.

5. Identify structures associated with synovial joints and knee joints.

6. Demonstrate and describe motions allowed at synovial joints.

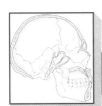

Name _____ Section _____ Date _____

PRE-LAB EXERCISES

Complete the following exercises prior to coming to lab, using your textbook and lab manual for reference.

Pre-Lab Exercise **6-1**

✎ Key Terms

You should be familiar with the following terms before coming to lab.

Term	Definition
Bone Tissue	
Compact bone	
Spongy bone	
Osteon	
Lamellae	
Osteocytes	
Periosteum	
Bone Shapes	
Long bone	
Short bone	
Flat bone	
Irregular bone	
Structures of Long Bones	
Diaphysis	

6

Epiphysis _____

_____

Epiphyseal plate/line _____

_____

Axial Skeleton

Cranial bones _____

Facial bones _____

Suture _____

Hyoid bone _____

Vertebrae _____

Ribs _____

Sternum _____

Appendicular Skeleton—Upper Limb

Pectoral girdle _____

Humerus _____

Radius _____

Ulna _____

Carpals _____

Metacarpals _____

Phalanges _____

Appendicular Skeleton—Lower Limb

Pelvic girdle _____

Femur _____

Tibia _____

Fibula _____

Tarsals _____

Metatarsals _____

Classes of Joints

Fibrous _____

Cartilaginous _____

Synovial _____

Types of Movement in Synovial Joints

Flexion _____

Extension _____

Abduction _____

Adduction _____

Circumduction _____

Rotation _____

Pre-Lab Exercise **6-2**

Microscopic Anatomy of Compact Bone

Label and color the microscopic anatomy of compact bone tissue depicted in **Figure 6.1** with the following terms from Exercise 6-1. Use your text and Exercise 6-1 in this unit for reference.

❑ Canaliculi
❑ Blood vessels in central (Haversian) canal
❑ Blood vessels in perforating (Volkmann's) canal
❑ Lacunae
  ❑ Osteocytes
❑ Lamellae
❑ Osteon
❑ Trabeculae (bone spicules)

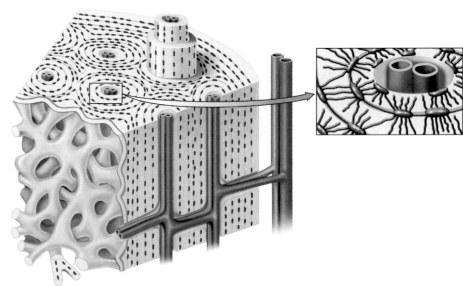

FIGURE **6.1** Microscopic anatomy of compact bone

Pre-Lab Exercise **6-3**
Bones of the Skull

Label and color the structures of the skull depicted in Figure 6.2 with the following terms from Exercise 6-3. Use your text and Exercise 6-3 in this unit for reference.

Cranial Bones

❏ Frontal bone
    ❏ Frontal sinuses
❏ Parietal bones
    ❏ Coronal suture
    ❏ Squamous suture
    ❏ Lambdoid suture

❏ Temporal bones
    ❏ External acoustic (auditory) meatus
    ❏ Styloid process
    ❏ Mastoid process
❏ Occipital bone
    ❏ Foramen magnum

❏ Sphenoid bone
    ❏ Sella turcica
    ❏ Sphenoid sinus
❏ Ethmoid bone
    ❏ Perpendicular plate

Facial Bones and Other Structures

❏ Mandible
    ❏ Mandibular condyle
    ❏ Mandibular ramus
    ❏ Mandibular body

❏ Maxilla
❏ Palatine bones
❏ Zygomatic bones
❏ Lacrimal bones

❏ Nasal bones
❏ Vomer

6

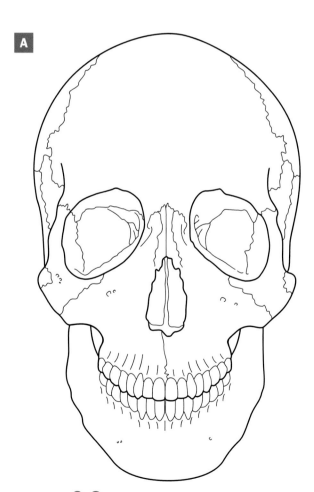

A

FIGURE **6.2** Skull: (**A**) anterior view *(continues)*

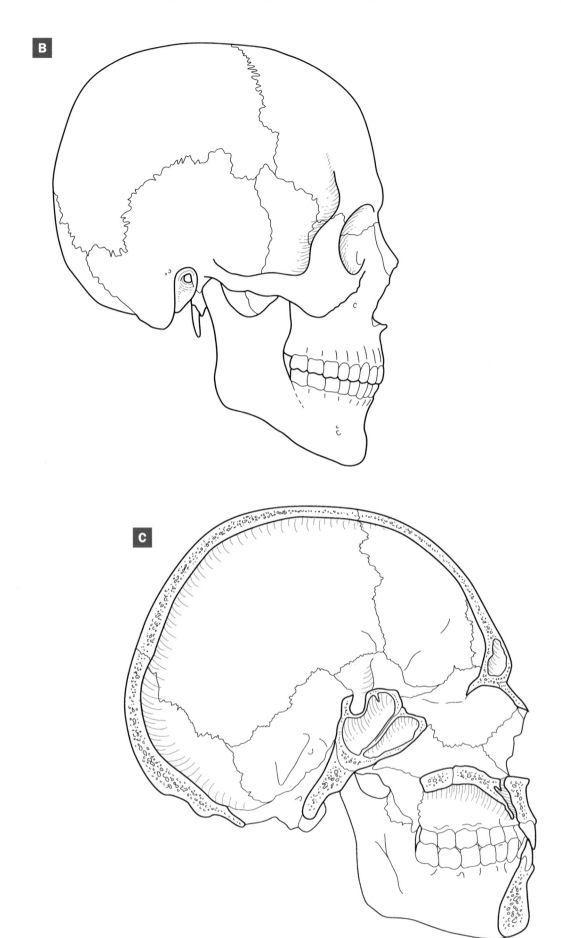

FIGURE **6.2** Skull *(cont.)*: **(B)** lateral view; **(C)** midsagittal section

Pre-Lab Exercise **6-4**

Whole Skeleton

Label and color the structures of the skeleton depicted in **Figure 6.3** with the following terms from Exercise 6-4. Use your text and Exercise 6-4 in this unit for reference.

Axial Skeleton

❏ Vertebrae
❏ Sacrum
❏ Coccyx
❏ Ribs
❏ Sternum

Pectoral Girdle and Upper Limb

❏ Clavicle
❏ Scapula
❏ Humerus
❏ Radius
❏ Ulna
❏ Carpals
❏ Metacarpals
❏ Phalanges

Pelvic Girdle and Lower Limb

❏ Ilium
❏ Ischium
❏ Pubis
❏ Femur
❏ Patella
❏ Tibia
❏ Fibula
❏ Tarsals
❏ Metatarsals
❏ Phalanges

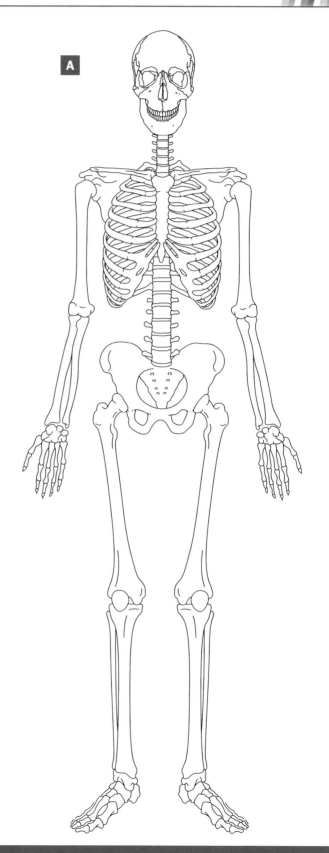

A

FIGURE **6.3** Skeleton:
(A) anterior view (continues)

6

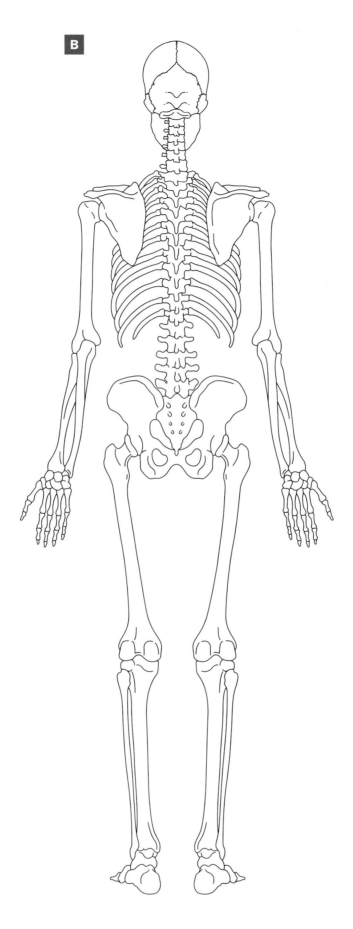

FIGURE **6.3** Skeleton *(cont.)*: **(B)** posterior view

EXERCISES

The **skeletal system** consists of the bones, associated cartilages, and joints. At first it might seem odd that a set of bones makes up an organ system, but remember that each bone is considered an organ.

A bone consists of many tissue types, including osseous tissue, epithelial tissue, dense connective tissue, and adipose tissue. The following exercises will introduce you to these organs and the histology of osseous tissue.

The two divisions of the skeletal system are the **axial skeleton** and the **appendicular skeleton**. The axial skeleton is composed of the bones of the head, neck, and trunk—specifically, the cranial bones, the facial bones, the vertebral column, the hyoid bone, the sternum, and the ribs. The appendicular skeleton consists of the bones of the upper limbs, the lower limbs, the pectoral girdle (the bones forming the shoulder joint), and the pelvic girdle (the bones forming the pelvis and hip joint).

In this unit we explore the anatomy of the bones and bone markings of the skeletal system, which will serve as a foundation for later units. For example, the radial and ulnar arteries parallel the radius and the ulna, and the frontal, parietal, temporal, and occipital lobes of the brain are named for the cranial bones under which they are located.

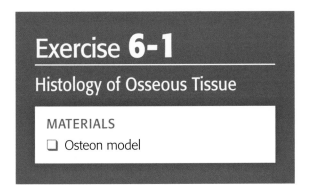

Exercise **6-1**

Histology of Osseous Tissue

MATERIALS
- ☐ Osteon model

The most superficial tissue of a bone is called the **periosteum (pair-ee-AHS-tee-um)**. The periosteum is composed of dense connective tissue richly supplied with blood vessels. The innermost layer of the periosteum contains the osteogenic cells, which become cells called **osteoblasts** that secrete bone matrix and build new bone, and cells called **osteoclasts** that secrete enzymes to catalyze the breakdown of bone matrix. Deep to the periosteum we find osseous tissue. The two general types of **osseous tissue** are

1. **compact bone**, and
2. **spongy bone**.

Compact bone is hard, dense bone tissue found immediately deep to the periosteum. Its hardness comes from its structure, which consists of repeating, densely packed subunits called **osteons** (AHS-tee-ahnz; Figure 6.4). Osteons contain several features, including the following:

1. **Lamellae.** Lamellae (la-MEL-ee) are concentric rings of bone matrix. The lamellae give compact bone a great deal of strength, much like a tree's rings.

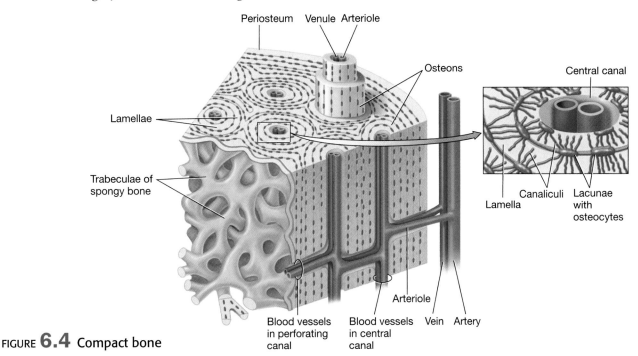

FIGURE **6.4** Compact bone

2. **Central canal.** Running down the center of each osteon is a central canal. Each central canal contains blood vessels and nerves and is lined with connective tissue membrane called the **endosteum** (en-DAHS-tee-um). Like the periosteum, the endosteum has an inner layer of osteoblasts that secrete bone matrix and osteoclasts that degrade bone.

3. **Lacunae.** Situated between the lamellae are small cavities called lacunae (la-KOO-nee). Lacunae contain mature osteoblasts, now called **osteocytes,** that monitor and maintain the bone matrix. Neighboring lacunae and osteocytes are connected to each other by tiny canals called **canaliculi** (kan-uh-LIK-yoo-lee).

4. **Perforating canals.** The perforating canals lie perpendicular to the osteon and carry blood vessels into the bone from the periosteum. Like the central canals, perforating canals are lined by endosteum.

Spongy bone is found on the inside of a bone deep to compact bone. As its name implies, it somewhat resembles a sponge and consists of a lattice-like structure with tiny bone spicules called **trabeculae** (tra-BEK-yoo-lee; Figure 6.5). The latticed structure of spongy bone allows it to house another important tissue, the **bone marrow.** The two types of bone marrow are: (1) **red bone marrow,** which produces blood cells, and (2) **yellow bone marrow,** composed primarily of adipose tissue. As you can see in Figure 6.5, trabeculae are composed of lamellae but are not organized into osteons. For this reason, spongy bone lacks the hardness of compact bone.

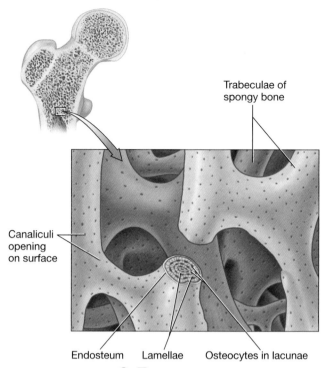

FIGURE **6.5** Microscopic anatomy of spongy bone tissue

Procedure **1** Model Inventory for Compact and Spongy Bone

Identify the following structures of compact and spongy bone on models and diagrams, using your textbook and this unit for reference. As you examine the anatomical models and diagrams, record on the model inventory in Table 6.1 the name of the model and the structures you were able to identify.

Compact Bone Structures

1. Canaliculi
2. Central canal
3. Lacunae
4. Lamellae
5. Osteocytes
6. Osteon
7. Perforating canal
8. Periosteum

Spongy Bone Structures

1. Endosteum
2. Lacunae
3. Osteocytes
4. Red bone marrow
5. Trabeculae (bone spicules)

TABLE **6.1** Model Inventory for Osseous Tissue

Model	Bone Structures Identified

Exercise 6-2

Bone Shapes

MATERIALS

❑ Disarticulated bones

❑ Articulated skeleton

❑ Long bone, sectioned

One way in which bones are classified is by their shape. Note in Figure 6.6 the four general shapes of bones:

1. **Long bones** are longer than they are wide and include the bones of the upper and lower extremities excluding the ankle and wrist bones.

2. **Short bones** are about as long as they are wide. The bones of the wrist and the ankle are short bones.

3. **Flat bones** are shaped exactly as they're named. Flat bones include the ribs, the sternum, the clavicle, certain skull bones, and the bones of the pelvis.

4. **Irregular bones** are those whose shape doesn't fit into any of the other classes. Irregular bones include the vertebrae and certain bones of the skull, such as the mandible (lower jaw bone).

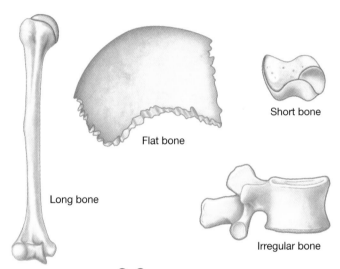

Long bone

Flat bone

Short bone

Irregular bone

FIGURE **6.6** Four shapes of bones

HINTS & TIPS

Bone Shape, not Length

Note that long bones are not named for their length but rather for their shape. Many long bones actually are quite short in length, including the bones of the fingers and the toes. Be careful when identifying bone shapes to look at the overall shape of the bone rather than its size.

6

Procedure 1 Identifying Bone Shapes

Obtain a set of disarticulated bones, and classify them according to their shape. Identify examples of long bones, short bones, flat bones, and irregular bones, and record them in Table 6.2. You may wish to use the figures in your text or Exercises 6-3 and 6-4 (pp. 118–140) to help you identify the disarticulated bones.

TABLE **6.2** Examples of Bone Shapes

Bone	Shape

Procedure 2 Anatomy of Long Bones

All long bones share common structures and parts, illustrated in **Figure 6.7** with the example of the femur. The **diaphysis** (dy-AF-ih-sis) is the shaft of the long bone. As you can see in the figure, it consists of a thick collar of compact bone surrounding a hollow area called the **medullary cavity**. This collar of compact bone makes long bones quite strong and able to support the body's weight. The medullary cavity has sparse trabeculae and generally is filled with yellow bone marrow in living bone.

Each end of a long bone is called the **epiphysis** (e-PIF-ih-sis). Each epiphysis contains a shell of compact bone surrounding the inner spongy bone. The spongy bone within the epiphyses contains either red or yellow bone marrow. The end of each epiphysis is covered with hyaline cartilage, which allows two bones to articulate during movement with minimal friction. At certain epiphysis-diaphysis junctions you will note a thin, calcified line called the **epiphyseal (e-PIF-ih-zee-ul) line**. This structure is the remnant of the **epiphyseal plate**, a band of hyaline cartilage from which long bones grow in length. When longitudinal growth ceases, the chondrocytes of the epiphyseal plate die and are replaced by calcified bone tissue.

Identify the following structures of long bones on specimens and X-rays (if available). Check off each structure as you identify it.

- ❏ Compact bone
- ❏ Diaphysis
- ❏ Epiphyseal line
- ❏ Epiphyseal plate
  (may be visible only on X-ray)

- ❏ Epiphysis
- ❏ Hyaline cartilage
- ❏ Medullary cavity

- ❏ Red bone marrow
- ❏ Spongy bone
- ❏ Yellow bone marrow

6

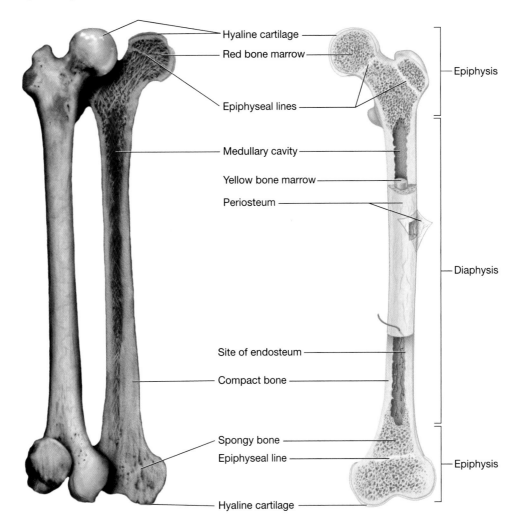

FIGURE **6.7** Long bone: Femur

Exercise 6-3

The Skull

MATERIALS
❑ Skulls, whole and sectioned
❑ Fetal skull

The skull is composed of two general types of bones—the **cranial bones** and the **facial bones** (Figures 6.8–6.12). The cranial bones encase the brain and together form the **calvaria** (kal-VAIR-ee-uh; also known as the *cranial vault*), which consists of several of the cranial bones joined at immovable joints called **sutures** (SOO-churz). These bones also form the cranial base, which contains indentations that accommodate the brain called the **anterior**, **middle**, and **posterior cranial fossae** (visible in Figure 6.11). The eight cranial bones include:

1. **Frontal bone.** The frontal bone forms the anterior portion of the cranium. Internally it contains hollow spaces called the **frontal sinuses** (visible in Figures 6.11 and 6.12). The frontal sinuses are part of a group of cavities called the **paranasal sinuses** that surrounds the nasal cavity. Air from the nasal cavity enters the paranasal sinuses via small openings in the bones, and in the sinuses the air gets filtered, warmed, and humidified.

2. **Parietal bones.** The paired parietal (puh-RY-ih-tul) bones form the superior and part of the lateral walls of the cranium. Note in Figures 6.8 and 6.9 that they articulate with one another and many other cranial bones at sutures: They meet one another at the **sagittal suture** (not visible in the figures), they meet the frontal bone at the **coronal suture**, they meet the temporal bones at the **squamous sutures**, and they meet the occipital bone at the **lambdoid suture**.

3. **Temporal bones.** The paired temporal bones form the lateral walls of the cranium (best seen in Figure 6.9). Each temporal bone houses an **external acoustic (auditory) meatus** that leads to the ear. Inferior to the external acoustic meatus are the needlelike **styloid process** and the large **mastoid process**.

4. **Occipital bone.** The posterior cranial bone is the occipital (ahk-SIP-ih-tul) bone, best seen in Figures 6.10 and 6.11. Its most conspicuous feature is found in its base—a large hole called the **foramen magnum** through which the spinal cord passes.

5. **Sphenoid bone.** The butterfly-shaped sphenoid bone (SFEE-noyd) is posterior to the frontal bone on the interior part of the skull (best seen in Figures 6.11 and 6.12). Its superior surface contains a saddle-like formation called the **sella turcica** (SEL-uh TUR-sih-kuh) that houses the pituitary gland. Inferior to the sella turcica is the body of the sphenoid, which contains the second paranasal sinus—the **sphenoid sinus**. Laterally it consists of two sets of "wings"—the small **lesser wings** and the larger **greater wings**. Inferiorly, it has another set of "wings" called the **pterygoid** (TAIR-ih-goyd) **processes**.

6. **Ethmoid bone.** The complex ethmoid (ETH-moyd) bone is the deepest cranial bone and the most difficult to see from standard views of the skull. It can best be seen in Figure 6.12. Located anterior to the sphenoid bone and posterior to the nasal bones of the face, it frames much of the nasal cavity. Its superior surface, called the **cribriform plate**, forms the roof of the nasal cavity. It has a superior projection called the **crista galli** (KRIS-tuh GAH-lee) to which the membranes surrounding the brain attach. The **lateral bodies** of the ethmoid bone form part of the orbit and the walls of the nasal cavity. Internally, these contain numerous cavities called the **ethmoid sinuses** that constitute the third set of paranasal sinuses. Extending medially from the lateral bodies are two projections into the nasal cavity—the **superior nasal conchae** (KAHN-kee) and **middle nasal conchae**. The middle portion of the ethmoid bone, called the **perpendicular plate**, forms the superior part of the bony nasal septum, which separates the two sides of the nasal cavity.

The 14 facial bones form the framework for the face, provide openings for breathing and eating, and form cavities for the sense organs. Several of the facial bones are located deeper in the skull, and you will want to refer to different figures (noted with each bone) to best locate them and appreciate their structures. These bones are the following:

1. **Mandible.** The mandible, or the lower jaw bone, consists of a central **body** and two "arms" called the **mandibular rami** (RAY-mee; singular, *ramus*). The mandibular rami have two processes—an anterior process called the **coronoid** (KOHR-oh-noyd) **process** and a posterior process called the **mandibular condyle**. The mandibular condyle fits into a depression in the temporal bone to form the **temporomandibular** (tem-pohr-oh-man-DIB-yoo-lur) **joint**.

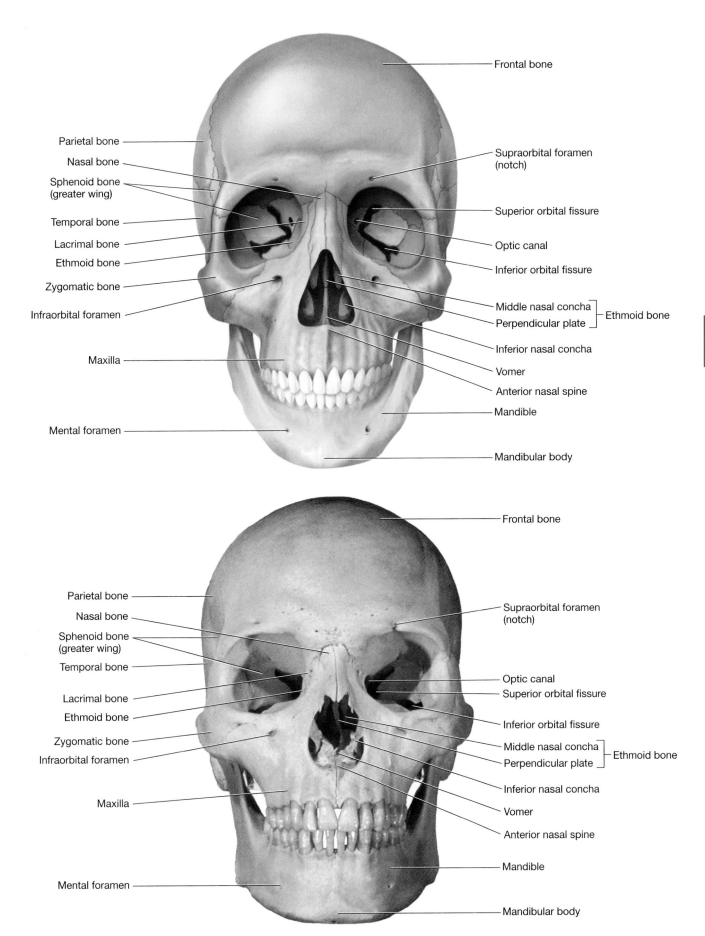

FIGURE **6.8** Anterior view of the skull

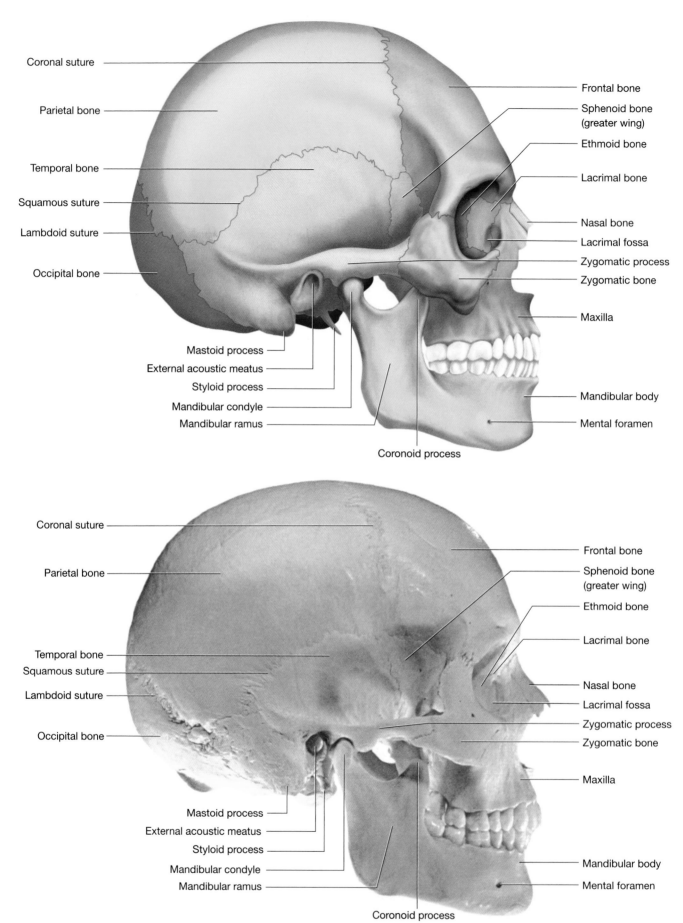

Coronal suture

Parietal bone

Temporal bone

Squamous suture

Lambdoid suture

Occipital bone

Mastoid process

External acoustic meatus

Styloid process

Mandibular condyle

Mandibular ramus

Coronoid process

Frontal bone

Sphenoid bone (greater wing)

Ethmoid bone

Lacrimal bone

Nasal bone

Lacrimal fossa

Zygomatic process

Zygomatic bone

Maxilla

Mandibular body

Mental foramen

Coronal suture

Parietal bone

Temporal bone

Squamous suture

Lambdoid suture

Occipital bone

Mastoid process

External acoustic meatus

Styloid process

Mandibular condyle

Mandibular ramus

Coronoid process

Frontal bone

Sphenoid bone (greater wing)

Ethmoid bone

Lacrimal bone

Nasal bone

Lacrimal fossa

Zygomatic process

Zygomatic bone

Maxilla

Mandibular body

Mental foramen

FIGURE **6.9** Lateral view of the skull

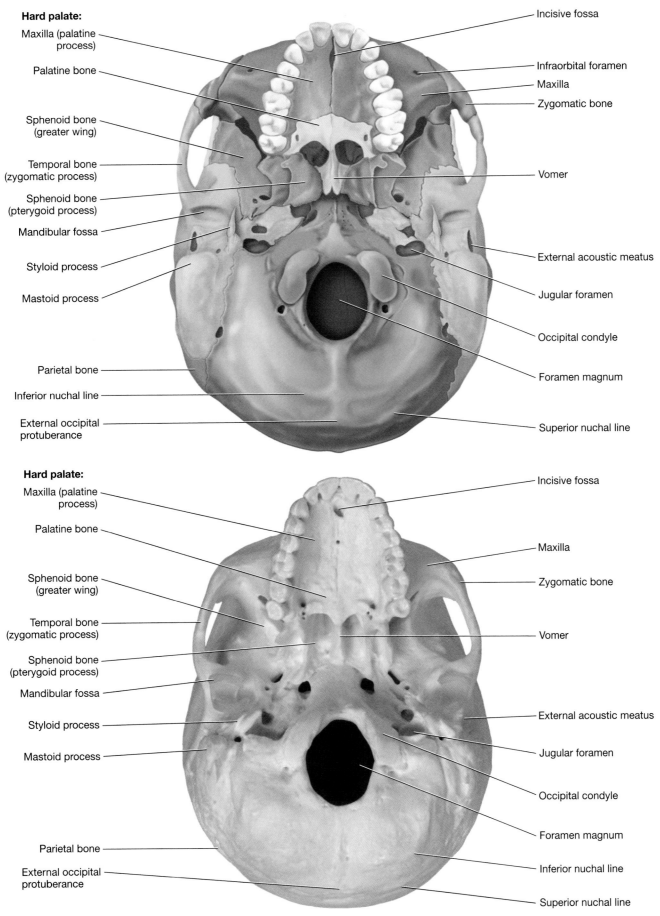

Hard palate:
Maxilla (palatine process)
Palatine bone
Sphenoid bone (greater wing)
Temporal bone (zygomatic process)
Sphenoid bone (pterygoid process)
Mandibular fossa
Styloid process
Mastoid process
Parietal bone
Inferior nuchal line
External occipital protuberance

Incisive fossa
Infraorbital foramen
Maxilla
Zygomatic bone
Vomer
External acoustic meatus
Jugular foramen
Occipital condyle
Foramen magnum
Superior nuchal line

Hard palate:
Maxilla (palatine process)
Palatine bone
Sphenoid bone (greater wing)
Temporal bone (zygomatic process)
Sphenoid bone (pterygoid process)
Mandibular fossa
Styloid process
Mastoid process
Parietal bone
External occipital protuberance

Incisive fossa
Maxilla
Zygomatic bone
Vomer
External acoustic meatus
Jugular foramen
Occipital condyle
Foramen magnum
Inferior nuchal line
Superior nuchal line

FIGURE **6.10** Inferior view of the skull (mandible removed)

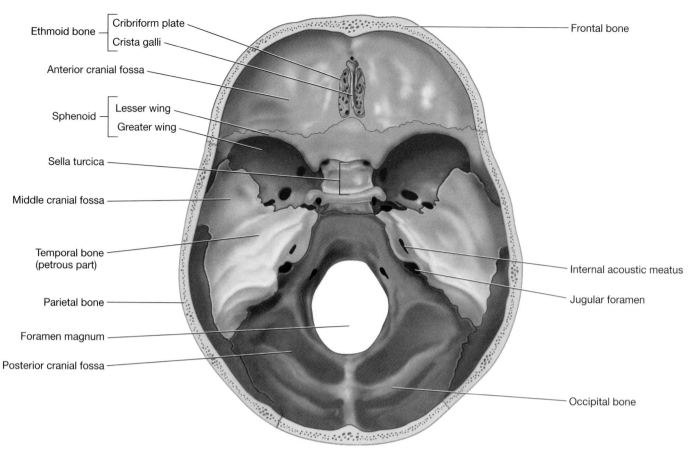

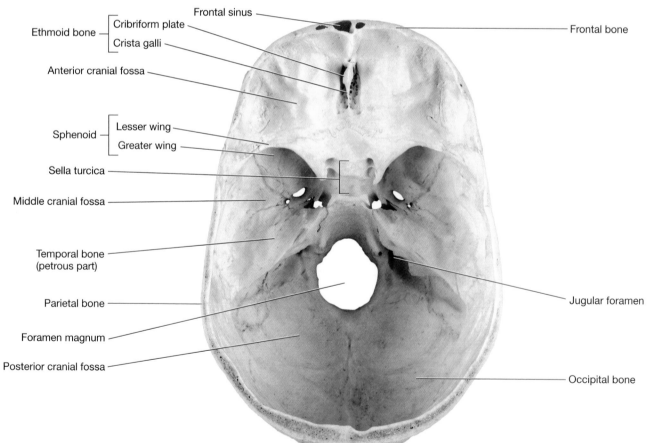

FIGURE **6.11** Inferior view of the skull (calvaria removed)

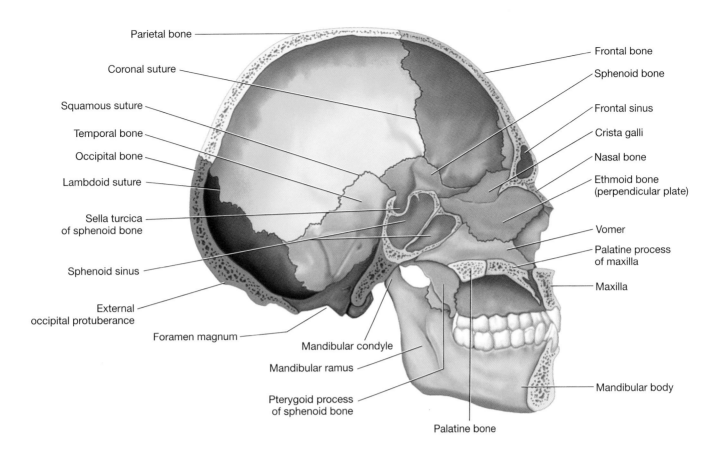

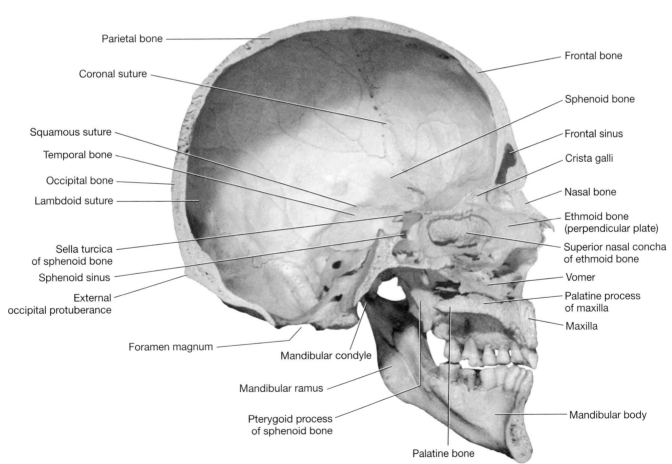

FIGURE **6.12** Midsagittal section of the skull

2. **Maxillae.** The two fused maxillae (**max-IL-ee**) are the upper jaw bones. They form part of the orbit and the anterior portion of the hard palate (via their **palatine processes**). Within their walls are cavities called the **maxillary sinuses**, the fourth and final set of paranasal sinuses.

3. **Lacrimal bones.** The tiny lacrimal (**LAK-rim-ul**) bones are located in the medial part of the orbit, where they form part of the structure that drains tears produced by the lacrimal gland of the eye. They are best seen in Figure 6.9.

4. **Nasal bones.** The two nasal bones form the anterior framework of the bridge of the nose.

5. **Vomer.** The single vomer forms the inferior portion of the bony nasal septum (best seen in Figure 6.12).

6. **Inferior nasal conchae.** The small inferior nasal conchae form part of the lateral walls of the nasal cavity. As their name implies, they are located inferior to the middle nasal conchae (Figure 6.8).

7. **Palatine bones.** The two palatine (**PAL-uh-teen**) bones form the posterior part of the hard palate (seen in Figure 6.10) and the posterolateral walls of the nasal cavity.

8. **Zygomatic bones.** The two zygomatic (**zy-goh-MAT-ik**) bones form the bulk of the cheek and a significant portion of the "cheekbone," or zygomatic arch.

The **orbit** is the bony cavity that houses the eyeball. It is formed by parts of seven bones: the frontal bone, the maxilla, the sphenoid bone, the ethmoid bone, the lacrimal bone, the zygomatic bone, and a tiny piece of the palatine bone.

As you can see in Figure 6.13, the fetal skull contains notable differences from the adult skulls you have seen so far. In adults, the sutures are fused, but in the fetus, the sutures have not yet fused and are instead joined by fibrous membranes. This can be seen with the **frontal suture**, where the two fetal frontal bones fuse. Where several sutures meet, we find large, membrane-covered areas called the **fontanels** (**fahn-tuh-NELZ**), known to many as "soft spots." The two main fontanels are the **anterior fontanel**, where the sagittal and coronal sutures meet, and the **posterior fontanel**, where the sagittal and lambdoid sutures meet.

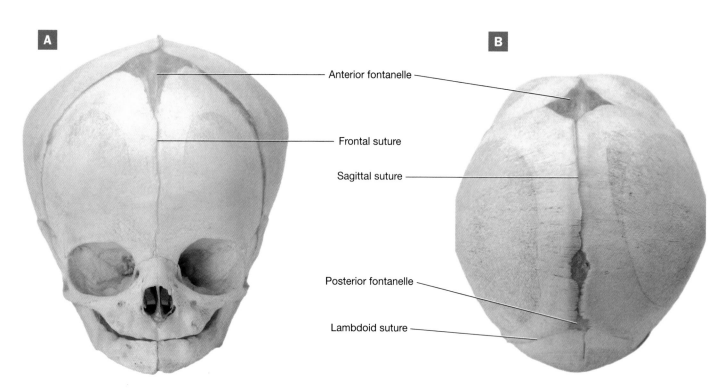

A

B

Anterior fontanelle

Frontal suture

Sagittal suture

Posterior fontanelle

Lambdoid suture

FIGURE **6.13** Fetal skull: (**A**) anterior view; (**B**) posterior view

Procedure 1 Cooperative Learning for the Skull

This exercise takes an approach called *cooperative learning*, in which you work with your lab partners to teach one another the bones and bone markings. The process may seem a bit confusing at first, but by the end of the first couple of rotations, it should move more quickly and smoothly.

1 Assemble into groups of a minimum of four students; five is optimum.

2 Distribute a skull to each member of the group, and assign each student one of the following five groups of bones and bone markings (the specific structures of each bone are listed on below and on the next page):

Group 1: calvaria, base, and structures of the frontal bone and parietal bones

Group 2: temporal bone and occipital bone structures

Group 3: ethmoid bone and sphenoid bone structures

Group 4: mandible and maxillary bone structures

Group 5: remainder of the facial bones, orbit, sutural bones, and anterior and posterior fontanels

3 Spend approximately three minutes learning the assigned structures on your own.

4 Then have each student spend approximately one to two minutes teaching the group his or her assigned structures.

5 Rotate the assigned structures clockwise so each student has a new set of structures to learn (the student assigned Group 1 will take Group 2, and so on).

6 Spend approximately two to three minutes learning your newly assigned structures.

7 Have each student spend approximately one to two minutes teaching the group his or her assigned structures.

8 Repeat this process (it begins to speed up significantly at this point) until each student has taught each group of structures once.

By the end of this activity, each group member will have learned and presented each group of structures.
The following is a list of bones and bone markings of the skull that will be covered in this exercise.

Cranial Bones

Group 1 Structures
1. Calvaria
2. Base of cranial cavity
   a. Anterior cranial fossa
   b. Middle cranial fossa
   c. Posterior cranial fossa
3. Frontal bone
   a. Frontal sinuses
4. Parietal bones
   a. Coronal suture
   b. Sagittal suture
   c. Squamous suture
   d. Lambdoid suture

Group 2 Structures
1. Temporal bones
   a. External acoustic (auditory) meatus
   b. Styloid process
   c. Mastoid process
2. Occipital bone
   a. Occipital condyles
   b. Foramen magnum

Group 3 Structures
1. Sphenoid bone
   a. Body
   b. Greater and lesser wings
   c. Sella turcica
   d. Sphenoid sinus
2. Ethmoid bone
   a. Perpendicular plate
   b. Superior and middle nasal conchae
   c. Crista galli
   d. Cribriform plate
   e. Ethmoid sinuses

Facial Bones and Other Structures

Group 4 Structures

1. Mandible
   a. Mandibular condyle
   b. Coronoid process
   c. Mandibular ramus
   d. Mandibular body
2. Maxilla
   a. Palatine processes
   b. Maxillary sinuses

Group 5 Structures

1. Palatine bones
2. Zygomatic bones and zygomatic arch
3. Lacrimal bones and lacrimal fossa
4. Nasal bones
5. Vomer
6. Inferior nasal conchae
7. Anterior fontanel
8. Posterior fontanel

Your instructor may wish to omit certain structures included above or add structures not included in these lists. List any additional structures below:

_____

_____

_____

_____

_____

6

Exercise 6-4

Remainder of the Skeleton

MATERIALS

❏ Vertebral column, articulated
❏ Disarticulated bones
❏ Skeleton, articulated

The **vertebral** (vur-TEE-brul) **column** consists of 24 vertebrae, the sacrum (SAY-krum), and the coccyx (CAHX-iks; Figures 6.14–6.15). The vertebrae are divided into 7 **cervical vertebrae**, 12 **thoracic vertebrae**, and 5 **lumbar vertebrae**. Nearly all vertebrae share certain general features, including a posterior **spinous process**, an anterior **vertebral body**, two lateral **transverse processes**, and a central **vertebral foramen**. Between each vertebral body is a fibrocartilage pad called an **intervertebral disc**.

The basic properties of each region of the vertebral column are as follows:

1. The seven cervical vertebrae are located in the neck (Figure 6.15A–C). All cervical vertebrae have holes in their transverse processes called **transverse foramina** through which blood vessels pass. In addition, the spinous processes of cervical vertebrae are often forked. Two cervical vertebrae are named differently than the others because of their unique features:

   a. **Atlas** (C_1): The atlas is the first cervical vertebra, which articulates with the occipital bone. It is easily identified because it has a large vertebral foramen, no body, and no spinous process (Figure 6.15B).

   b. **Axis** (C_2): The axis is the second cervical vertebra. It is also easily identified by a superior projection called the **dens** (Figure 6.15C). The dens fits up inside the atlas to form the *atlanto-axial joint*, which allows rotation of the head.

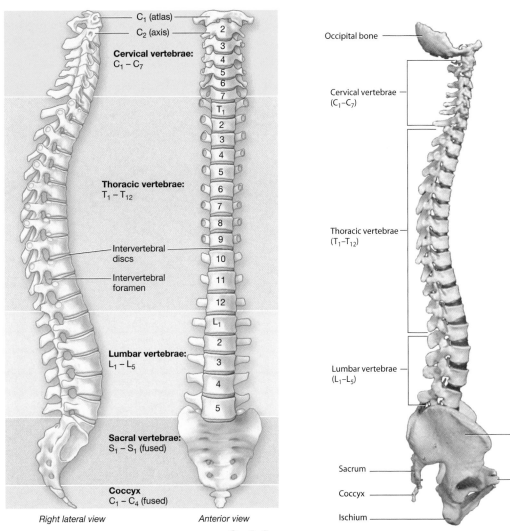

FIGURE **6.14** Vertebral column

2. The 12 thoracic vertebrae have the following common features (Figure 6.15D):

a. The spinous processes are thin and point inferiorly.

b. All have two *costal facets* that articulate with the ribs (there are 12 pairs of ribs).

c. All have triangular vertebral foramina.

d. If you look at a thoracic vertebra from the posterior side, it looks like a giraffe (seriously!).

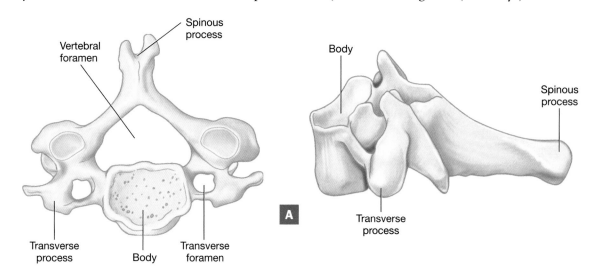

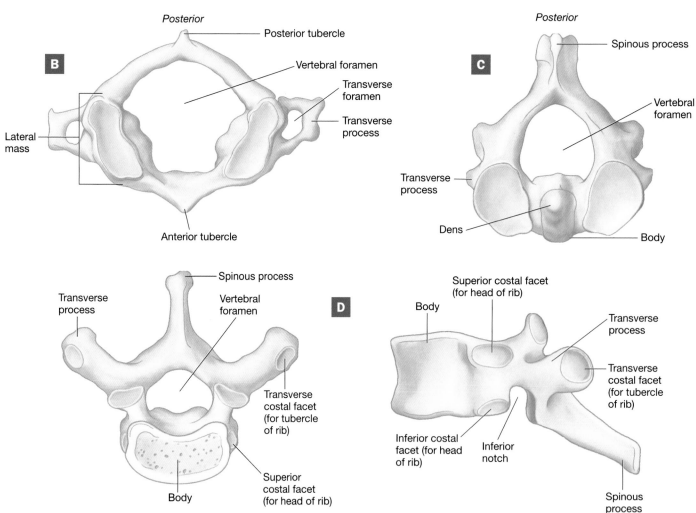

FIGURE **6.15** Vertebrae: (**A**) typical cervical vertebra, superior and lateral views;
(**B**) atlas (C$_1$); (**C**) axis (C$_2$); (**D**) typical thoracic vertebrae, superior and lateral views; *(continues)*

3. The five lumbar vertebrae have the following common features (Figure 6.15E):

   a. All have a large, block-like body.

   b. The spinous processes are thick and point posteriorly.

   c. If you look at a lumbar vertebra from the posterior side, it looks like a moose (really!).

4. The sacrum consists of five fused vertebrae (Figures 6.15F and 6.15G). Branches of spinal nerves pass through holes called **sacral foramina** that flank both sides of the sacral bodies. The lateral surfaces of the sacrum articulate with the hip bones to form the **sacroiliac (say-kroh-IL-ee-ak) joints.**

5. The coccyx consists of three to five small, fused vertebrae that articulate superiorly with the sacrum.

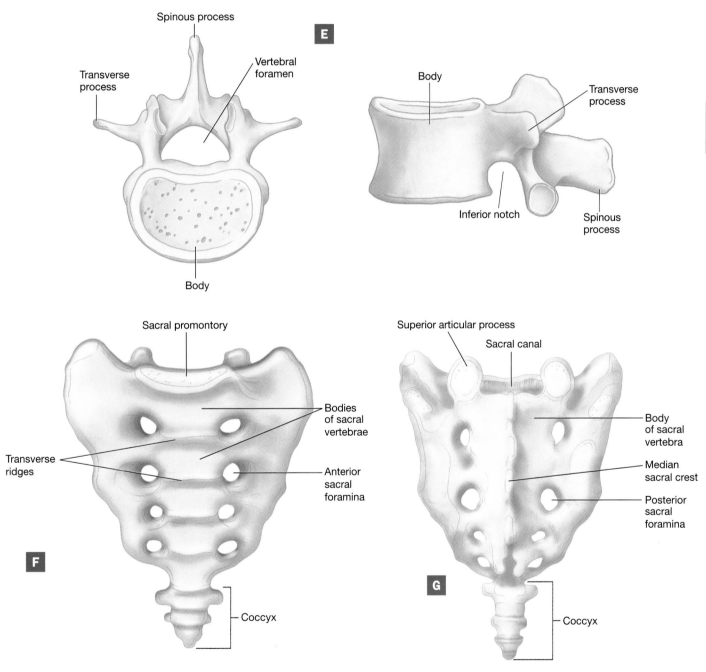

FIGURE **6.15** Vertebrae *(cont.)*: (**E**) typical lumbar vertebra, superior and lateral views; (**F**) sacrum, anterior view; (**G**) sacrum, posterior view

The remainder of the axial skeleton consists of the bones of the thoracic cavity (the **sternum** and the **ribs**, Figure 6.16) and the **hyoid** (HYE-oyd) **bone** in the neck (Figure 6.17). Note that the photo (Figure 6.16) also shows the bones of the pectoral (PEK-tohr-ul) girdle. The sternum is divided into three parts—the upper **manubrium** (man-OO-bree-um), the middle **body**, and the lower **xiphoid** (ZYE-foyd) **process**. The ribs are classified according to how they attach to the sternum: Ribs 1–7 are considered **true ribs** because they attach directly to the sternum by their own cartilage, ribs 8–10 are classified as **false ribs** because they attach to the cartilage of the true ribs rather than directly to the sternum, and ribs 11–12 are called **floating ribs** because they lack an attachment to the sternum.

The hyoid bone is held in place in the superior neck by muscles and ligaments, and it helps form part of the framework for the larynx (voice box). It also serves as an attachment site for the muscles of the tongue and aids in swallowing. When a person is choked manually, the hyoid bone is often broken. (I would not recommend testing this on your lab partner!)

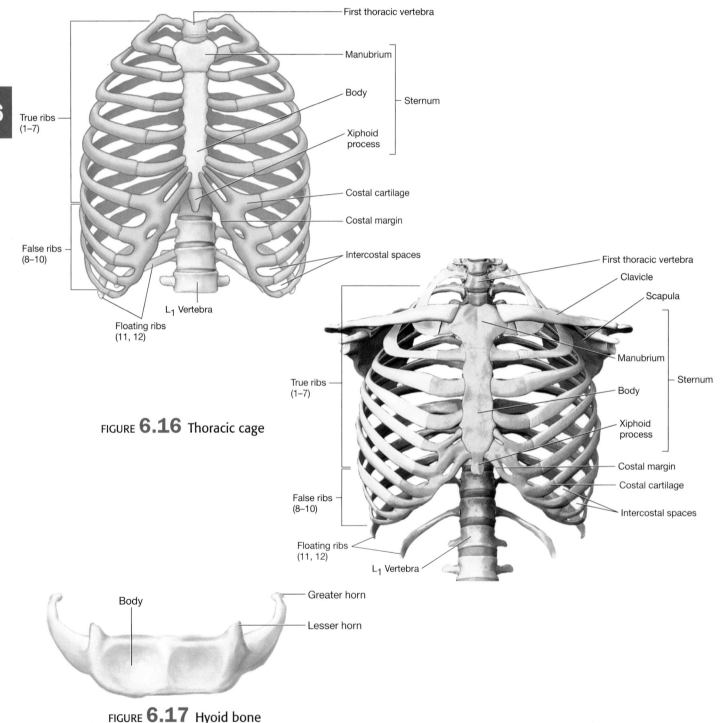

FIGURE **6.16** Thoracic cage

FIGURE **6.17** Hyoid bone

Let's move on to the appendicular skeleton, starting with the **pectoral girdle**. The pectoral girdle consists of the two bones that frame the shoulder—the **scapula** (SKAP-yoo-luh) and the **clavicle**. The scapula, shown in Figure 6.18, has a posterior ridge called the **spine** and a lateral depression called the **glenoid** (GLEN-oyd) **cavity** that forms the shoulder joint with the humerus. Superiorly it has two projections—the anterior **coracoid** (KOHR-uh-koyd) **process** and the posterior **acromion** (ah-KROH-mee-ahn), which forms a joint with the clavicle called the **acromioclavicular** (ah-KROH-mee-oh-cla-VIK-yoo-lur, or AC) joint.

The upper limb consists of the arm, the forearm, the wrist, and the hand. The only bone within the arm is the **humerus** (HYOO-mur-us; Figures 6.19 and 6.21). The humerus has a number of features, some of which include the following:

■ At the proximal end of the humerus is a rounded **head** that fits into the glenoid cavity. Just lateral to the head is the **lesser tubercle** and the larger **greater tubercle**.

■ The middle of the humerus features a projection called the **deltoid tuberosity**, where the deltoid muscle attaches.

■ At the humerus' distal end we find two condyles—the medial **trochlea** (TROH-klee-uh), shaped like a spool of thread, and the ball-shaped lateral **capitulum** (ka-PIT-yoo-lum). Just proximal to these condyles are indentations in the humerus where the bones of the forearm articulate—the anterior **coronoid fossa** and the posterior **olecranon** (oh-LEK-ruh-nahn) **fossa**.

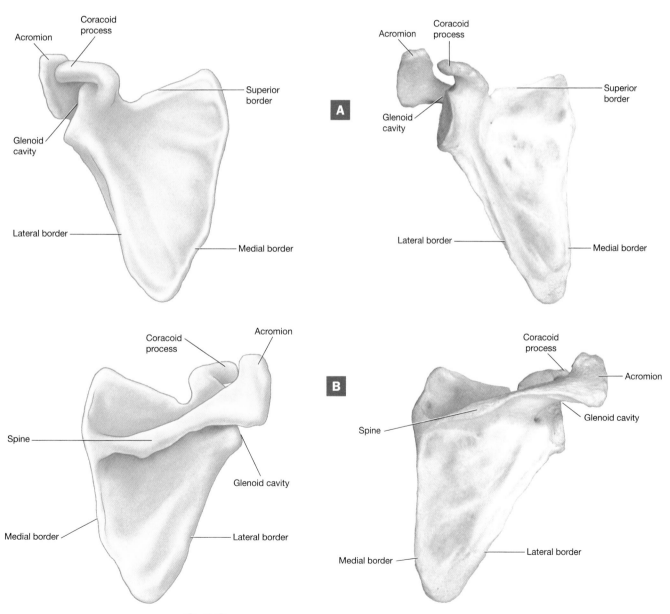

FIGURE **6.18** Right scapula: (**A**) anterior view; (**B**) posterior view

The two forearm bones, shown in Figures 6.20 and 6.21, are the lateral **radius** (RAY-dee-us) and medial **ulna** (UL-nuh; if you have a hard time remembering which is which, stand in anatomical position and take your radial pulse; it is on the lateral side of the forearm, just like the radius). The ulna is wide proximally where it articulates with the humerus and thin distally where it articulates with the bones of the wrist. Its proximal end has two processes—the large, posterior **olecranon process** and the smaller, anterior **coronoid process**—separated by a deep curve called the **trochlear notch**.

As its name implies, the trochlear notch fits around the trochlea of the humerus to form the elbow joint. The olecranon process is the actual "elbow bone," which you can feel on your posterior arm. The trochlear notch and the ulna's two processes form a U shape when the ulna is held on its side. This makes the ulna easy to differentiate from the radius.

The radius has a width distribution opposite from that of the ulna—it is skinny proximally and wide distally. Proximally it consists of a **radial head** that articulates with the ulna at the **proximal radioulnar joint**. Note in Figure 6.20 that the two bones also articulate at their distal ends at the **distal radioulnar joint**. Both the radius and the ulna have projections on their distal ends called **styloid processes**.

The wrist is composed of eight short bones called **carpals** (KAR-pulz), labeled individually in Figure 6.22. The carpals articulate with the radius and the ulna as well as the five long bones in the hand called **metacarpals** (met-uh-KAR-pulz). The metacarpals articulate distally with the fingers, which are formed from 14 long bones called **phalanges** (fuh-LAN-jeez; singular, *phalanx*). The second through fifth digits have three phalanges each (the *proximal*, *middle*, and *distal phalanges*); the thumb has only two (a *proximal* and a *distal phalanx*).

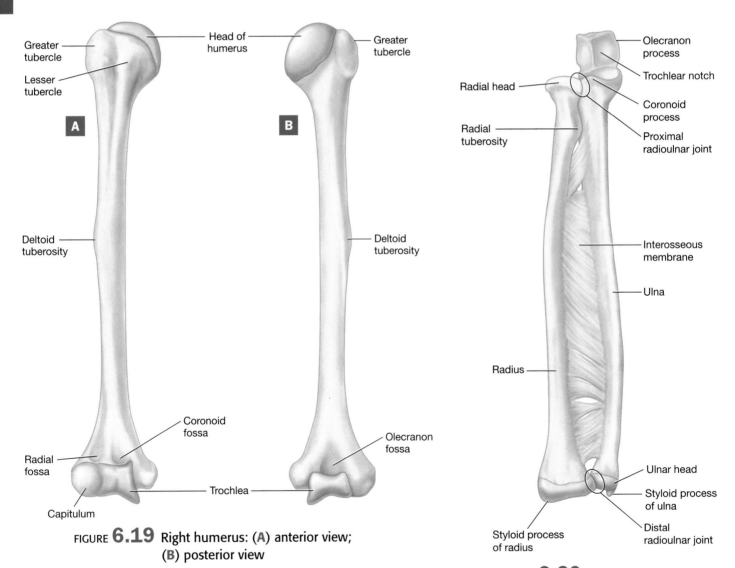

FIGURE **6.19** Right humerus: (**A**) anterior view; (**B**) posterior view

FIGURE **6.20** Right radius and ulna, anterior view

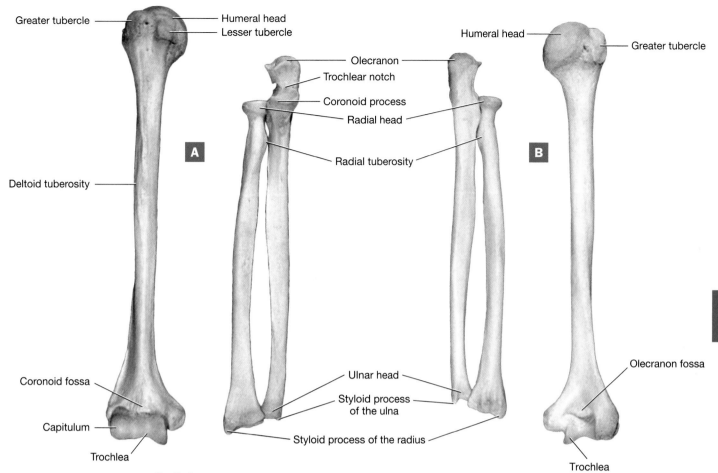

FIGURE **6.21** Bones of the upper limb: (**A**) humerus, radius, and ulna, anterior view; (**B**) humerus, radius, and ulna, posterior view

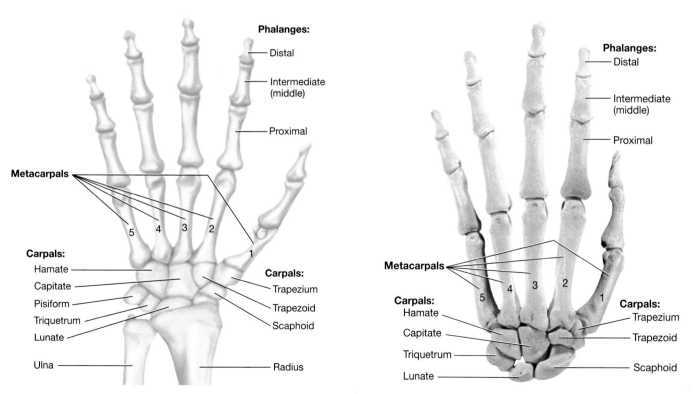

FIGURE **6.22** Right wrist and hand, anterior view

The pelvic girdle connects the lower limbs to the trunk, supports the pelvic organs, and transmits the weight of the trunk to the legs. It is formed by two **coxal bones**. Three fused bones—the **ilium** (IL-ee-um), the **ischium** (ISS-kee-um), and the **pubis** (PYOO-bis)—make up each coxal bone (Figures 6.23 and 6.24). Notice that the lateral side of the hip (Figure 6.24) has a place where all three bones come together to form a deep socket. This socket, called the **acetabulum** (ass-e-TAB-yoo-lum), forms the hip joint with the femur. Notice also that where the ischium and pubis meet there is a large hole called the **obturator** (AHB-tur-ay-tur) **foramen**. In a living person this hole is covered with a membrane and allows only small blood vessels and nerves to pass through.

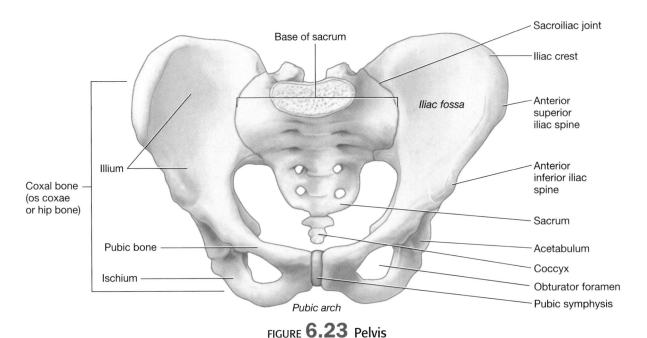

FIGURE **6.23** Pelvis

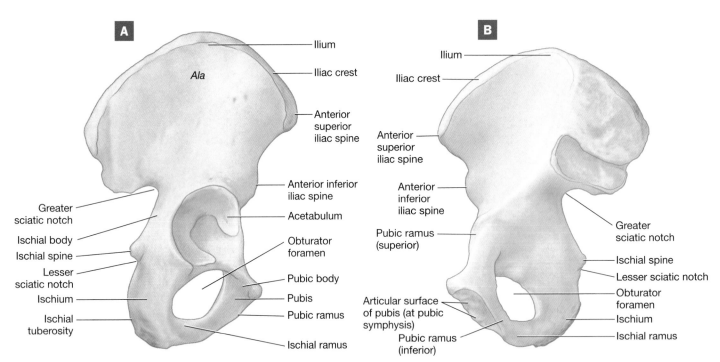

FIGURE **6.24** Pelvis: (**A**) right coxal bone, lateral view; (**B**) right coxal bone, medial view

The three bones of the hip have the following features:

1. **Ilium.** The ilium is the largest of the three bones. Its main portion is called the **body**, and its superior "wing" is called the **ala**. The ridge of the ala, called the **iliac crest,** is where you rest your hands when your hands are on your hips. At the anterior end of the crest we find a projection called the **anterior superior iliac spine.** The posterior ilium also features the **greater sciatic (SY-a-tik) notch,** which allows the large greater sciatic nerve to pass between the pelvis and the thigh.

2. **Ischium.** The ischium makes up the posteroinferior pelvis. It contains three features on its posterior side: the superior **ischial spine,** the middle **lesser sciatic notch,** and the thick, inferior **ischial tuberosity.** The ischial tuberosities are the "butt bones," the bones that bear your weight when you sit down.

3. **Pubis.** The pelvis' anterior portion is formed by the pubis, or the **pubic bone.** The pubis consists of a **body** and two extensions called the **superior** and **inferior rami.** The bodies of the two pubic bones meet at a fibrocartilage pad called the **pubic symphysis (SIM-fih-sis).**

The lower limb consists of the thigh, the **patella** (puh-TEL-uh, or kneecap), the leg, the ankle, and the foot. The thigh contains only a single bone, the large, heavy **femur** (FEE-mur; Figures 6.25 and 6.27). Proximally, the femur articulates with the acetabulum at its rounded **head.** Just distal to the femoral head is the **neck** of the femur, the weakest part of the femur and the most common location for it to fracture (when the femoral neck fractures, it is usually called a "broken hip"). Where the femoral neck meets the femoral shaft, we find two large prominences—the anterolateral **greater trochanter** (troh-KAN-tur) and the posteromedial **lesser trochanter.**

Distally, the femur expands into the **medial** and **lateral condyles,** which form the knee joint with the largest bone of the leg, the **tibia** (TIH-bee-uh). The tibia is flattened proximally at its articular surface, and its **medial** and **lateral condyles** fit together with those of the femur (Figures 6.26 and 6.27). Just distal to the knee joint is an anterior projection known as the **tibial tuberosity,** which is where the patellar ligament inserts. Distally, the tibia articulates with a tarsal bone called the **talus,** with which it forms the ankle joint. At its terminal end is a projection called the **medial malleolus** (mal-ee-OH-lus), the medial ankle bone.

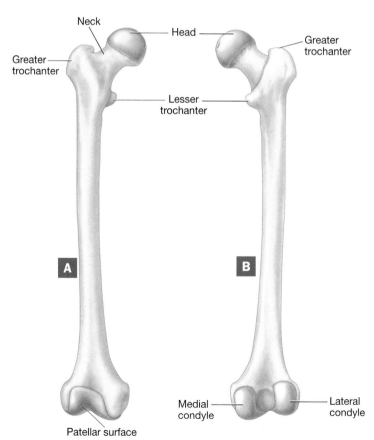

FIGURE **6.25** Right femur: (**A**) anterior view; (**B**) posterior view

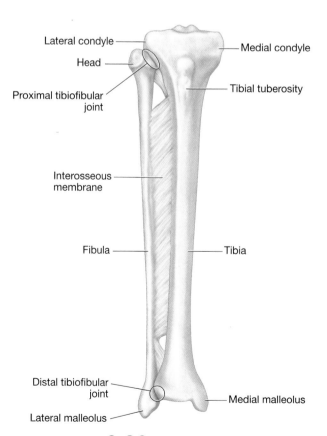

FIGURE **6.26** Right tibia and fibula, anterior view

The other leg bone is the thin, lateral **fibula** (FIB-yoo-luh). The proximal fibular end is called the **head**, and its distal end is the **lateral malleolus** (*lateral ankle bone*). The fibula doesn't articulate directly with either the femur or the talus. It does, however, articulate with the lateral side of the tibia at *proximal* and *distal tibiofibular joints*.

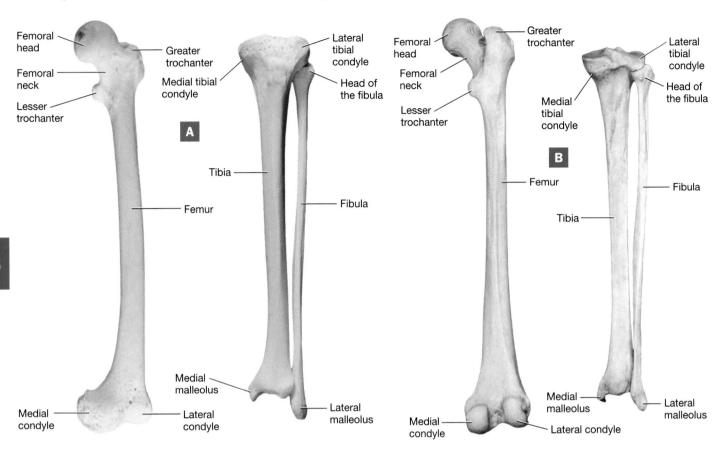

FIGURE **6.27** Bones of the lower limb: (**A**) femur, tibia, and fibula, anterior view; (**B**) femur, tibia, and fibula, posterior view

The ankle is composed of seven short bones called **tarsals** (TAHR-sulz), labeled individually in Figure 6.28. The tarsals articulate with the five long bones in the foot called **metatarsals** (met-uh-TAHR-sulz). Like the bones of the fingers, the bones of the toes also consist of 14 **phalanges**. The second through fifth digits have three phalanges each (the *proximal*, *intermediate* [or *middle*], and *distal phalanges*), and the big toe, or *hallux*, has only two (a *proximal* and a *distal phalanx*).

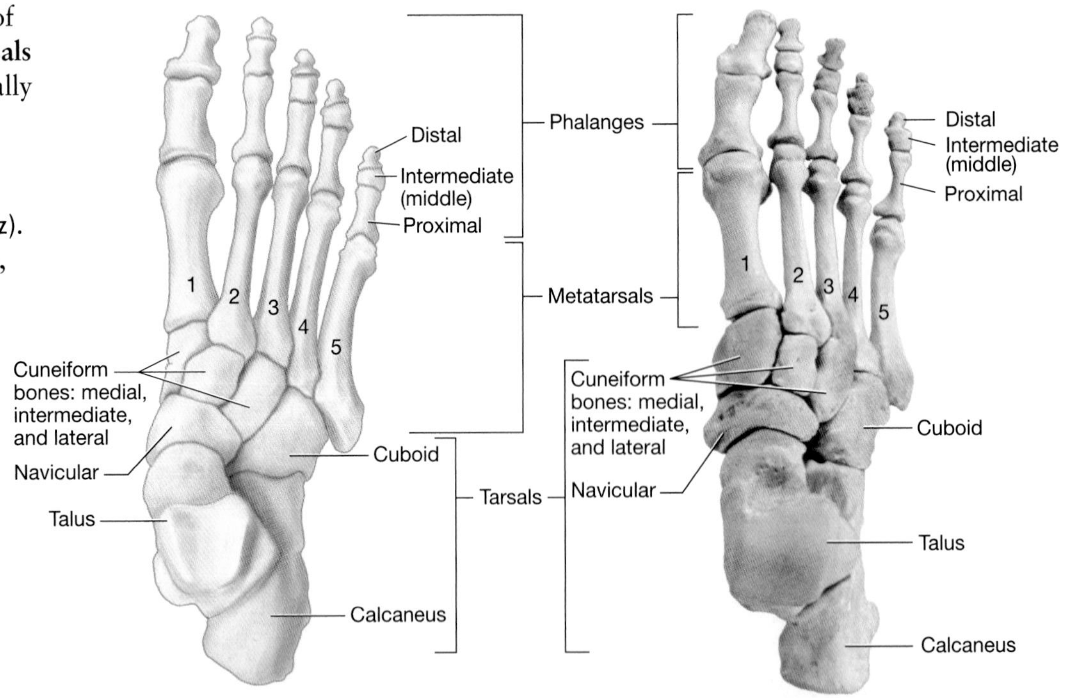

FIGURE **6.28** Right foot and ankle, superior view

Procedure 1 Cooperative Learning for the Skeleton

We will follow essentially the same procedure here as we did in Exercise 6-3, but with different groups of bones and bone markings. Note that this cooperative learning exercise includes the structures from Exercise 6-2.

1 Assemble into groups with a minimum of four students; five is optimum.

2 Distribute a bone or set of bones to each member of the group, and assign each student one of the following five groups of bones and bone markings (the specific structures of each bone are listed below and on the next page:

Group 1: cervical, thoracic, and lumbar vertebrae and vertebral markings; ribs and rib markings; sternum structures and the hyoid bone

Group 2: scapula structures, clavicle structures, humerus structures

Group 3: radius and ulna markings, carpals, metacarpals, and phalanges

Group 4: ilium, ischium, and pubis structures, and the difference between the male and female pelvises

Group 5: femur, tibia, fibula structures, tarsals, metatarsals, phalanges

3 Spend approximately three minutes learning the assigned structures on your own.

4 Ask each student to spend approximately one to two minutes teaching the group his or her assigned structures.

5 Rotate the assigned structures clockwise so each student has a new set of structures to learn (the student assigned Group 1 will take Group 2, and so on).

6 Spend approximately two to three minutes learning your newly assigned structures.

7 Then ask each student to take approximately one to two minutes to teach the group his or her assigned structures.

8 Repeat this process (it begins to speed up significantly at this point) until each student has been taught each group of structures once. By the end of this "game," each group member will have learned and presented each group of structures.

The following is a list of bone and bone markings of the appendicular skeleton covered in this exercise.

Remaining Structures of the Axial Skeleton

Group 1 Structures
1. Vertebrae
   a. Body
   b. Spinous process
   c. Vertebral foramen
   d. Transverse processes
   e. Intervertebral discs
2. Cervical vertebrae
   a. Atlas

   b. Axis
      ▌ Dens
   c. Transverse foramina
3. Thoracic vertebrae
4. Lumbar vertebrae
5. Sacrum
6. Coccyx
7. Ribs

   a. True ribs
   b. False ribs
   c. Floating ribs
8. Sternum
   a. Manubrium
   b. Body
   c. Xiphoid process
9. Hyoid bone

Pectoral Girdle and Upper Limb

Group 2 Structures
1. Clavicle
2. Scapula
   a. Acromion
   b. Spine
   c. Coracoid process
   d. Glenoid cavity (fossa)

3. Humerus
   a. Head
   b. Greater tubercle
   c. Deltoid tuberosity
   d. Capitulum
   e. Trochlea
   f. Olecranon fossa
   g. Coronoid fossa

Group 3 Structures

1. Radius
2. Ulna
   a. Olecranon process
   b. Coronoid process
   c. Trochlear notch
3. Carpals
4. Metacarpals
5. Phalanges

Pelvic Girdle and Lower Limb

Group 4 Structures

1. Ilium
   a. Iliac crest
   b. Anterior superior iliac spine
   c. Greater sciatic notch
2. Ischium
   a. Ischial tuberosity
   b. Lesser sciatic notch
   c. Obturator foramen
3. Pubis
   a. Pubic symphysis
4. Acetabulum

Group 5 Structures

1. Femur
   a. Head
   b. Neck
   c. Greater trochanter
   d. Lesser trochanter
   e. Medial and lateral condyles
2. Patella
3. Tibia
   a. Tibial tuberosity
   b. Medial malleolus
4. Fibula
   a. Head
   b. Lateral malleolus
5. Tarsals
   a. Talus
   b. Calcaneus
6. Metatarsals
7. Phalanges

Your instructor may wish to omit certain structures included above or add structures not included in these lists. List any additional structures below:

_____

_____

_____

_____

_____

_____

Procedure 2 Building a Skeleton

1 Obtain a set of disarticulated bones (real bones are best).

2 Assemble the bones into a full skeleton. (If you have an articulated vertebral column and rib cage, go ahead and use them.)

3 Be certain to keep your skeleton in anatomical position. Figure 6.29 gives an overall "big picture" view of the skeleton you may use for reference.

4 Assemble the bones into a full skeleton.

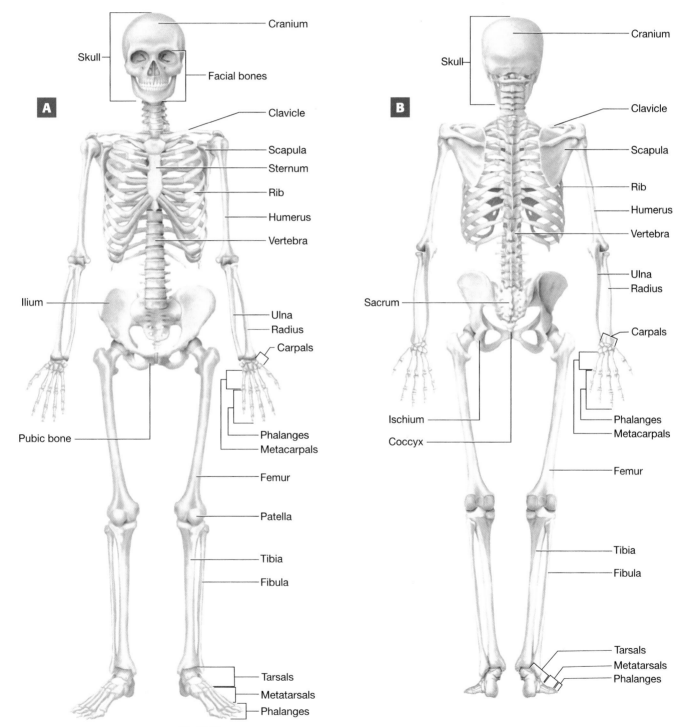

FIGURE **6.29** Articulated skeleton: (**A**) anterior view; (**B**) posterior view

Procedure 3 Identifying Bones Blindly

1 Place your set of disarticulated bones in a box.

2 Working with your lab partner, close your eyes, reach into the box, grab a bone randomly, and attempt to identify it only by its feel.

3 If you are unable to identify the bone, have your lab partner give you hints to help you find out the bone's identity.

6

Exercise 6-5

Articulations

MATERIALS

❏ Skeleton, articulated
❏ Skull

Let's now turn to the other structures of the skeletal system: joints, or **articulations**, where two bones come together. There are three structural classes of joints, which include the following (Figure 6.30):

1. **Fibrous joints.** Fibrous joints consist of two bones joined by short connective tissue fibers. Most fibrous joints allow no motion.

2. **Cartilaginous joints.** Cartilaginous joints consist of bones united by cartilage rather than fibrous connective tissue. Most cartilaginous joints allow some motion; however, the epiphyseal plate, a structure composed of hyaline cartilage found in growing bones, is an immovable cartilaginous joint.

3. **Synovial joints.** Synovial (sin-OH-vee-ul) joints are freely movable joints. They have a true joint cavity and consist of two bones with articular ends covered with hyaline, or **articular**, **cartilage**. The joint is surrounded by a **joint capsule** composed of dense connective tissue. Internally, the capsule is lined by a **synovial membrane** that secretes a watery fluid called **synovial fluid** similar in composition to blood plasma without the proteins. The fluid bathes the joint to permit frictionless motion. The bones in a synovial joint are held together by **ligaments** that reinforce the joint. Certain synovial joints feature structures known as **menisci** (men-IH-sky; singular, *meniscus*) or *articular discs*, fibrocartilage pads that improve the fit of two bones to prevent dislocation. Synovial joints typically are surrounded by tendons that move the bones involved in the joint. The tendons generally are wrapped in a sheath of connective tissue in which they can slide with a minimum of friction. Fluid-filled sacs called **bursae** (BUR-see) are often located between tendons and joints, and this also reduces friction.

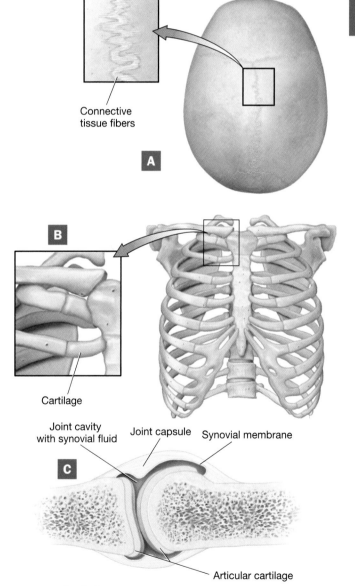

Connective tissue fibers

A

B

Cartilage

Joint cavity with synovial fluid   Joint capsule   Synovial membrane

C

Articular cartilage

FIGURE **6.30** Three classes of joints: (**A**) fibrous joint; (**B**) cartilaginous joint; (**C**) synovial joint

6

Procedure 1 Classifying Joints by Structure

Classify each joint listed in Table 6.3 by its structure. Then examine and manipulate the joint to determine the amount of motion allowed at the joint (freely movable, slightly movable, or immovable).

TABLE **6.3** Structural Classification of Joints

Joint	Structural Classification	Amount of Motion
Intervertebral joint		
Shoulder (glenohumeral) joint		
Coronal suture		
Interphalangeal joint		

Procedure 2 Identifying Structures of Synovial Joints

Identify the following structures on fresh specimens, such as pigs' feet. If fresh specimens are not available, use anatomical models instead.

- ❏ Joint cavity
- ❏ Joint capsule
- ❏ Articular cartilage
- ❏ Articular discs (menisci)
- ❏ Synovial membrane
- ❏ Synovial fluid
- ❏ Bursae
- ❏ Tendon with tendon sheath
- ❏ Ligaments

Procedure 3 Identifying Structures of the Knee Joint

The knee joint, illustrated in Figures 6.31 and 6.32, is formed by the articulation of the distal femur and proximal tibia. It is stabilized by ligaments and by the **medial** and **lateral menisci**. Four important ligaments are:

1. **Anterior cruciate ligament.** The anterior cruciate (KROO-shee-it) ligament, or ACL, extends from the anterior tibia to the lateral femoral condyle. Its function is to prevent hyperextension of the knee.

2. **Posterior cruciate ligament.** The posterior cruciate ligament, or PCL, extends from the posterior tibia to the medial femoral condyle. It crosses under the ACL, and together the two form an "X." The PCL prevents posterior displacement of the tibia on the femur.

3. **Medial collateral** and **lateral collateral ligaments.** The medial and lateral collateral ligaments (MCL and LCL) extend from the medial tibia and the lateral fibula to the femur, respectively. They resist medial and lateral stresses.

Identify the following structures of the knee joint on anatomical models or fresh specimens. Check off each structure as you identify it.

- ❑ Joint capsule
- ❑ Ligaments
  - ❑ Lateral collateral ligament
  - ❑ Medial collateral ligament
  - ❑ Anterior cruciate ligament (ACL)
  - ❑ Posterior cruciate ligament (PCL)
  - ❑ Patellar ligament (tendon)
- ❑ Menisci
  - ❑ Medial meniscus
  - ❑ Lateral meniscus
- ❑ Medial and lateral femoral condyles

6

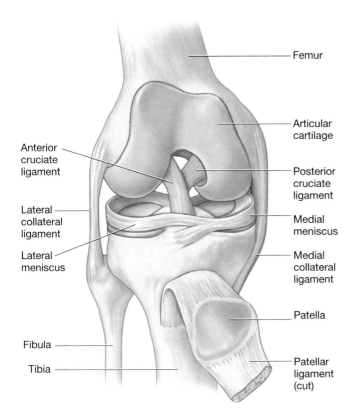

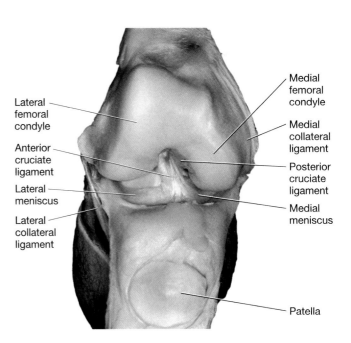

FIGURE **6.31** Right knee joint, anterior view

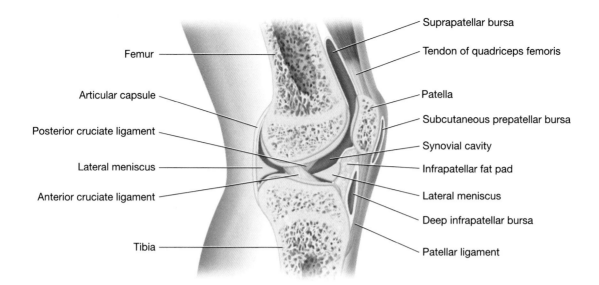

Femur

Articular capsule

Posterior cruciate ligament

Lateral meniscus

Anterior cruciate ligament

Tibia

Suprapatellar bursa

Tendon of quadriceps femoris

Patella

Subcutaneous prepatellar bursa

Synovial cavity

Infrapatellar fat pad

Lateral meniscus

Deep infrapatellar bursa

Patellar ligament

FIGURE **6.32** Right knee joint, midsagittal section

Exercise **6-6**

Motions of Synovial and Cartilaginous Joints

Each time you move your body in a seemingly routine fashion (such as walking or climbing stairs), you are producing motion at numerous joints. Many possible motions can occur at synovial and cartilaginous joints. These motions are illustrated in Figure 6.33.

In the following procedure you will perform two common movements: walking up the stairs and doing jumping jacks. You will determine which joints you are moving with each action, and then which motions are occurring at each joint.

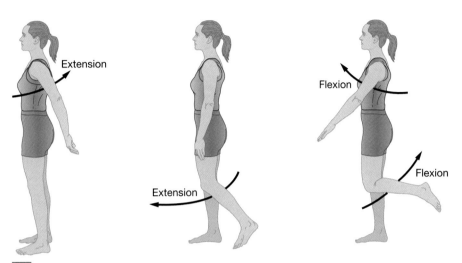

A Angular movements: Extension and flexion at the shoulder and knee

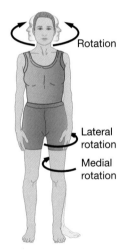

B Rotation of the head, neck, and lower limb

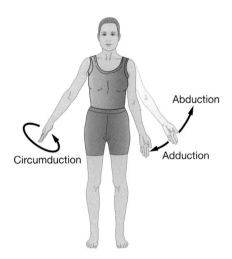

C Angular movements: adduction, abduction, and circumduction of the upper limb at the shoulder

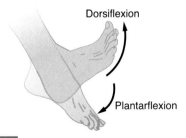

D Dorsiflexion and plantarflexion

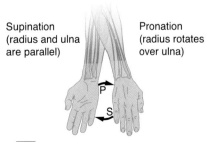

E Pronation (P) and supination (S)

FIGURE **6.33** Motions of synovial and cartilaginous joints

Procedure 1   Identifying Joint Motions of Common Movements

Team up with a partner, and have your partner perform the following actions. Watch carefully as the actions are performed, and list the joints in motion.

Ask your instructor if he or she wants you to use the technical name or the common name for each joint (e.g., glenohumeral versus shoulder joint). Some of the joints, such as the hip joint and knee joint, will be obvious. Others, such as the radioulnar joint, the fingers and toes, and the intervertebral joints, are less obvious and easily overlooked.

After you have listed the joints being used, determine which motions are occurring at each joint. Keep in mind the type and the range of motion of each joint as you answer each question.

1 Walking up stairs

Joints moving: Motions occurring:

_____   _____

_____   _____

_____   _____

_____   _____

_____   _____

_____   _____

_____   _____

_____   _____

2 Doing jumping jacks

Joints moving: Motions occurring:

_____   _____

_____   _____

_____   _____

_____   _____

_____   _____

_____   _____

_____   _____

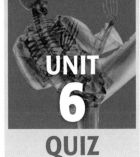

UNIT
6
QUIZ

1 Label the following parts of compact bone on Figure 6.34.

- ❑ Blood vessels
- ❑ Central canal
- ❑ Lacunae
- ❑ Lamellae
- ❑ Osteon
- ❑ Perforating canal
- ❑ Trabeculae of spongy bone

6

FIGURE **6.34** Microscopic anatomy of compact bone tissue

2 Which of the following statements about long bones is/are false? *Mark all that apply.*
a. A long bone is longer than it is wide.
b. They include the bones of the upper and lower extremities except the fingers and toes.
c. They include the bones of the upper extremities except the bones of the ankle and wrist.
d. A long bone is named for its length.

3 Short bones are
a. short in length.
b. about as long as they are wide.
c. irregular in shape.
d. flat.

4 The epiphyseal plate is
a. the structure from which long bones grow in length.
b. a remnant of the structure from which long bones grow in length.
c. composed of osseous tissue.
d. found lining the surface of the epiphysis.

5 A bone tumor disrupts the normal structure of osteons, replacing the organized rings with disorganized, irregular masses of bone. How will this affect the ability of a bone to perform its functions?

_____

_____

_____

_____

_____

_____

6 Label the following bones in Figure 6.35.

❏ Clavicle
❏ Femur
❏ Fibula
❏ Humerus
❏ Ilium
❏ Metacarpals
❏ Pubis
❏ Radius
❏ Sternum
❏ Tarsals
❏ Tibia
❏ Ulna

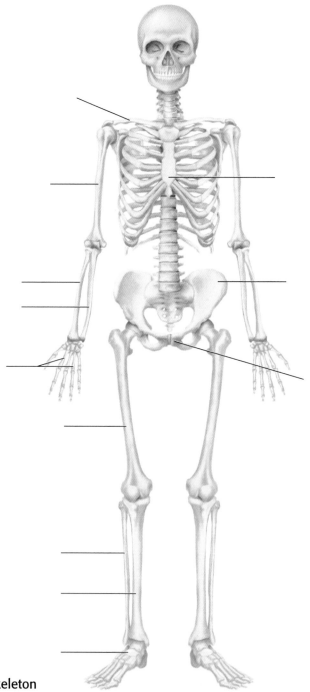

FIGURE **6.35** Anterior view of the skeleton

6

7 Label the following bones of the skull in Figure 6.36.

- ❑ Ethmoid bone
- ❑ Frontal bone
- ❑ Mandible
- ❑ Maxilla
- ❑ Nasal bones
- ❑ Occipital bone
- ❑ Parietal bone
- ❑ Sphenoid bone
- ❑ Temporal bone
- ❑ Zygomatic bone

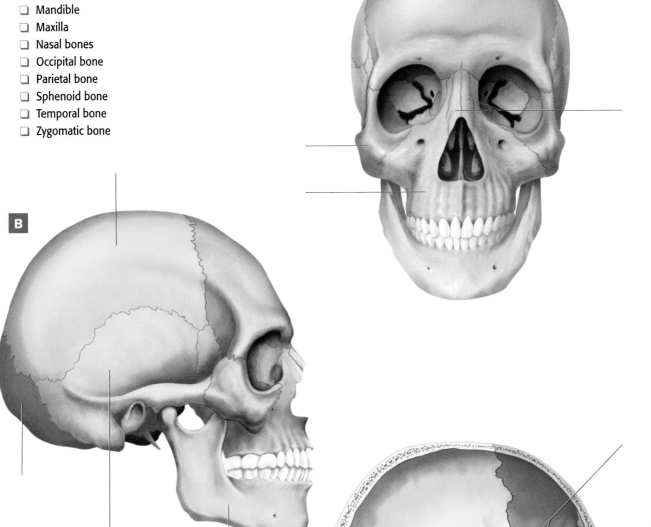

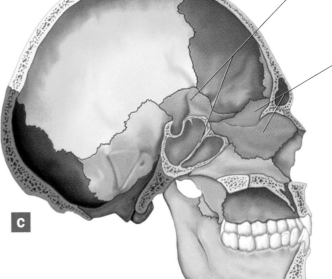

FIGURE **6.36** Skull: (**A**) anterior view; (**B**) lateral view; (**C**) midsagittal section

8 Label the following parts of
the upper limb in Figure 6.37.

- ❑ Capitulum
- ❑ Coronoid process
- ❑ Deltoid tuberosity
- ❑ Olecranon
- ❑ Trochlea
- ❑ Trochlear notch

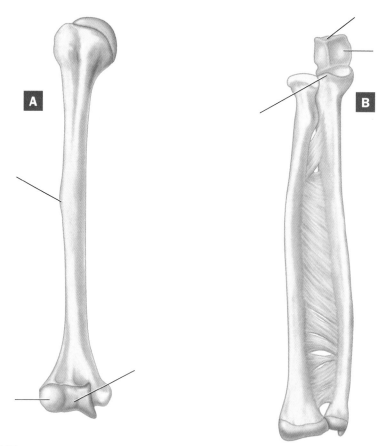

FIGURE **6.37** Upper limb: (**A**) arm, anterior view; (**B**) forearm, anterior view

9 Label the following parts of the
coxal bone (hemipelvis) in Figure 6.38.

- ❑ Acetabulum
- ❑ Anterior superior iliac spine
- ❑ Iliac crest
- ❑ Ilium
- ❑ Ischium
- ❑ Obturator foramen
- ❑ Pubis

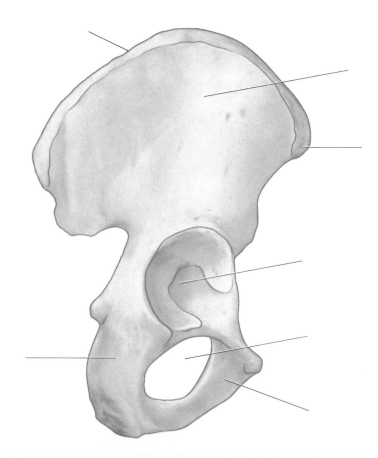

FIGURE **6.38** Right coxal bone, lateral view

10 Label the following parts of the lower limb in Figure 6.39.

❑ Greater trochanter
❑ Head
❑ Lateral malleolus
❑ Lesser trochanter
❑ Medial malleolus

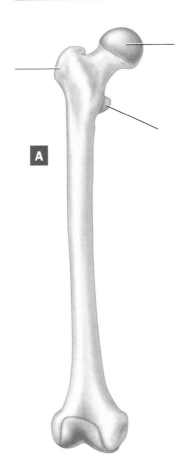

A

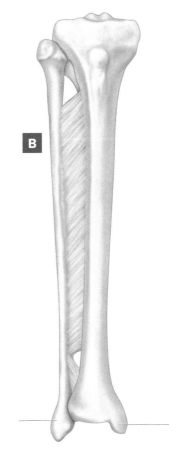

B

FIGURE **6.39** Lower limb:
(**A**) thigh, anterior view;
(**B**) leg, anterior view

11 You are presented the following X-ray from a 6-year-old child (Figure 6.40).

a Identify the bones in the X-ray.

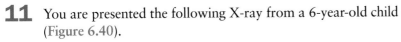

_____

_____

_____

_____

_____

b Your colleague thinks there may be a fracture present at the arrow in Figure 6.40. What do you think? Is this a fracture or a normal anatomical feature? Explain.

_____

_____

_____

_____

_____

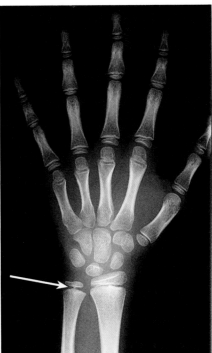

FIGURE **6.40** X-ray from 6-year-old child

6

12 Most cartilaginous joints allow _____.

    a. no motion

    b. some motion

13 Synovial joints are filled with _____, which _____ the joint.

    a. serous fluid; lubricates

    b. synovial fluid; lubricates

    c. serous fluid; increases range of motion of

    d. synovial fluid; increases range of motion of

14 Label the following parts of the knee joint in Figure 6.41.

    ❑ Anterior cruciate ligament
    ❑ Lateral collateral ligament
    ❑ Lateral meniscus
    ❑ Medial collateral ligament
    ❑ Medial meniscus
    ❑ Posterior cruciate ligament

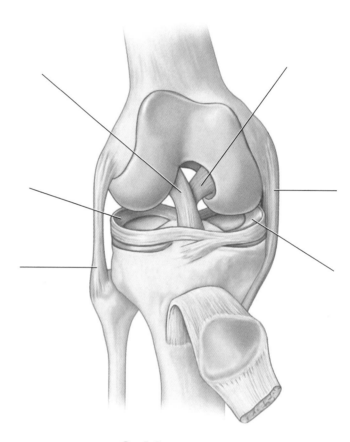

FIGURE **6.41** Knee joint

15 Which of the following correctly describes abduction?

    a. Abduction decreases the angle between two bones.

    b. Abduction moves a body part toward the midline of the body.

    c. Abduction moves a bone around its own axis.

    d. Abduction moves a body part away from the midline of the body.

Muscle Tissue and Muscular System

OBJECTIVES

Once you have completed this unit, you should be able to:

1. Describe the microscopic anatomy of skeletal muscle fibers.

2. Identify structures of skeletal muscle.

3. Identify muscles of the upper and lower limbs, trunk, head, and neck.

4. List the muscles required to perform common movements.

Name _____ Section _____ Date _____

PRE-LAB EXERCISES

Complete the following exercises prior to coming to lab, using your textbook and lab manual for reference.

Pre-Lab Exercise 7-1

✎ **Key Terms**

You should be familiar with the following terms before coming to lab. For the skeletal muscles, describe the muscles' location and appearance.

Pre-Lab Exercise 7-1

✎ Key Terms
You should be familiar with the following terms before c
describe the muscles' location and appearance.

Term
Skeletal Muscle Structures
Epimysium
      icle

Perimysium

Term	Definition

Skeletal Muscle Structures

Epimysium _____

_____

Fascicle _____

_____

Perimysium _____

_____

Muscle fiber _____

_____

Endomysium _____

_____

Structures of the Skeletal Muscle Fiber

Sarcolemma _____

_____

T-tubule _____

_____

Sarcoplasmic reticulum _____

_____

Myofibril _____

_____

Myofilament _____

_____

Sarcomere _____

_____

A band _____

_____

I band _____

_____

General Terms

Origin _____

_____

Insertion _____

_____

Muscle action _____

_____

Skeletal Muscles of the Head, Neck, and Thorax

Sternocleidomastoid _____

_____

Trapezius _____

_____

Erector spinae _____

_____

Intercostal muscles _____

_____

Diaphragm _____

_____

Rectus abdominis _____

_____

Skeletal Muscles That Move the Upper Limb

Deltoid _____

_____

Latissimus dorsi _____

_____

Pectoralis major _____

_____

Biceps brachii _____

_____

Triceps brachii _____

_____

Brachioradialis _____

_____

Skeletal Muscles That Move the Lower Limb

Gluteus muscles _____

_____

Sartorius _____

_____

Quadriceps femoris group _____

_____

Hamstrings group _____

_____

Gastrocnemius _____

_____

Pre-Lab Exercise **7-2**

Basic Skeletal Muscle Anatomy

Label and color the basic structures of skeletal muscles depicted in Figure 7.1 with the following terms from Exercise 7-1. Use your text and Exercise 7-1 in this unit for reference.

❑ Endomysium
❑ Fascicle
❑ Muscle fiber (cell)
❑ Tendon

Connective Tissue Coverings
❑ Epimysium
❑ Perimysium

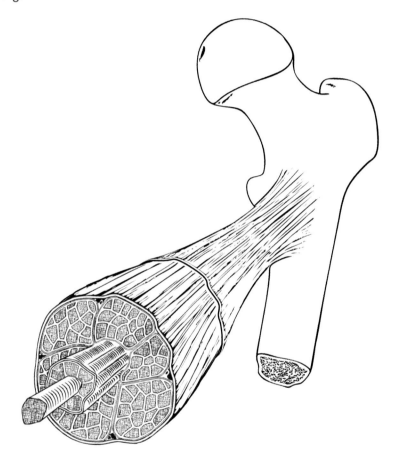

FIGURE **7.1** Basic skeletal muscle structure

Label and color the microscopic anatomy of the skeletal muscle fiber depicted in **Figure 7.2** with the following terms from Exercise 7-1. Use your text and Exercise 7-1 in this unit for reference.

- ❏ Myofibril
- ❏ Sarcolemma
- ❏ Sarcomere
  - ❏ A band
  - ❏ I band
  - ❏ Z disc
- ❏ Transverse tubules
- ❏ Sarcoplasmic reticulum
- ❏ Terminal cisternae
- ❏ Triad

7

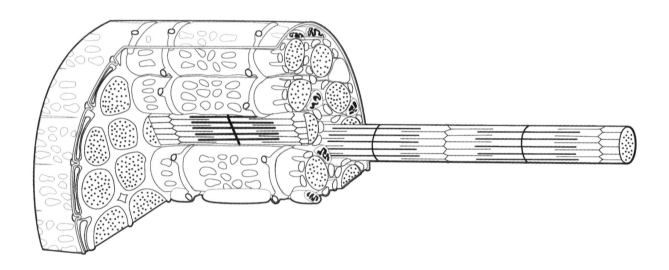

FIGURE **7.2** Skeletal muscle fiber

Pre-Lab Exercise 7-4

Skeletal Muscle Anatomy

Label and color the muscles depicted in Figure 7.3 with the following terms from Exercise 7-2. Use your text and Exercise 7-2 in this unit for reference.

Muscles That Move the Face and Head

- ❏ Orbicularis oculi
- ❏ Zygomaticus
- ❏ Orbicularis oris
- ❏ Temporalis
- ❏ Masseter
- ❏ Sternocleidomastoid
- ❏ Trapezius

Muscles That Move the Trunk

- ❏ Rectus abdominis
- ❏ External oblique

Muscles That Move the Shoulder

- ❏ Deltoid
- ❏ Pectoralis major
- ❏ Latissimus dorsi

Muscles That Move the Forearm

- ❏ Biceps brachii
- ❏ Triceps brachii
- ❏ Brachialis
- ❏ Brachioradialis

Muscles That Move the Hip and Knee

- ❏ Gluteus maximus
- ❏ Sartorius
- ❏ Quadriceps femoris group
  - ❏ Rectus femoris
  - ❏ Vastus lateralis
  - ❏ Vastus medialis
- ❏ Hamstring muscles
  - ❏ Semitendinosus
  - ❏ Semimembranosus
  - ❏ Biceps femoris

Muscles That Move the Ankle

- ❏ Gastrocnemius
- ❏ Soleus
- ❏ Tibialis anterior

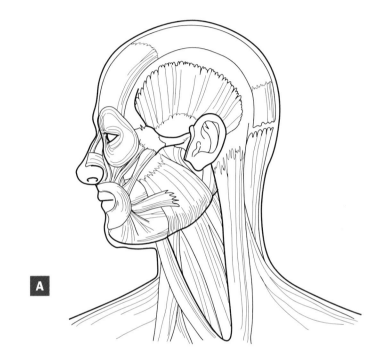

FIGURE **7.3** Human musculature: **(A)** lateral view of the face *(continues)*

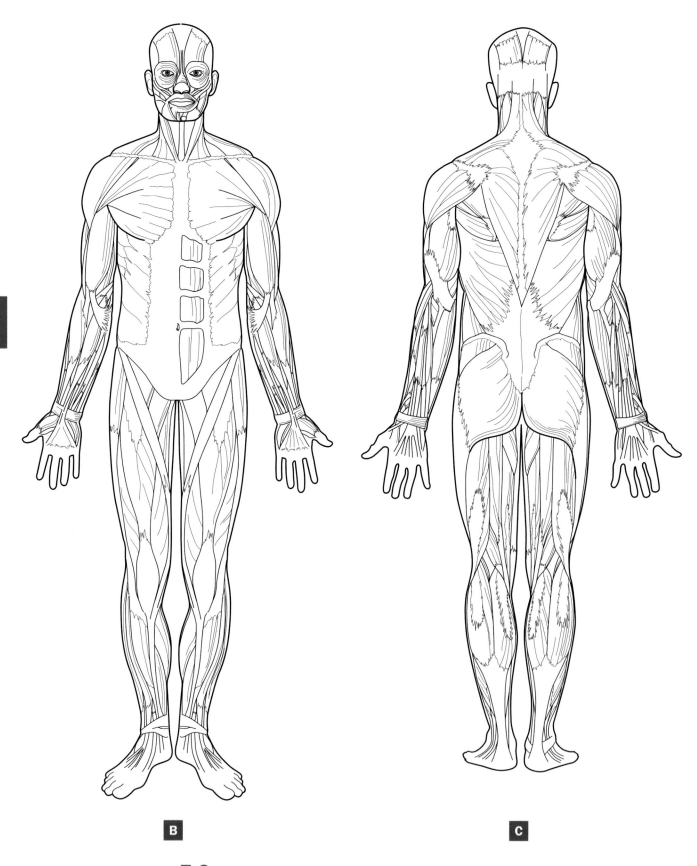

FIGURE **7.3** Human musculature *(cont.)*: **(B)** anterior view **(C)** posterior view

EXERCISES

The human body has nearly 700 **skeletal muscles** that range dramatically in size and shape from the large trapezius muscle to the tiny corrugator supercilii muscle. Luckily for you, we will be learning only about 40 muscles rather than the full 700. The exercises in this unit help you become familiar with the basic gross and microscopic anatomy of skeletal muscles, the main muscle groups, and their component muscles.

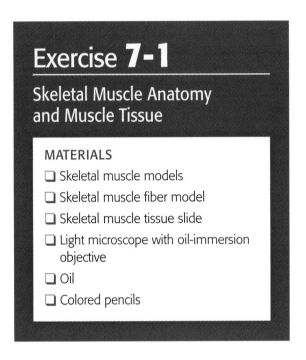

Exercise **7-1**

Skeletal Muscle Anatomy and Muscle Tissue

MATERIALS

❏ Skeletal muscle models
❏ Skeletal muscle fiber model
❏ Skeletal muscle tissue slide
❏ Light microscope with oil-immersion objective
❏ Oil
❏ Colored pencils

A skeletal muscle is composed of skeletal muscle cells, also called **muscle fibers**, arranged into groups called **fascicles** (FAS-ih-kulz; Figure 7.4). The muscle as a whole is covered by a connective tissue sheath called the **epimysium** (ep-ih-MY-see-um) that blends with the thick, superficial fascia that binds muscles into groups. The epimysium also blends with the fibers of tendons and aponeuroses, which connect the muscle to bones or soft tissue. Each fascicle is surrounded by another connective tissue sheath called the **perimysium** (pair-ih-MY-see-um). Individual skeletal muscle fibers are surrounded by their extracellular matrix, known as the **endomysium** (en-doh-MY-see-um).

Skeletal muscle fibers are long, cylindrical cells wrapped by their plasma membrane, known as the **sarcolemma** (sahr-koh-LEM-uh; Figures 7.5 and 7.6). About 80% of the skeletal muscle fiber's cytoplasm, also called its **sarcoplasm** (SAHR-koh-plazm), is filled with small cylindrical organelles called **myofibrils** (my-oh-FY-brilz) composed of protein subunits called **myofilaments**. The remainder of the sarcoplasm contains abundant mitochondria, multiple nuclei, and a modified endoplasmic reticulum called the **sarcoplasmic reticulum** (SR) that wraps around the myofibrils. Notice that at certain points along the myofibril, the SR swells to form **terminal cisternae** (sis-TUR-nee). Running down the middle of each terminal cisterna is an inward extension of the sarcolemma known as a **T-tubule**. A group of two terminal cisternae and a T-tubule is called a **triad**.

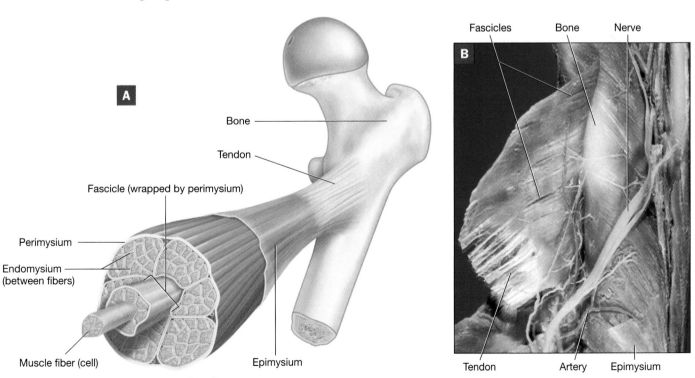

FIGURE **7.4** (**A**) Basic skeletal muscle structure; (**B**) dissected muscle

There are two types of myofilaments involved in contraction: (1) **thick filaments**, and (2) **thin filaments**. The arrangement of thick and thin filaments within the myofibrils is what gives skeletal muscle its characteristic **striated** appearance. The dark regions of the striations, called **A bands**, are dark because this is where the thick and thin filaments overlap. The light regions, called **I bands**, appear light because they contain only thin filaments. Bisecting the I band is a dark line called the **Z disc**. The terms of this alphabet soup are used to describe the fundamental unit of contraction: the **sarcomere** (SAR-koh-meer). A sarcomere, defined as the space from one Z disc to the next Z disc, consists of a full A band and two half-I bands.

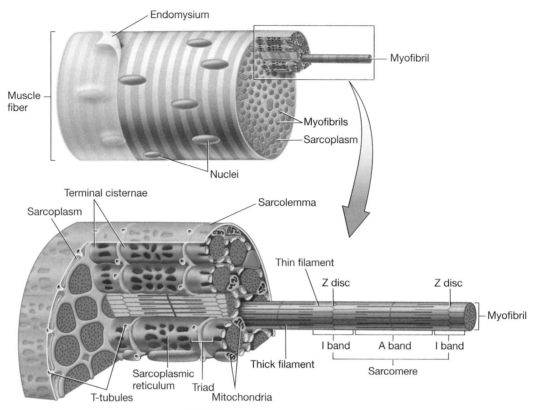

FIGURE **7.5** Skeletal muscle fiber

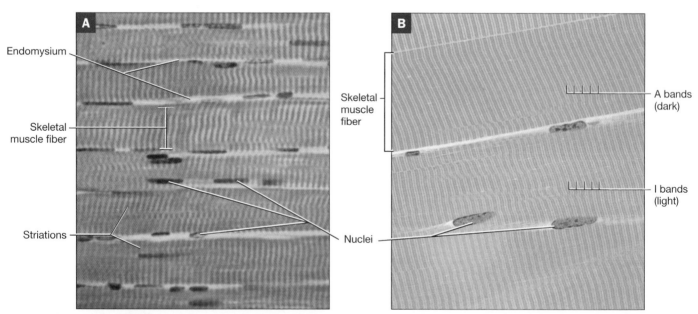

FIGURE **7.6** Skeletal muscle tissue: (**A**) 40× objective; (**B**) 100× objective (oil immersion)

Procedure 1 Model Inventory for Skeletal Muscle and Skeletal Muscle Fibers

Identify the following structures of skeletal muscle and skeletal muscle fibers on models and diagrams, using your textbook and this unit for reference. As you examine the anatomical models and diagrams, record on the model inventory in Table 7.1 the name of the model and the structures you were able to identify.

Skeletal Muscle Anatomy

1. Connective tissue coverings
   a. Epimysium
   b. Perimysium
2. Fascicle
3. Muscle fiber (cell)
4. Tendon

Muscle Fiber Microanatomy

1. Myofibrils
2. Sarcolemma
3. Sarcomere
   a. A band
   b. I band
   c. Z disc
4. Transverse tubules
5. Sarcoplasmic reticulum
6. Terminal cisternae
7. Triad
8. Endomysium

TABLE **7.1** Model Inventory for Skeletal Muscle Anatomy and Microanatomy

Model/Diagram	Structures Identified

Procedure 2 Microscopy of Skeletal Muscle Tissue

View a prepared slide of skeletal muscle tissue.

1 First examine the slide with the regular high-power objective of your light microscope.

2 Draw and color what you see, and label your drawing with the terms indicated.

3 Then switch to an oil-immersion lens (your instructor may have one set up as a demonstration), and identify the structures of the sarcomere.

High-Power (40×) Objective

1. Striations
   a. A band
   b. I band
2. Sarcolemma
3. Nuclei
4. Endomysium

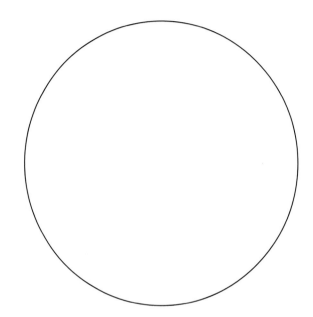

Oil-Immersion Lens

1. Sarcomere
2. A band
3. I band
4. Z disc

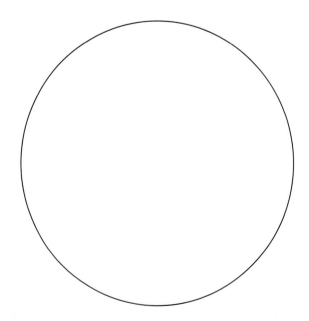

Exercise **7-2**

Skeletal Muscles

MATERIALS

❏ Muscle models: upper limb, lower limb, trunk, head, neck

In this exercise, we divide skeletal muscles into muscle groups that have similar functions. For example, the latissimus dorsi muscle is located on the back, but we classify it with the muscles of the upper limb because that is what it moves. We will use the following groupings of skeletal muscles in this unit:

1. **Muscles that move the head, neck, and face.** We can subdivide the muscles that move the head, neck, and face into the muscles of **facial expression**, the muscles of **mastication** (mas-tih-KAY-shun), and the muscles that move the head. The muscles of facial expression control the various facial expressions humans are capable of making, and they all insert into skin or other muscles. Examples include the **orbicularis oculi** (ohr-bik-yoo-LAIR-is AHK-yoo-lye), which closes and squints the eye, the **orbicularis oris** (OHR-is), which purses the lips, and the **zygomaticus** (zy-goh-MAT-ih-kus), which pulls the corners of the mouth laterally during smiling. The other muscles of facial expression are illustrated in Figure 7.7.

The muscles of mastication are involved in chewing. They include the **masseter** (MAS-e-tur), a thick muscle over the lateral jaw, and the fan-shaped **temporalis** (tem-pohr-AL-is) **muscle**, which rests over the lateral skull.

Several muscles move the head, including the **trapezius** (tra-PEE-zee-us), which holds the head upright and hyperextends the neck (note that it also elevates the shoulders), and the **sternocleidomastoid** (stur-noh-kly-doh-MAS-toyd), a strap-like muscle in the neck that flexes the head and neck, rotates the neck laterally, and flexes the neck laterally.

FIGURE **7.7** Facial musculature, lateral view

2. **Muscles that move the trunk.** The muscles that move the trunk are the muscles of the thorax, muscles of the abdominal wall, and postural muscles of the back (Figures 7.8, 7.9, and 7.10).

   a. The muscles of the thorax are generally involved in the muscle movements that produce ventilation (breathing). The small **pectoralis** (pek-tohr-AL-is) **minor** draws the scapula anteriorly and the rib cage superiorly during forced inspiration and expiration, the **internal** and **external intercostal** muscles are located between the ribs and are involved in both quiet and forced inspiration and expiration, and the circular **diaphragm** (DY-uh-fram) is the main muscle for inspiration. Note that the diaphragm and pectoralis minor are not visible in Figure 7.9.

   b. The abdominal muscles move the vertebral column and increase intra-abdominal pressure. The **rectus abdominis** (REK-tus ab-DAHM-in-us) is the central and superficial muscle that flexes the vertebral column, the **internal** and **external obliques** are located laterally and rotate the vertebral column, and the deep **transversus** (tranz-VUR-sus) **abdominis** compresses the abdominal contents to increase intra-abdominal pressure.

   c. The three postural muscles of the back are all part of the long muscle known as the **erector spinae** (SPY-nee) that runs the length of the vertebral column.

3. **Muscles that move the shoulder.** Only three muscles are "prime movers" of the shoulder: the **deltoid**, or "shoulder muscle," the prime abductor of the shoulder; the **pectoralis major**, or "chest muscle," the prime muscle of shoulder

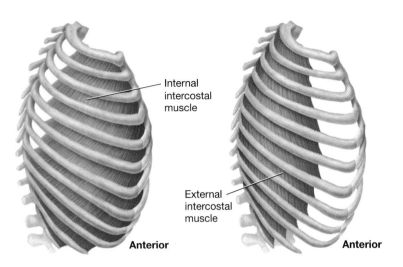

FIGURE **7.8** Internal and external intercostal muscles, lateral view

flexion; and the posterior **latissimus dorsi** (lah-TIS-ih-mus DOHR-sye), the prime muscle of shoulder extension (Figures 7.10, 7.11, and 7.12).

4. **Muscles that move the forearm.** The main muscles that move the forearm are the anterior **biceps brachii** (BY-seps BRAY-kee-eye), the anterior and lateral **brachioradialis** (bray-kee-oh-ray-dee-AL-is), and the posterior **triceps brachii** (TRY-seps BRAY-kee-eye; Figures 7.11 and 7.12). The first three muscles play a role in forearm flexion, and the triceps brachii extends the forearm. The rest of the muscles of the upper limb act on the wrist, the hand, and the digits.

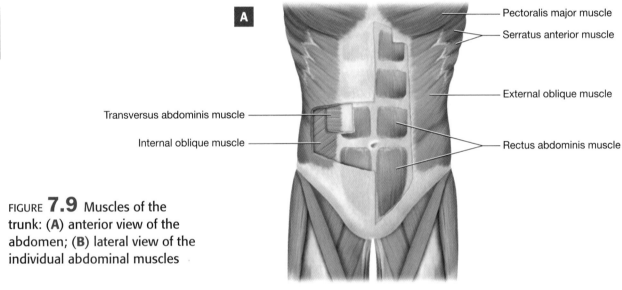

FIGURE **7.9** Muscles of the trunk: (**A**) anterior view of the abdomen; (**B**) lateral view of the individual abdominal muscles

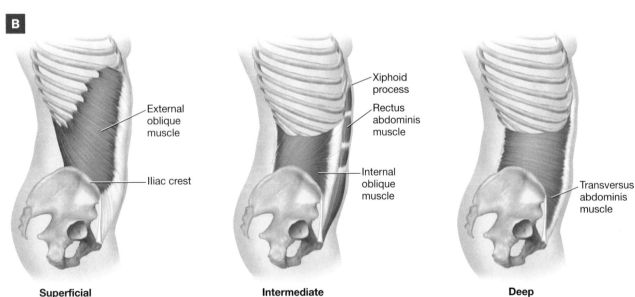

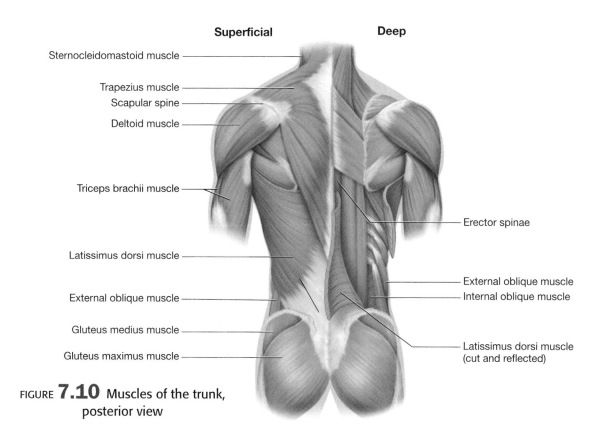

Superficial   Deep

Sternocleidomastoid muscle

Trapezius muscle

Scapular spine

Deltoid muscle

Triceps brachii muscle

Erector spinae

Latissimus dorsi muscle

External oblique muscle

Internal oblique muscle

External oblique muscle

Gluteus medius muscle

Gluteus maximus muscle

Latissimus dorsi muscle
(cut and reflected)

FIGURE **7.10** Muscles of the trunk,
posterior view

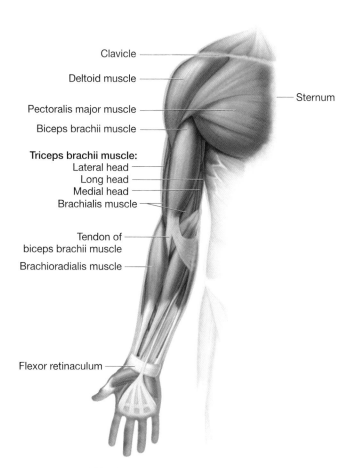

Clavicle

Deltoid muscle

Pectoralis major muscle

Biceps brachii muscle

Sternum

Triceps brachii muscle:
   Lateral head
   Long head
   Medial head
Brachialis muscle

Tendon of
biceps brachii muscle

Brachioradialis muscle

Flexor retinaculum

FIGURE **7.11** Anterior view of the muscles
of the right upper limb

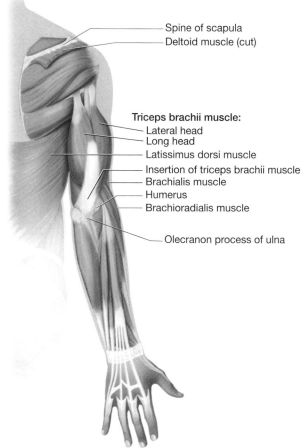

Spine of scapula

Deltoid muscle (cut)

Triceps brachii muscle:
   Lateral head
   Long head
Latissimus dorsi muscle
Insertion of triceps brachii muscle
Brachialis muscle
Humerus
Brachioradialis muscle

Olecranon process of ulna

FIGURE **7.12** Posterior view of the muscles
of the right upper limb

7

5. **Muscles that move the hip and knee.** Muscles that move the hip joint exclusively include the deep **iliopsoas** (il-ee-oh-SOH-us), the anterior **adductor group**, and the posterior **gluteus** (GLOO-tee-us) **maximus** and **gluteus medius** (Figure 7.13). The iliopsoas is the prime flexor of the hip joint. As implied by their names, the muscles in the adductor group are the prime adductors of the hip joint. The gluteus maximus is the prime extensor of the hip joint, and the gluteus medius is a major abductor of the hip joint. The rest of the thigh muscles generally move both the knee and hip joints. The anterior thigh muscles include the **sartorius** (sahr-TOHR-ee-us), the medial **gracilis** (grah-SIH-lis), and the four muscles of the **quadriceps femoris** (QWAH-drih-seps fem-OHR-is) **group**: the **rectus femoris, vastus lateralis, vastus intermedius**, and **vastus medialis** muscles. Note that the vastus intermedius isn't visible in Figure 7.13 because it is deep to the rectus femoris. Most of these muscles both flex the hip joint and extend the knee joint. The posterior thigh muscles include the three muscles of the **hamstrings group**: the lateral **biceps femoris** and the medial **semitendinosus** (sem-eye-ten-din-OH-sus) and **semimembranosus** (sem-eye-mem-bray-NOH-sus) muscles. These three muscles both extend the hip joint and flex the knee joint.

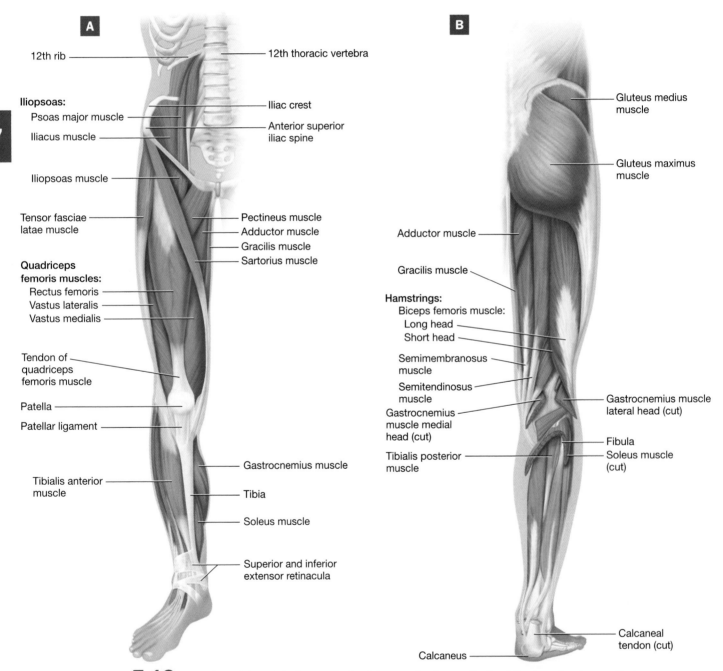

FIGURE **7.13** Muscles of the right lower limb: (**A**) anterior lower limb; (**B**) posterior lower limb

6. **Muscles that move the ankle.** The most obvious muscle of the posterior leg is the large **gastrocnemius (gas-trahk-NEE-mee-us)** muscle, also known as the "calf muscle." This two-headed muscle originates on the distal femur and inserts into the posterior calcaneus via the **calcaneal tendon**, more commonly called the **Achilles tendon**. Deep to the gastrocnemius is the **soleus (SOH-lee-us)** muscle, which unites with the gastrocnemius and contributes to the calcaneal tendon. Together these two muscles are the prime muscles that plantarflex the ankle joint. The gastrocnemius also produces some flexion at the knee joint. Anteriorly are the extensors, such as the **tibialis (tih-bee-AL-us) anterior**, which dorsiflexes the foot and the ankle joint. The muscles of the leg are best seen in Figures 7.13 and 7.14.

Figures 7.15 and 7.16 provide whole body views of many of the muscles we have just discussed.

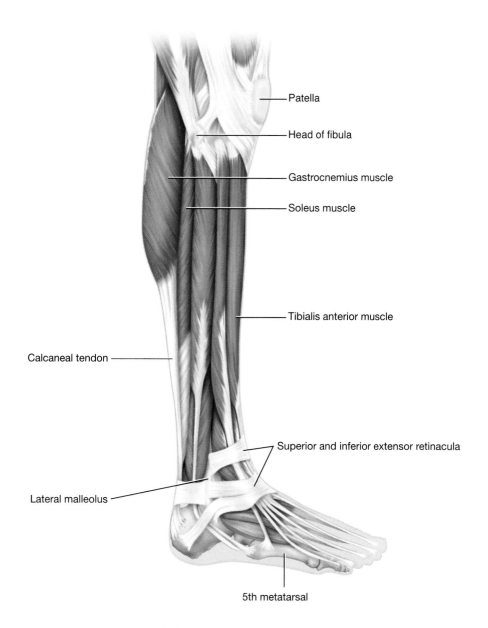

FIGURE **7.14** Lateral view of muscles of the leg

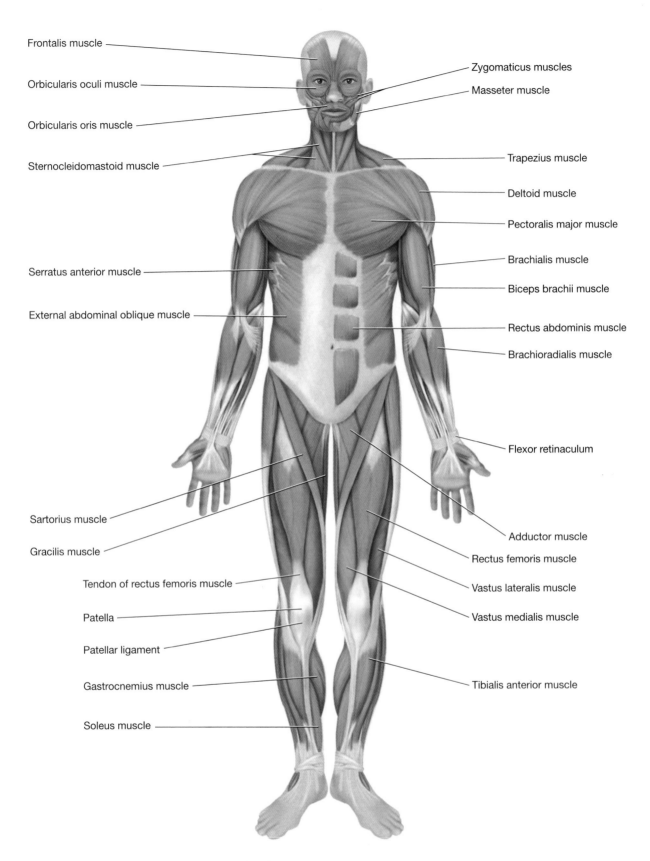

Frontalis muscle

Orbicularis oculi muscle

Orbicularis oris muscle

Sternocleidomastoid muscle

Serratus anterior muscle

External abdominal oblique muscle

Sartorius muscle

Gracilis muscle

Tendon of rectus femoris muscle

Patella

Patellar ligament

Gastrocnemius muscle

Soleus muscle

Zygomaticus muscles

Masseter muscle

Trapezius muscle

Deltoid muscle

Pectoralis major muscle

Brachialis muscle

Biceps brachii muscle

Rectus abdominis muscle

Brachioradialis muscle

Flexor retinaculum

Adductor muscle

Rectus femoris muscle

Vastus lateralis muscle

Vastus medialis muscle

Tibialis anterior muscle

FIGURE **7.15** Muscles of the body, anterior view

7

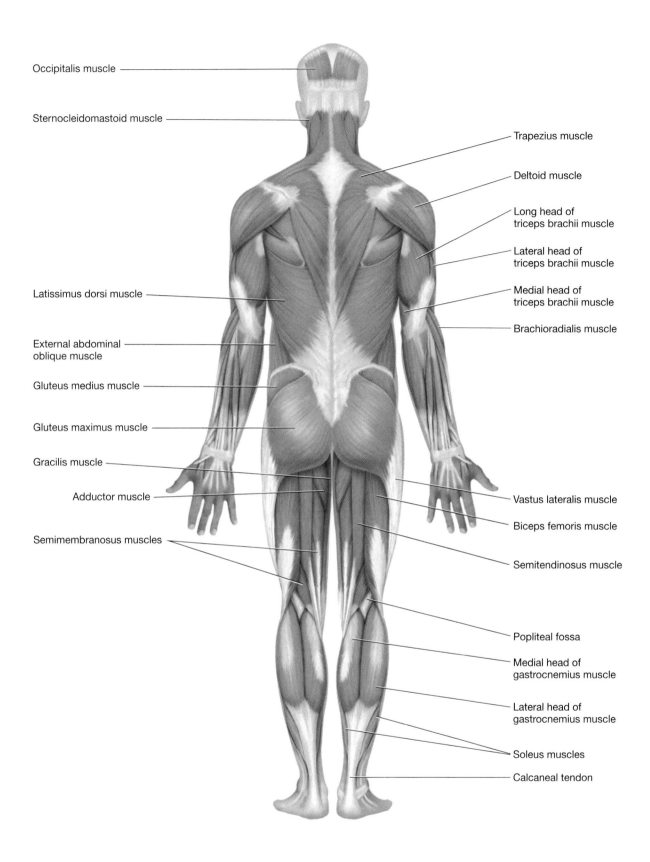

Occipitalis muscle

Sternocleidomastoid muscle

Trapezius muscle

Deltoid muscle

Long head of triceps brachii muscle

Lateral head of triceps brachii muscle

Medial head of triceps brachii muscle

Brachioradialis muscle

Latissimus dorsi muscle

External abdominal oblique muscle

Gluteus medius muscle

Gluteus maximus muscle

Gracilis muscle

Adductor muscle

Semimembranosus muscles

Vastus lateralis muscle

Biceps femoris muscle

Semitendinosus muscle

Popliteal fossa

Medial head of gastrocnemius muscle

Lateral head of gastrocnemius muscle

Soleus muscles

Calcaneal tendon

FIGURE **7.16** Muscles of the body, posterior view

Procedure 1   Model Inventory for the Skeletal Muscles

Identify the following muscles on models and diagrams, using your textbook and this unit for reference. As you examine the anatomical models and diagrams, record on the model inventory in Table 7.2 the name of the model and the structures you were able to identify.

Muscles That Move the Head, Neck, and Face

1. Orbicularis oculi
2. Zygomaticus
3. Buccinator
4. Orbicularis oris
5. Temporalis
6. Masseter
7. Sternocleidomastoid
8. Trapezius

Muscles That Move the Trunk

1. Pectoralis minor
2. External intercostals
3. Internal intercostals
4. Diaphragm
5. Rectus abdominis
6. External obliques
7. Internal obliques
8. Transversus abdominis
9. Erector spinae

Muscles That Move the Shoulder

1. Deltoid
2. Pectoralis major
3. Latissimus dorsi

Muscles That Move the Forearm

1. Biceps brachii
2. Triceps brachii
3. Brachioradialis

Muscles That Move the Hip and Knee

1. Iliopsoas
2. Gluteus maximus
3. Sartorius
4. Gracilis
5. Quadriceps femoris group
   a. Rectus femoris
   b. Vastus medialis
   c. Vastus intermedius
   d. Vastus lateralis
6. Adductor group
7. Hamstring muscles
   a. Biceps femoris
   b. Semimembranosus
   c. Semitendinosus

Muscles That Move the Ankle

1. Gastrocnemius
2. Soleus
3. Tibialis anterior

Your instructor may wish to omit certain muscles included above or add muscles not included in these lists. List any additional structures below:

_____

_____

_____

_____

_____

_____

TABLE **7.2** Model Inventory for Skeletal Muscles

Model/Diagram	Structures Identified

Exercise 7-3

Muscle Origins and Insertions

MATERIALS

❑ Small skeleton
❑ Modeling clay

You can best understand a muscle's actions by first understanding its origin and insertion. A muscle begins at its **origin**, generally the more stationary part, and attaches to its **insertion**, generally the part the muscle moves. For example, you can see in **Figure 7.17** that the biceps brachii muscle originates on the scapula and crosses the elbow joint, where it inserts into the proximal radius. Notice also that the triceps brachii originates from the humerus and the inferior scapula and crosses the elbow joint to insert into the posterior ulna.

After you determine a muscle's origin and insertion, figuring out its actions becomes easy. Let's examine the biceps brachii and triceps brachii muscles again. The biceps brachii inserts into the radius, so we know it will move the forearm. Given how it crosses the anterior elbow joint, we can conclude it will cause forearm flexion at the elbow joint. The triceps brachii inserts into the ulna, so we know it also will move the forearm. Given how it crosses the posterior elbow joint, we can conclude it will cause forearm extension at the elbow joint. Now wasn't that easy?

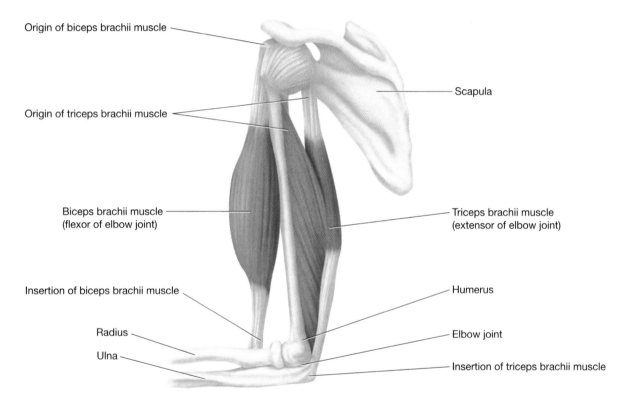

FIGURE **7.17** Origin and insertion of the biceps brachii and triceps brachii muscles, posterior view

Procedure 1 Build Muscles

In this procedure you will use small skeletons and modeling clay to build specific muscle groups using your text for reference. This may sound easy, but there is a catch: You must determine the actions of the muscle by looking only at the origin and insertion of each muscle you build.

1 Obtain a small skeleton and four colors of modeling clay.

2 Build the indicated muscles, using a different color of clay for each muscle. As you build, pay careful attention to the origin and insertion of each muscle.

3 Determine the primary actions for each muscle you have built by looking *only* at the origin and insertion. Record this information in Tables 7.3–7.5.

TABLE **7.3** Muscles and Actions for Group 1

Muscle	Actions
Biceps femoris	
Semitendinosus	
Semimembranosus	
Gracilis	

TABLE **7.4** Muscles and Actions for Group 2

Muscle	Actions
Biceps brachii	
Triceps brachii	
Deltoid	
Latissimus dorsi	

TABLE **7.5** Muscles and Actions for Group 3

Muscle	Actions
Pectoralis major	
Trapezius	
Masseter	
Temporalis	

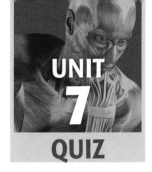

1 Label the following terms on Figure 7.18.

- ❏ Epimysium
- ❏ Fascicle
- ❏ Muscle fiber
- ❏ Perimysium
- ❏ Tendon

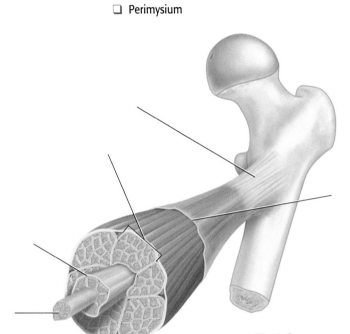

FIGURE **7.18** Basic skeletal muscle structure

2 Label the following terms on Figure 7.19.

- ❏ A band
- ❏ I band
- ❏ Myofibril
- ❏ Sarcolemma
- ❏ Sarcomere
- ❏ Sarcoplasmic reticulum
- ❏ T-tubule
- ❏ Z disc

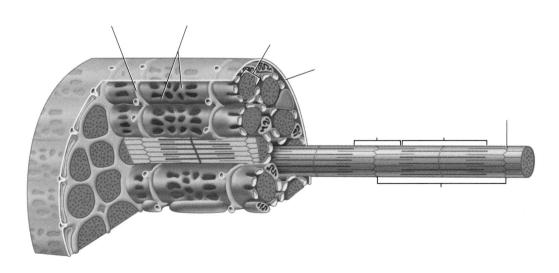

FIGURE **7.19** Skeletal muscle fiber

3 The striations in skeletal muscle fibers are attributable to

    a. light and dark pigments found in the sarcoplasm.

    b. the arrangement of thick and thin filaments in the myofibril.

    c. overlapping Z discs.

    d. overlapping adjacent skeletal muscle fibers.

4 Label the following muscles on Figure 7.20.

    ❏ Masseter
    ❏ Orbicularis oculi
    ❏ Orbicularis oris
    ❏ Sternocleidomastoid
    ❏ Temporalis
    ❏ Zygomaticus

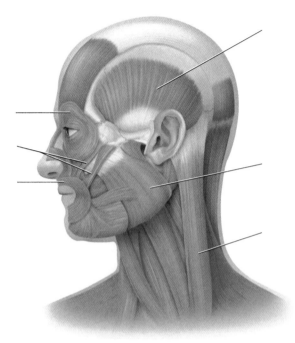

FIGURE **7.20** Facial musculature, lateral view

5 Which of the following muscles is *not* a forearm flexor at the elbow?

    a. Brachioradialis

    b. Triceps brachii

    c. Biceps brachii

    d. Brachialis

6 Which of the following muscles does *not* extend the hip and flex the knee?

    a. Sartorius

    b. Biceps femoris

    c. Semimembranosus

    d. Semitendinosus

7 Which of the following muscles is the prime abductor of the arm at the shoulder joint?

    a. Pectoralis major

    b. Latissimus dorsi

    c. Pectoralis minor

    d. Deltoid

8 Label the following muscles on Figure 7.21.

- ❏ Biceps brachii
- ❏ Biceps femoris
- ❏ Brachioradialis
- ❏ Deltoid

- ❏ External oblique
- ❏ Gastrocnemius
- ❏ Gluteus maximus
- ❏ Latissimus dorsi

- ❏ Pectoralis major
- ❏ Rectus abdominis
- ❏ Rectus femoris
- ❏ Sartorius

- ❏ Semimembranosus
- ❏ Tibialis anterior
- ❏ Trapezius
- ❏ Triceps brachii

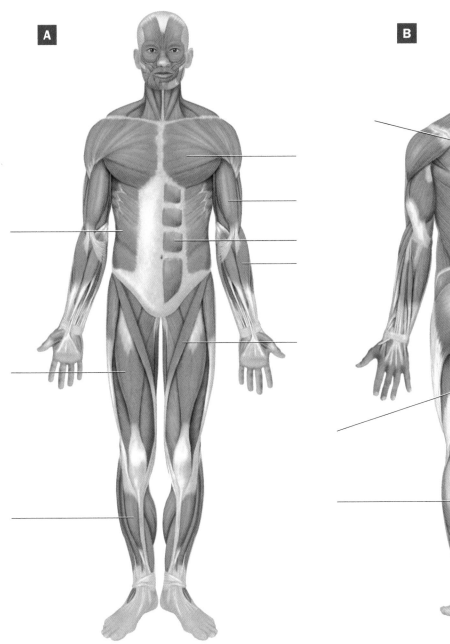
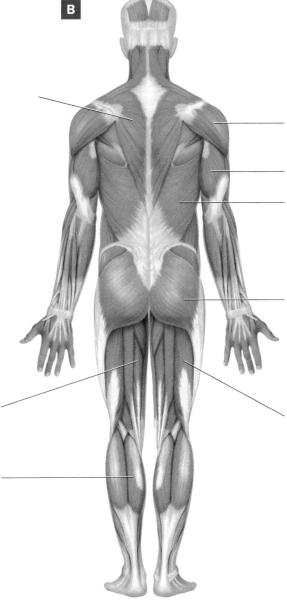

A

B

7

FIGURE **7.21** Muscles of the body: **A** anterior view; **B** posterior view

9 Muscle strain, or "pulling a muscle," may result from overuse injuries or from trauma. Typically muscle strain results in pain with muscle movement and with pressure. Predict which muscle or muscles may be strained from pain in each of the following locations:

a Lateral thigh _____

b Posterior arm _____

c Lateral neck _____

d Abdomen just medial to the midline _____

10 One of the most commonly performed orthopedic surgeries is rotator cuff repair. Often this involves removing and reattaching the deltoid muscle at its insertion. What functional impairment would be present after this procedure?

_____

_____

_____

_____

_____

_____

11 Radical mastectomy is a type of surgery for breast cancer that involves removing all of the breast tissue, the lymph nodes, and the pectoralis major muscle. What functional impairment would be present following this surgery?

_____

_____

_____

_____

_____

_____

12 A stroke, caused by a clot in a blood vessel of the brain, may lead to a loss of function of certain muscles. Which motions would an individual be unable to perform if the following muscles lost function?

a Orbicularis oculi _____

b Sternocleidomastoid _____

c Gluteus maximus _____

Nervous System

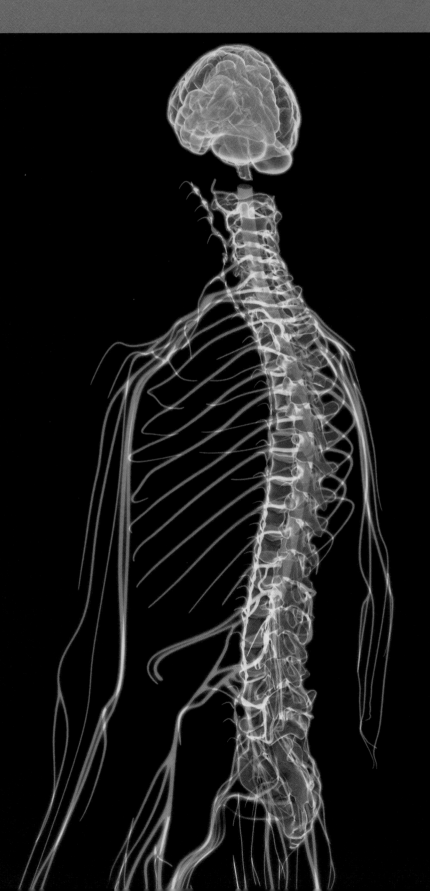

OBJECTIVES

Once you have completed this unit, you should be able to:

1. Describe the microanatomy of nervous tissue.

2. Describe and identify the gross structures of the brain.

3. Describe and identify structures of the spinal cord.

4. Identify, describe, and demonstrate functions of cranial nerves.

5. Identify spinal nerves and plexuses.

6. Describe a simple spinal reflex arc.

7. Describe the effects of the two branches of the autonomic nervous system on the body systems.

PRE-LAB EXERCISES

Complete the following exercises prior to coming to lab, using your textbook and lab manual for reference.

Pre-Lab Exercise 8-1

Key Terms

You should be familiar with the following terms before coming to lab.

Term	Definition
Parts of the Neuron	
Neuron	
Cell body	
Axon	
Dendrite	
Myelin sheath	
Node of Ranvier	
Structures of the Brain	
Cerebral hemispheres	
Cerebral cortex	
Corpus callosum	
Diencephalon	
Thalamus	

Hypothalamus _____

_____

Midbrain _____

_____

Pons _____

_____

Medulla oblongata _____

_____

Cerebellum _____

_____

Dura mater _____

_____

Arachnoid mater _____

_____

Pia mater _____

_____

Ventricles _____

_____

Structures of the Spinal Cord

Gray matter horns (anterior, posterior, lateral) _____

_____

_____

Cauda equina _____

_____

General Terms

Cranial nerve _____

_____

Spinal nerve _____

_____

Nerve plexus _____

_____

Spinal Nerve Plexuses

Cervical plexus _____

_____

Brachial plexus _____

_____

Lumbar plexus _____

_____

Sacral plexus _____

_____

8

Pre-Lab Exercise 8-2

Nervous Tissue Microanatomy

Label and color the microscopic anatomy of nervous tissue depicted in Figure 8.1 with the following terms from Exercise 8-1, using your text and Exercise 8-1 in this unit for reference.

❑ Axon
  ❑ Axon hillock
  ❑ Telodendria
  ❑ Axon terminal

❑ Dendrite(s)
❑ Cell body (soma)

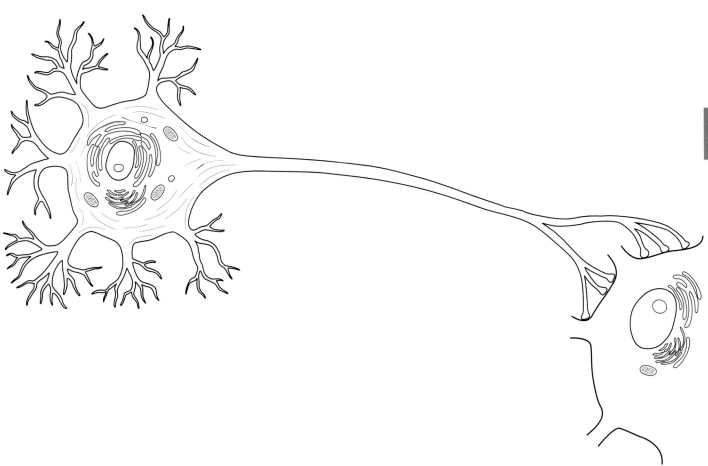

FIGURE **8.1** Neuron

Pre-Lab Exercise **8-3**
Brain Anatomy

Label and color the diagrams of the brain depicted in Figures 8.2, 8.3, and 8.4 with the following terms from Exercise 8-2, using your text and Exercise 8-2 in this unit for reference.

Cerebrum
❑ Corpus callosum (cerebral white matter)

Lobes of the cerebrum
- ❑ Frontal lobe
- ❑ Parietal lobe
- ❑ Occipital lobe
- ❑ Temporal lobe

Sulci
- ❑ Central sulcus
- ❑ Lateral sulcus

Diencephalon
- ❑ Thalamus
- ❑ Hypothalamus
  - ❑ Infundibulum
  - ❑ Pituitary gland
- ❑ Pineal gland

Brainstem
- ❑ Midbrain
- ❑ Pons
- ❑ Medulla oblongata
❑ Cerebellum

Ventricles
- ❑ Third ventricle
- ❑ Cerebral aqueduct

Brain coverings
- ❑ Dura mater
  - ❑ Subdural space
- ❑ Arachnoid mater
  - ❑ Subarachnoid space
- ❑ Pia mater

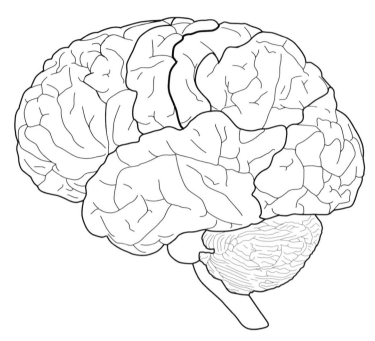

FIGURE **8.2** Brain, lateral view

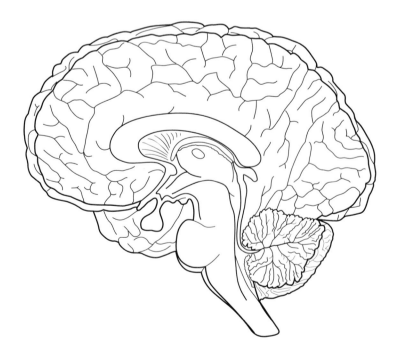

FIGURE **8.3** Brain, midsagittal section

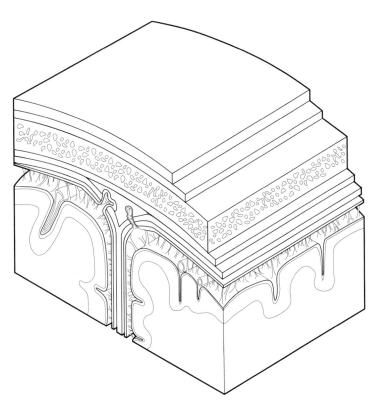

FIGURE **8.4** Brain and meninges, frontal and parasagittal section

Pre-Lab Exercise 8-4

Spinal Cord Anatomy

Label and color the diagrams of the spinal cord depicted in Figure 8.5 with the following terms from Exercise 8-3, using your text and Exercise 8-3 in this unit for reference.

❏ Meninges
    ❏ Dura mater
    ❏ Arachnoid mater
    ❏ Pia mater

❏ Spinal gray matter
    ❏ Anterior horn
    ❏ Lateral horn
    ❏ Posterior (dorsal) horn

❏ Spinal white matter
❏ Central canal

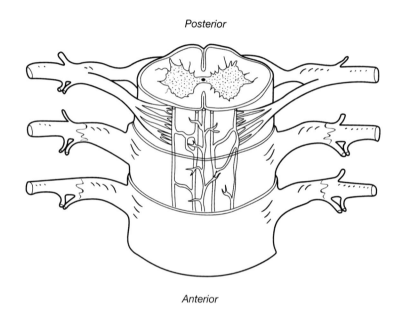

FIGURE **8.5** Spinal cord, transverse section

Pre-Lab Exercise 8-5

Cranial Nerve Functions

Complete Table 8.1 with the functions of each pair of cranial nerves, and indicate whether the nerve is motor, sensory, or mixed.

TABLE **8.1** Cranial Nerves

Cranial Nerve	Functions	Motor, Sensory, or Mixed
CN I: Olfactory nerve		
CN II: Optic nerve		
CN III: Oculomotor nerve		
CN IV: Trochlear nerve		
CN V: Trigeminal nerve		
CN VI: Abducens nerve		
CN VII: Facial nerve		
CN VIII: Vestibulocochlear nerve		
CN IX: Glossopharyngeal nerve		
CN X: Vagus nerve		
CN XI: Accessory nerve		
CN XII: Hypoglossal nerve		

Pre-Lab Exercise 8-6

Nerve Plexus and Spinal Nerve Anatomy

Label the diagram of the nerve plexuses and their spinal nerves depicted in Figure 8.6 with the following terms from Exercise 8-5, using your text and Exercise 8-5 in this unit for reference. Note that this diagram is presented in color to facilitate identification of the nerves.

❑ Cervical plexus
❑ Brachial plexus
    ❑ Axillary nerve
    ❑ Radial nerve
    ❑ Musculocutaneous nerve
    ❑ Ulnar nerve
    ❑ Median nerve
❑ Thoracic (intercostal) nerves
❑ Lumbar plexus
    ❑ Femoral nerve
❑ Sacral plexus
    ❑ Sciatic nerve

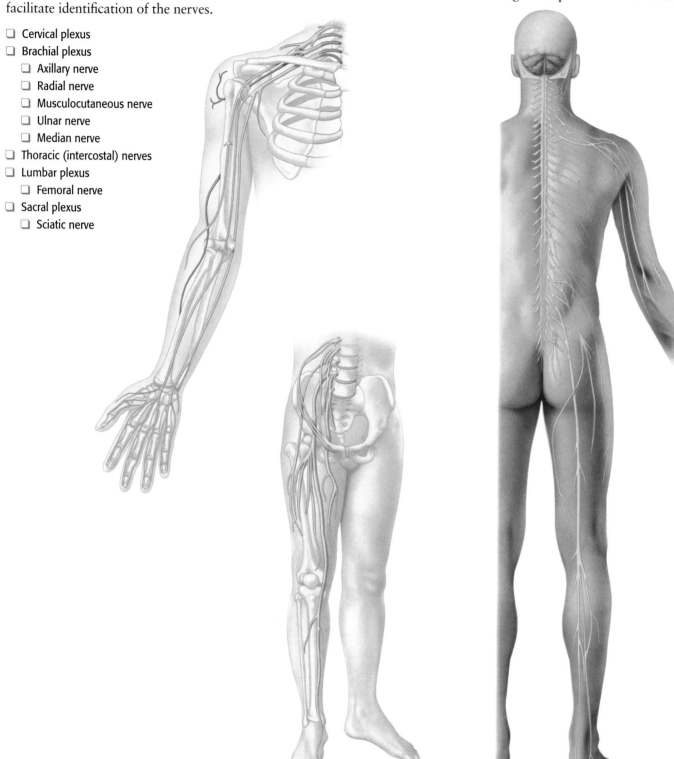

FIGURE **8.6** Nerve plexuses and ventral rami of the spinal nerves

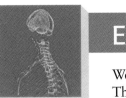

EXERCISES

We now begin our study of one of the major homeostatic systems in the body: the **nervous system**. This group of organs regulates cellular activities by sending nerve impulses, also called **action potentials**, via cells called **neurons**. Neurons are supported by a variety of smaller cells collectively called **neuroglial cells**, and together these two cell types make up **nervous tissue**.

Nervous tissue makes up the bulk of the organs of the two divisions of the nervous system: (1) the **central nervous system** (**CNS**), which consists of the **brain** and the **spinal cord**, and (2) the **peripheral nervous system** (**PNS**), which consists of organs called **peripheral nerves**, or simply *nerves* (Figure 8.7*)*. There are two types of nerves classified by location:

1. Nerves that originate from the brain and the brainstem, called **cranial nerves**, and

2. nerves that originate from the spinal cord, called **spinal nerves**.

The following exercises will introduce you first to nervous tissue, after which you will examine the anatomy of the brain, spinal cord, and peripheral nerves. You will also look at some of the functions of the nervous system, including those of the cranial nerves and spinal reflexes.

Nervous System			
Central Nervous System		Peripheral Nervous System	
Brain	Spinal cord	Cranial nerves	Spinal Nerves

FIGURE **8.7** Anatomical organization of the nervous system

Exercise **8-1**

Nervous Tissue

MATERIALS
❑ Neuron models
❑ Modeling clay in four colors

There are two types of cells within nervous tissue: **neurons** (NOOR-ahnz) and **neuroglial** (noor-oh-GLEE-ul; Figure 8.8) **cells**. Neurons are large cells that transmit and generate messages in the form of nerve impulses, or **neuronal action potentials**. Although they vary widely in size and structure, most have the following features in common (Figure 8.9):

1. **Cell body.** The cell body is the biosynthetic center of the neuron, containing the nucleus and many of the organelles. Cell bodies are

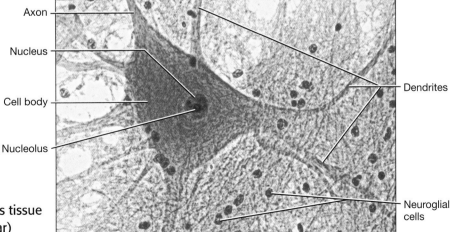

Axon
Nucleus
Cell body
Nucleolus
Dendrites
Neuroglial cells

FIGURE **8.8** Nervous tissue (motor neuron smear)

Nervous System | UNIT **8** | **191**

8

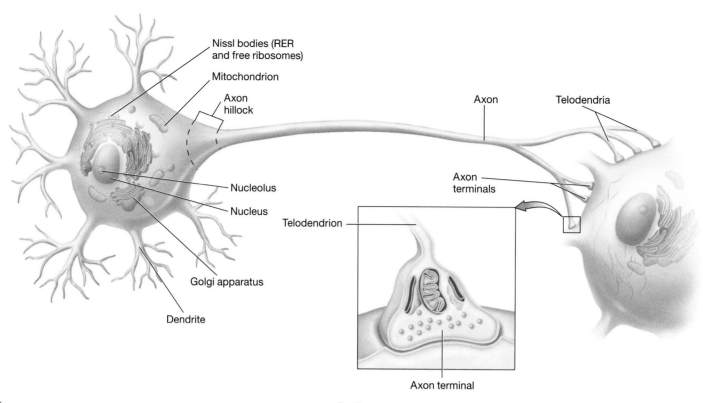

Nissl bodies (RER and free ribosomes)

Mitochondrion

Axon hillock

Axon

Telodendria

Axon terminals

Nucleolus

Nucleus

Telodendrion

Golgi apparatus

Dendrite

Axon terminal

FIGURE **8.9** Neuron

often found in clusters. In the CNS, clusters of cell bodies are called **nuclei** (NOO-klee-eye), and in the PNS, such clusters are called **ganglia** (GAYNG-lee-uh).

2. **Axon.** A single axon exits the cell body to transmit messages to other neurons, muscles, and glands. The axon's initial portion is known as the **axon hillock,** and its multiple terminal branches are called **telodendria** (tel-oh-DEN-dree-uh). At the end of each telodendrion is an **axon terminal** where the axon communicates with its target cell.

3. **Dendrites.** Most neurons have one or more branching processes called dendrites (DEN-drytz) that receive messages from other neurons they transmit to the neuron's cell body.

Neuroglial cells are much smaller than neurons, and they outnumber neurons about 50 to 1—no small feat considering the nervous system contains about 1 trillion neurons! Neuroglial cells include the following (Figure 8.10; note that this figure shows only neuroglial cells of the CNS):

1. **Astrocytes.** Astrocytes are the most numerous neuroglial cell in the CNS. These star-shaped cells have many functions, including anchoring neurons and blood vessels in place with processes called **perivascular feet** and regulating the extracellular environment of the brain. In addition, they facilitate the formation of the **blood-brain barrier,** which consists of tight junctions in the brain capillaries that prevent many substances in the blood from entering the brain tissue.

2. **Microglial cells.** The small microglial cells are very active phagocytes that clean up debris surrounding the neurons. Microglia also degrade and ingest damaged or dead neurons.

3. **Ependymal cells.** The ciliated ependymal cells line the hollow spaces of the brain and spinal cord. They assist in forming the fluid that bathes the brain and spinal cord, called **cerebrospinal fluid,** and circulate it with their cilia.

4. **Oligodendrocytes.** Oligodendrocytes, shown in Figure 8.11A, have long extensions that wrap around the axons of certain neurons in the CNS to form the myelin sheath. Note that one oligodendrocyte can myelinate several axons.

5. **Schwann cells.** Schwann cells form a structure called the **myelin** (MY-e-lin) **sheath** around the axons of certain neurons in the PNS. As you can see in Figure 8.11B, Schwann cells can myelinate only one axon, and they do

so by wrapping clockwise around the axon. The outer edge of the Schwann cell, called the **neurilemma** (noor-ih-LEM-uh), contains most of its cytoplasm and the nucleus. The myelin sheath protects and insulates the axons and speeds up conduction of action potentials. Because the sheath is made up of individual neuroglial cells, there are small gaps between the cells where the plasma membrane of the axon is exposed. These gaps are called **nodes of Ranvier** (rahn-vee-AY), and the myelin-covered segments between the nodes are called **internodes**.

6. **Satellite cells**. Satellite cells surround the cell bodies of neurons in the PNS. These cells are believed to enclose and support the cell bodies, although their precise function is unknown.

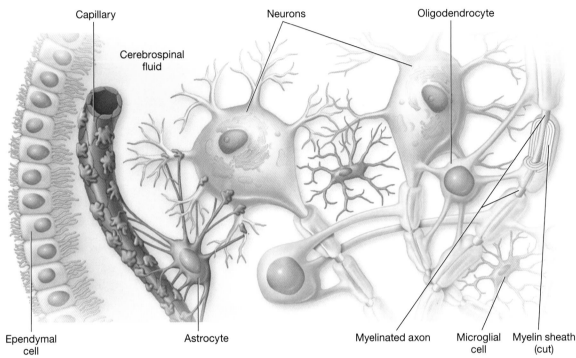

FIGURE **8.10** Neuroglial cells of the CNS

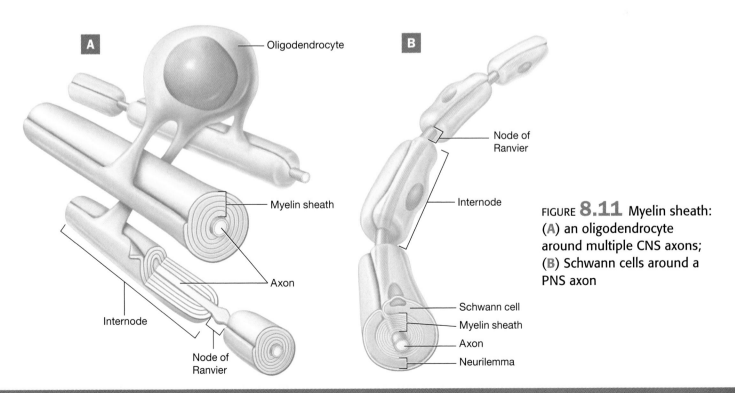

FIGURE **8.11** Myelin sheath: (**A**) an oligodendrocyte around multiple CNS axons; (**B**) Schwann cells around a PNS axon

Procedure 1 Model Inventory for Nervous Tissue

Identify the following structures of nervous tissue on models and diagrams using your textbook and this unit for reference. As you examine the anatomical models and diagrams, record on the model inventory in Table 8.2 the name of the model and the structures you were able to identify.

1. Neuron
   a. Axon
      (1) Axon hillock
      (2) Telodendria
      (3) Axon terminal
   b. Dendrite(s)
   c. Cell body (soma)
2. Neuroglial cells
   a. Oligodendrocytes
   b. Schwann cells
3. Other structures
   a. Myelin sheath
   b. Node of Ranvier

Table **8.2** Model Inventory for Nervous Tissue

Model/Diagram	Structures Identified

Procedure 2 Building a Myelin Sheath

In this procedure you will demonstrate the difference between the methods by which Schwann cells and oligodendrocytes myelinate the axons of neurons in the peripheral nervous system and the central nervous system, respectively. Both types of cells create the myelin sheath by wrapping themselves around the axon repeatedly (as many as 100 times). Recall, however, that Schwann cells can myelinate only one axon, whereas oligodendrocytes send out "arms" to myelinate several axons in their vicinity.

1 Obtain four colors of modeling clay (blue, green, yellow, and red, if available).

2 Use the following color code to build three central nervous system (CNS) axons, one peripheral nervous system (PNS) axon, one oligodendrocyte, and two Schwann cells:

   a CNS axons: blue

   b PNS axon: green

   c Oligodendrocyte: yellow

   d Schwann cells: red

3 Build your oligodendrocyte so it reaches out to myelinate the three CNS axons.

4 Build your Schwann cells so they myelinate the single PNS axon, making sure to leave a gap for the node of Ranvier.

Exercise 8-2

Anatomy of the Brain

MATERIALS

❏ Brain models: whole and sectioned

❏ Ventricle models

❏ Brainstem models

❏ Dural sinus model

❏ Sheep brain

❏ Dissection equipment and trays

Although the brain may look complex, it is really just a highly folded hollow organ. We divide the brain into four regions: the **cerebral hemispheres** (collectively called the *cerebrum*; sair-EE-brum), the *diencephalon* (dy-en-SEF-uh-lahn), the *brainstem*, and the **cerebellum** (sair-e-BEL-um). Within and around these four divisions are hollow spaces called **ventricles** filled with a fluid similar to plasma called **cerebrospinal** (sair-ee-broh-SPY-nul) **fluid**, or CSF. As you can see in Figure 8.12, the largest ventricles, called the **lateral ventricles**, are located in the right and left cerebral hemispheres. Note in Figure 8.12A that the lateral ventricles resemble a ram's horns when viewed from the anterior side. The smaller **third ventricle** is housed within the diencephalon. It is continuous with the **fourth ventricle**, found in the brainstem, via a small canal called the **cerebral aqueduct**. The fourth ventricle is continuous with the **central canal**, a hollow channel that runs down the middle of the spinal cord.

Within each of the four ventricles are collections of blood vessels known as **choroid (KOHR-oyd) plexuses**. As blood flows through the choroid plexuses, fluid filters out into the ventricles, and at that point it is called CSF. The largest choroid plexuses are within the lateral ventricles. One of the main functions of CSF is to reduce brain weight (the brain is buoyant in the CSF). Without CSF, your brain literally would crush itself under its own weight!

The **cerebrum** is the largest and most superior portion of the brain (Figure 8.13). Its surface consists of elevated ridges called **gyri** (JY-ree; singular, *gyrus*) and shallow grooves called **sulci** (SUL-kee; singular, *sulcus*). Deep grooves, called **fissures**, separate major regions of the cerebral hemispheres. The **longitudinal fissure** separates the right and left hemispheres. The cerebrum consists of five lobes: the **frontal, parietal, temporal, occipital,** and deep **insula** lobes (remember this last one by the mnemonic "the *insula* is *insula*ted"). The cerebral hemispheres are responsible for the brain's cognitive functions, including learning and language, conscious interpretation of sensory information, conscious planning of movement, and personality.

The cell bodies and unmyelinated axons and dendrites of the cerebral neurons lie in the cerebrum's outer 2 millimeters in a region called the **cerebral cortex**. These portions of the neurons are unmyelinated, which gives the cerebral cortex a gray color, and for this reason it is called **gray matter**. The cell bodies and processes of the cerebral cortex communicate with other parts of the nervous system via bundles of myelinated axons called **white matter tracts**. The largest tract of cerebral white matter is called the **corpus callosum,** which connects the right and left cerebral hemispheres.

8

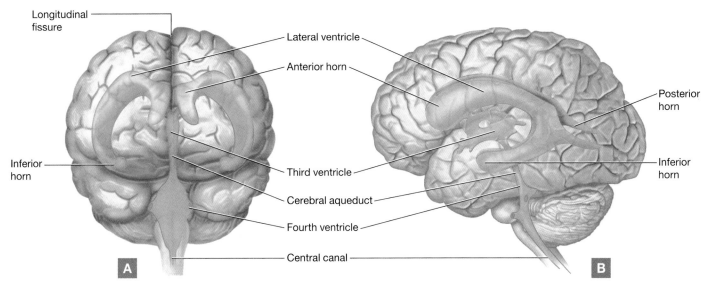

FIGURE **8.12** Ventricles: (**A**) anterior view; (**B**) left lateral view

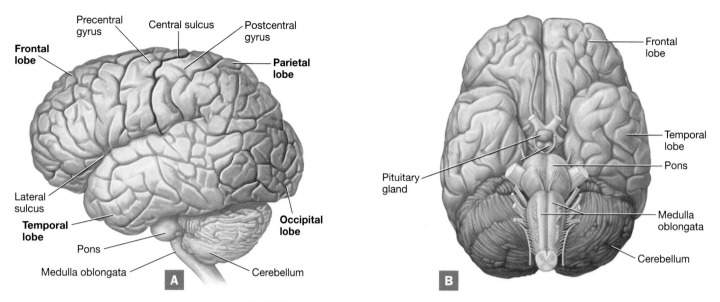

FIGURE **8.13** Brain: (**A**) lateral view; (**B**) inferior view

Gray matter isn't confined to the cerebral cortex. Clusters of cell bodies called **nuclei** are found throughout the cerebrum. An important group of nuclei, the **basal nuclei,** monitors voluntary motor functions. The neurons of these nuclei are connected to other parts of the nervous system by various tracts of white matter in the cerebrum.

Deep to the cerebral hemispheres in the central core of the brain is the **diencephalon,** composed of three main parts (Figure 8.14):

1. **Thalamus.** The thalamus (THAL-uh-mus) is a large, egg-shaped mass of gray and white matter that constitutes 80% of the diencephalon. It is a major integration and relay center that edits and sorts information going into the cerebrum. It essentially functions as the "gateway" into the cerebrum.

2. **Hypothalamus.** The small organ called the hypothalamus (hy-poh-THAL-uh-mus) is located on the anterior and inferior aspect of the diencephalon. It contains nuclei with neurons that carry out many of the body's homeostatic functions, including helping to regulate the endocrine system; monitoring the sleep-wake cycle; controlling thirst, hunger, and body temperature; and helping to monitor the autonomic nervous system (good things do come in small packages, after all!). An endocrine organ called the **pituitary** (pih-TOO-ih-tair-ee) **gland** is connected to the hypothalamus by a stalk called the **infundibulum** (in-fun-DIB-yoo-lum).

3. **Epithalamus.** The epithalamus (ep-ih-THAL-uh-mus) is located on the posterior and superior aspect of the diencephalon. It contains an endocrine organ called the **pineal** (pih-NEE-ul) **gland** that secretes the hormone **melatonin** (mel-uh-TOH-nin), which helps to regulate the sleep-wake cycle.

The third major portion of the brain, the **brainstem,** influences the automatic functions of the body, such as the rhythm for breathing, heart rate, blood pressure, and certain reflexes. The most superior portion of the brainstem is the **midbrain,** and inferior to it we find the rounded **pons,** which bulges anteriorly. The last segment of the brainstem, the **medulla oblongata** (muh-DOO-luh ahb-lahn-GAH-tuh, or simply *medulla*), is continuous inferiorly with the spinal cord.

The fourth major component of the brain is the large posterior **cerebellum.** It consists of two highly convoluted lobes with an outer **cerebellar cortex** composed of gray matter and inner white matter. The cerebellum coordinates and plans ongoing motor activities and is critical in reducing and preventing motor error with movement.

Note in Figure 8.15 that a set of three membranes, collectively called the **meninges** (men-IN-jeez; singular, *meninx*), surrounds the brain. The meninges include the following:

1. **Dura mater.** The outermost meninx is the thick, leathery, double-layered dura mater (DUR-uh MAH-tur). The two layers of the dura are fused, but in three regions the deep layer separates from the superficial layer and dives into the brain to form structures that separate certain areas of the brain. At these locations there are spaces between the two dural layers collectively called the **dural sinuses.** All deoxygenated blood from the brain drains into the dural sinuses, which in turn drain into veins exiting the head and neck.

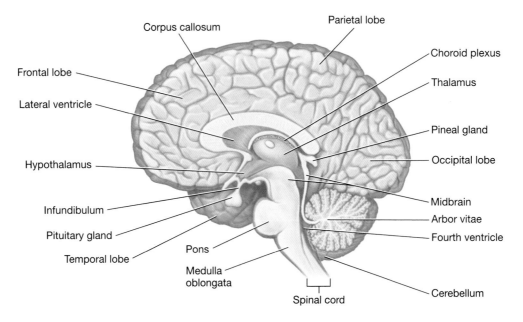

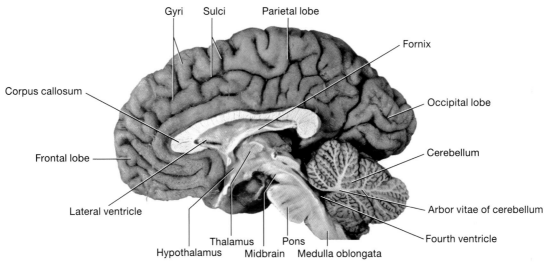

FIGURE **8.14** Midsagittal section of the brain

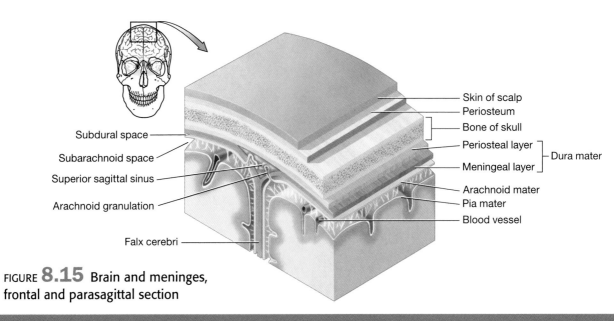

FIGURE **8.15** Brain and meninges,
frontal and parasagittal section

2. **Arachnoid mater.** The middle meninx, the arachnoid mater (**ah-RAK-noyd MAH-tur**), is separated from the dura by a space called the **subdural space.** This space contains little bundles of the arachnoid mater called the **arachnoid granulations,** vascular structures that project into the dural sinuses and allow CSF to reenter the blood. In Figure 8.16 you can see the pattern of CSF circulation from its formation by the choroid plexuses to its return to the blood.

3. **Pia mater.** The thinnest, innermost meninx is the pia mater (**PEE-uh MAH-tur**). The pia mater clings to the surface of the cerebral hemispheres and is richly supplied with blood vessels. A space between the pia mater and the arachnoid mater, called the **subarachnoid space,** is filled with CSF.

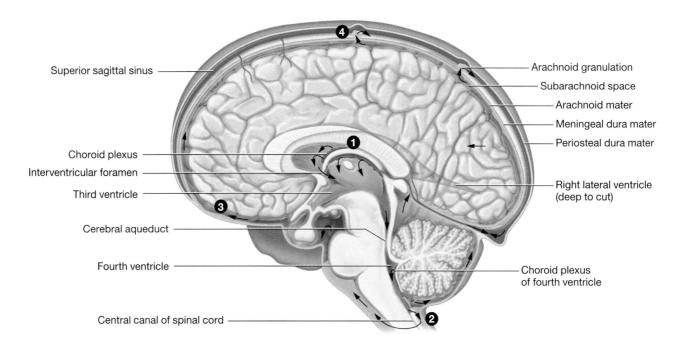

Superior sagittal sinus

Arachnoid granulation

Subarachnoid space

Arachnoid mater

Meningeal dura mater

Periosteal dura mater

Choroid plexus

Interventricular foramen

Third ventricle

Right lateral ventricle (deep to cut)

Cerebral aqueduct

Fourth ventricle

Choroid plexus of fourth ventricle

Central canal of spinal cord

1 CSF is produced by the choroid plexus of each ventricle.

2 CSF flows through the ventricles and into the subarachnoid space. Some CSF flows through the central canal of the spinal cord.

3 CSF flows through the subarachnoid space.

4 CSF is absorbed into the dural venous sinuses via the arachnoid granulations.

FIGURE **8.16** Circulation of CSF through the brain and spinal cord

Procedure 1 Model Inventory for the Brain

Identify the following structures of the brain on models and diagrams, using your textbook and this unit for reference. As you examine the anatomical models and diagrams, record on the model inventory in Table 8.3 the name of the model and the structures you were able to identify. The brain's structure is fairly complex, and it's best to examine models in as many different planes of section as possible.

1. Cerebrum
   a. Cerebral hemispheres
   b. Corpus callosum (cerebral white matter)
   c. Cerebral cortex (gray matter)
   d. Lobes of the cerebrum
      (1) Frontal lobe
      (2) Parietal lobe
      (3) Occipital lobe
      (4) Temporal lobe
      (5) Insula lobe
   e. Fissures
      (1) Longitudinal fissure
      (2) Transverse fissure
   f. Sulci
      (1) Central sulcus
      (2) Lateral sulcus
2. Diencephalon
   a. Thalamus
   b. Hypothalamus
      (1) Infundibulum
      (2) Pituitary gland
   c. Pineal gland
3. Brainstem
   a. Midbrain
   b. Pons
   c. Medulla oblongata
4. Cerebellum
5. Brain coverings
   a. Dura mater
      (1) Subdural space
   b. Arachnoid mater
      (1) Subarachnoid space
   c. Pia mater
6. Ventricles
   a. Lateral ventricles
   b. Third ventricle
   c. Fourth ventricle
   d. Cerebral aqueduct
   e. Choroid plexus

TABLE **8.3** Model Inventory for the Brain

Model	Structures Identified

8

Procedure 2 Brain Dissection

Often structures of the brain and spinal cord are difficult to see on anatomical models. This procedure will allow you to examine these structures more closely by dissecting a preserved sheep brain. Note that the process of preservation makes many structures of the brain and spinal cord much tougher than they would be in a fresh specimen.

1 First note the thick part of the dura mater covering the longitudinal fissure. If you cut through this with scissors, you will enter a dural sinus called the superior sagittal sinus.

2 Next remove the dura mater to reveal the thin membrane on top of the brain. This is the arachnoid mater.

3 Remove an area of the arachnoid mater to see the shiny inner membrane—the pia mater—directly touching the surface of the brain. Note that the pia mater follows the convolutions of the gyri and sulci.

4 Examine the surface anatomy of both the superior and the inferior surfaces of the sheep brain (Figures 8.17 and 8.18).

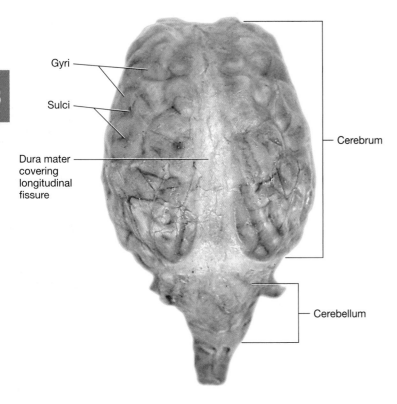

FIGURE **8.17** Superior view of the sheep brain

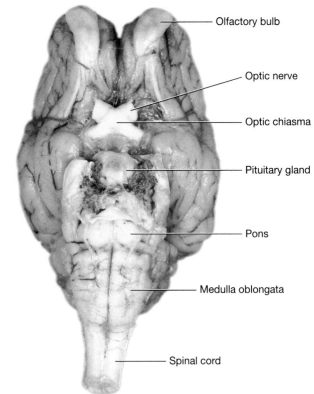

FIGURE **8.18** Inferior view of the sheep brain

Below, draw what you see on both surfaces, and label your drawing with the following structures:

- ❏ Arachnoid mater
- ❏ Cerebellum
- ❏ Cerebrum
- ❏ Dura mater
- ❏ Gyri
- ❏ Longitudinal fissure
- ❏ Medulla oblongata
- ❏ Pituitary gland
- ❏ Pons
- ❏ Sulci

5 Separate the two cerebral hemispheres with your fingers, and identify the corpus callosum.

6 Make a cut along the brain's midsagittal plane through the corpus callosum to separate the two cerebral hemispheres.

7 Examine the brain's internal anatomy (Figure 8.19), and stick your finger in the lateral ventricle. You will see (or feel) that it is much larger than it appears.

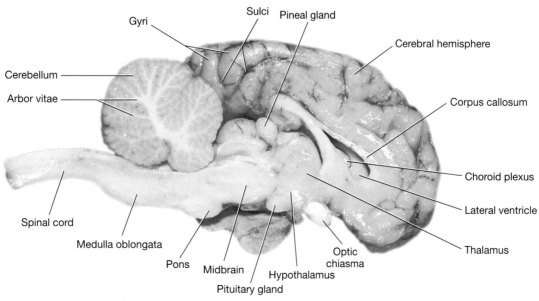

FIGURE **8.19** Lateral view of the sheep brain; midsagittal section

Draw what you see in the space below, and label your drawing with the following structures:

- ❏ Corpus callosum
- ❏ Hypothalamus
- ❏ Lateral ventricle
- ❏ Medulla oblongata
- ❏ Midbrain
- ❏ Pons
- ❏ Thalamus

8

8 Section one of the halves of the brain in the frontal plane, approximately along the central sulcus. Notice the outer cerebral cortex (the gray matter) and the inner white matter. From this view you also can see the lateral and third ventricles. Again, draw what you see in the space below and label your drawing with the following structures:

- ❏ Cerebral cortex
- ❏ Cerebral white matter
- ❏ Lateral ventricle
- ❏ Thalamus
- ❏ Third ventricle

Exercise 8-3

Spinal Cord

MATERIALS

❑ Spinal cord models: whole and sectioned

The medulla oblongata passes through the foramen magnum of the occipital bone and becomes the **spinal cord** (Figure 8.20). Note in Figure 8.20A that the spinal cord does not extend the entire length of the vertebral column; rather, it ends between the first and second lumbar vertebrae. At this point it tapers to form the end of the spinal cord, which gives off a tuft of nerve roots called the **cauda equina** (CAW-duh ee-KWYNE-uh, or "horse's tail"). The cauda equina fills the remainder of the vertebral column to the sacrum and exits out of the appropriate foramina to become spinal nerves.

The cranial meninges are continuous with spinal meninges and are similar in name and structure (Figure 8.20B and 8.21). One notable difference between the cranial and spinal meninges involves the spinal dura mater, which consists of only *one* layer rather than two like the cranial dura. This single dural layer does not attach to the vertebral column, which creates a space between the spinal dura and the interior vertebral foramen called the **epidural** (ep-ih-DOO-rul) **space**. Because the cranial dura is fused to the interior of the skull, there is no epidural space around the brain.

Internally, the spinal cord consists of a butterfly-shaped core of gray matter that surrounds the CSF-filled **central canal** (Figure 8.21), continuous with the fourth ventricle of the brain. The gray matter is divided into regions, or **horns**. The **anterior** (or *ventral*) **horns** contain the cell bodies of motor neurons. The **posterior** (or *dorsal*) **horns** contain the cell bodies of spinal sensory neurons. In the thoracic and lumbar regions of the spinal cord are the **lateral horns**, which contain the cell bodies of autonomic neurons.

As you can see in Figure 8.21, it is possible to discern the anterior from the posterior spinal cord by looking at the shapes of the anterior and posterior horns. The anterior horns are broad and flat on the ends, whereas the posterior horns are more tapered, and they extend farther out toward the edge.

8

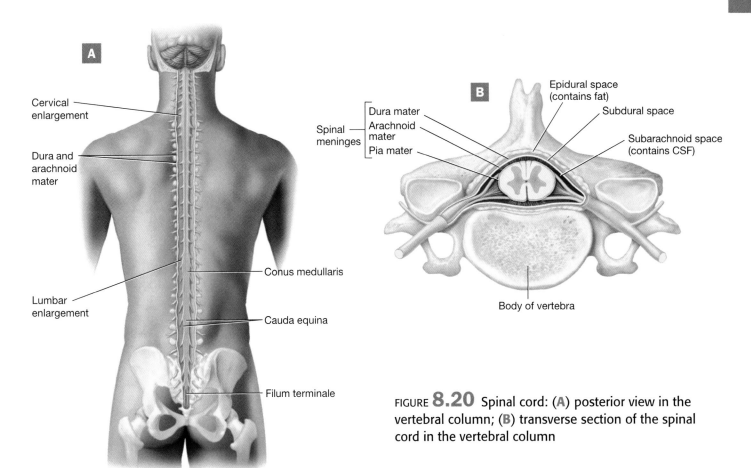

A

Cervical enlargement

Dura and arachnoid mater

Lumbar enlargement

Conus medullaris

Cauda equina

Filum terminale

B

Spinal meninges
- Dura mater
- Arachnoid mater
- Pia mater

Epidural space (contains fat)

Subdural space

Subarachnoid space (contains CSF)

Body of vertebra

FIGURE **8.20** Spinal cord: (**A**) posterior view in the vertebral column; (**B**) transverse section of the spinal cord in the vertebral column

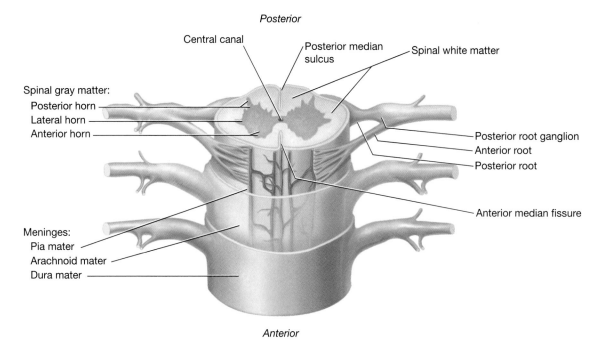

Posterior

Central canal

Posterior median sulcus

Spinal white matter

Spinal gray matter:
  Posterior horn
  Lateral horn
  Anterior horn

Posterior root ganglion

Anterior root

Posterior root

Anterior median fissure

Meninges:
  Pia mater
  Arachnoid mater
  Dura mater

Anterior

FIGURE **8.21** Transverse section of the spinal cord

Surrounding the spinal gray matter is the spinal white matter, which contains myelinated axons grouped into bundles called **tracts**. Tracts contain axons that have the same beginning and end points and the same general function. **Ascending tracts** carry sensory information from sensory neurons to the brain, and **descending tracts** carry motor information from the brain to motor neurons.

Procedure **1** Model Inventory for the Spinal Cord

Identify the following structures of the spinal cord on models and diagrams, using your textbook and this unit for reference. As you examine the anatomical models and diagrams, record on the model inventory in Table 8.4 the name of the model and the structures you were able to identify.

1. Meninges
   a. Dura mater
      (1) Epidural space
   b. Arachnoid mater
      (1) Subarachnoid space
   c. Pia mater

2. Spinal gray matter
   a. Anterior horn
   b. Posterior (dorsal) horn
   c. Lateral horn

3. Spinal white matter
4. Cauda equina
5. Central canal

TABLE **8.4** Model Inventory for the Spinal Cord

Model	Structures Identified

Exercise 8-4

Cranial Nerves

MATERIALS

❑ Penlight

❑ Snellen vision chart

❑ Tuning fork

❑ Unknown samples to smell

❑ PTC, thiourea, and sodium benzoate tasting papers

The 12 pairs of **cranial nerves** attach to the brain (Figure 8.22). Each nerve is given two names: (1) a sequential Roman numeral in order of its attachment to the brain, and (2) a name that describes the nerve's location or function. For example, cranial nerve III is the third cranial nerve to arise from the brain. It is also called the oculomotor nerve because one of its functions is to provide motor fibers to some of the muscles that move the eyeball.

All cranial nerves innervate structures of the head and neck. Three cranial nerves are **sensory nerves** with fibers that have purely sensory functions, four are **mixed nerves** that contain both sensory and motor fibers, and five are **motor nerves** that contain primarily motor fibers. Following is an overview of the main functions of each cranial nerve (note that CN = cranial nerve):

1. **CN I: Olfactory nerve.** The olfactory nerve is a purely sensory nerve that provides for the sense of smell.

2. **CN II: Optic nerve.** The optic nerve is also a purely sensory nerve that provides for the sense of vision. Its fibers emerge from the retina of the eye and meet at the **optic chiasma** (ky-AZ-muh), where the nerves partially exchange fibers before diverging to form the **optic tracts**.

3. **CN III: Oculomotor nerve.** The oculomotor (ahk-yoo-loh-MOH-tohr) nerve is a motor cranial nerve that innervates four of the six muscles that move the eyeball, the muscle that opens the eyelid, the muscle that constricts the pupil, and the muscle that changes the shape of the lens for near vision.

4. **CN IV: Trochlear nerve.** The trochlear (TROH-klee-ur) nerve is a small motor nerve that innervates one of the six muscles that move the eyeball (the *superior oblique muscle*).

5. **CN V: Trigeminal nerve.** The trigeminal nerve is a large mixed nerve named for the three branches that together provide sensory innervation to the face and motor innervation to the muscles of mastication (chewing).

6. **CN VI: Abducens nerve.** The abducens (ab-DOO-senz) nerve is a small motor nerve that innervates the final muscle that moves the eyeball (the *lateral rectus muscle*).

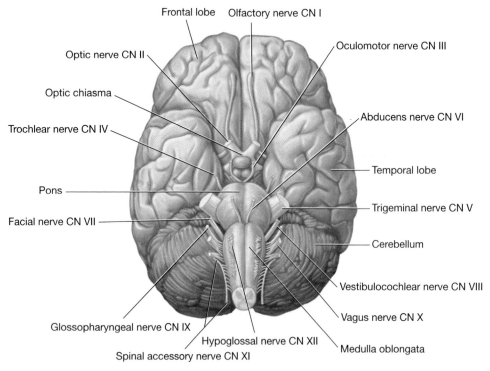

FIGURE **8.22** Inferior view of the brain with the cranial nerves

7. **CN VII: Facial nerve.** The mixed fibers of the facial nerve provide for the following: motor to the muscles of facial expression; taste to the anterior two-thirds of the tongue; motor to the glands that produce tears (the lacrimal glands), mucus, and saliva; and sensory to part of the face and mouth.

8. **CN VIII: Vestibulocochlear nerve.** The final sensory nerve, the vestibulocochlear (**ves-tib-yoo-loh-KOHK-lee-ur**) nerve, innervates the structures of the inner ear and provides for the senses of hearing and balance.

9. **CN IX: Glossopharyngeal nerve.** The small mixed glossopharyngeal (**glah-soh-fair-IN-jee-ul**) nerve provides motor fibers to the muscles of the pharynx (throat) involved in swallowing and sensory fibers to the posterior one-third of the tongue for taste sensation.

10. **CN X: Vagus nerve.** The mixed vagus (**VAY-gus**) nerve is the only cranial nerve that "wanders" outside of the head and neck ("vagus" means "wanderer"). In the head and the neck it provides some sensory fibers to the skin of the head and the pharynx, motor fibers to muscles involved in speech and swallowing, and motor fibers to certain salivary glands. Outside the head and the neck it innervates most of the thoracic and abdominal viscera as the main nerve of the parasympathetic nervous system.

11. **CN XI: Accessory nerve.** The accessory nerve is the only cranial nerve that has both a cranial component originating from the brainstem and a spinal component originating from the spinal cord. Its motor fibers innervate the muscles that move the head and the neck, such as the trapezius and sternocleidomastoid muscles.

12. **CN XII: Hypoglossal nerve.** The hypoglossal (**hy-poh-GLAH-sul**) nerve is a small motor nerve that innervates the muscles that move the tongue. Note that the hypoglossal nerve *moves* the tongue but does not provide any taste sensation to the tongue.

HINTS & TIPS

Remembering the Order of the Cranial Nerves

Many cranial nerve mnemonics have been created over the years to help students remember their correct order. Following is one of my favorite mnemonics, but if this one doesn't stick for you, try making up your own or doing an Internet search for "cranial nerve mnemonics":

Oh (Olfactory)
Once (Optic)
One (Oculomotor)
Takes (Trochlear)
The (Trigeminal)
Anatomy (Abducens)
Final (Facial)
Very (Vestibulocochlear)
Good (Glossopharyngeal)
Vacations (Vagus)
Are (Accessory)
Happening (Hypoglossal)

You also can help yourself remember the olfactory and optic nerves by reminding yourself that you have one nose (CN I, the *olfactory* nerve) and two eyes (CN II, the *optic* nerve).

Procedure 1 Testing the Cranial Nerves

A component of every complete physical examination performed by health-care professionals is the cranial nerve exam. In this procedure you will put on your "doctor hat," and perform the same tests of the cranial nerves done during a physical examination. Pair up with another student, and take turns performing the following tests. For each test, first document your observations (in many cases, this will be "able to perform" or "unable to perform"). Then state which cranial nerve(s) you have checked with each test. Keep in mind some tests check more than one cranial nerve, some cranial nerves are tested more than once, and each nerve is tested in this procedure at least once.

1 Have your partner perform the following actions individually (not all at once—your partner may have difficulty smiling and frowning at the same time!): smile, frown, raise his or her eyebrows, and puff his or her cheeks.

Observations: _____

_____

_____

_____

CN(s) tested: _____

2 Have your partner open and close his or her jaw and clench his or her teeth.

Observations: _____

_____

_____

_____

CN(s) tested: _____

3 Have your partner elevate and depress his or her shoulders and turn his or her head to the right and the left.

Observations: _____

_____

_____

_____

CN(s) tested: _____

4 Draw a large, imaginary Z in the air with your finger. Have your partner follow your finger with his or her eyes without moving his or her head. Repeat the procedure, this time drawing the letter H in the air with your finger.

Observations: _____

_____

_____

_____

CN(s) tested: _____

5 Test pupillary response:

   a Dim the lights in the room about halfway.

   b Place your hand vertically against the bridge of your partner's nose as illustrated in Figure 8.23. This forms a light shield to separate the right and left visual fields.

   c Shine the penlight indirectly into the left eye from an angle as illustrated in Figure 8.23. Watch what happens to the pupil in the left eye.

   d Move the penlight away, and watch what happens to the left pupil.

   e Shine the light into the left eye again, and watch what happens to the pupil in the right eye. Move the penlight away, and watch what happens to the right pupil.

   f Repeat this process with the right eye.

   g Record your results in Table 8.5.

      CN(s) tested: _____

FIGURE **8.23** Method for testing the pupillary response

TABLE **8.5** Pupillary Response Results

Action	Response of Left Pupil	Response of Right Pupil
Light shined into left eye		
Light removed from left eye		
Light shined into right eye		
Light removed from right eye		

6 Place your hand lightly on your partner's throat, and have him or her swallow and speak. Feel for symmetrical movement of the larynx (throat).

Observations: _____

_____

_____

_____

CN(s) tested: _____

7 Have your partner protrude his or her tongue. Check for abnormal deviation or movement (e.g., does the tongue move straight forward or does it move to one side?).

Observations: _____

_____

_____

_____

CN(s) tested: _____

8 Test your partner's vision by having him or her stand 20 feet from a Snellen chart and read the chart, starting at the largest line and progressing to the smallest line he or she is able to see clearly. Record the ratio (e.g., 20/30) next to the smallest line your partner can read.

Observations: _____

_____

_____

_____

CN(s) tested: _____

9 Hold a tuning fork by its handle, and strike the tines with a rubber mallet (or just tap it lightly on the lab table). Touch the stem to the top of your partner's head along the midsagittal line in the manner shown in Figure 8.24. This is called the Weber test. Ask your partner if he or she hears the vibration better in one ear, or if he or she hears the sound equally well in both ears.

Observations: _____

_____

_____

_____

CN(s) tested: _____

FIGURE **8.24** Weber test for hearing

10 Have your partner stand with his or her eyes closed and arms at his or her sides for several seconds. Evaluate his or her ability to remain balanced.

Observations: _____

_____

_____

_____

CN(s) tested: _____

11 Hold an unknown sample near your partner's nose, and fan the odor toward him or her by waving your hand over the container. Have him or her identify the substance by its scent.

Observations: _____

_____

_____

_____

CN(s) tested: _____

12 Evaluate your partner's ability to taste using tasting papers. Have your partner place a piece of PTC paper on his or her tongue, and determine if he or she can taste it (the ability to taste PTC is genetically determined; about half of the population can taste it). If your partner cannot taste the PTC, try the thiourea paper instead (a word of warning— thiourea tastes bad). If your partner cannot taste either of these papers, try the sodium benzoate paper.

Observations: _____

_____

_____

_____

CN(s) tested: _____

Exercise 8-5

Spinal Nerves and Reflexes

MATERIALS
☐ Model of the spinal nerves
☐ Reflex hammer

Axons enter and exit the spinal cord as a group of fibers called **nerve roots**. The **ventral roots** carry motor impulses from the anterior horn of the spinal cord to the PNS, and the **dorsal roots** are axons that transmit sensory impulses from the PNS to the posterior horn of the spinal cord. Each of the 31 pairs of **spinal nerves** forms from the fusion of the ventral and dorsal roots. Because each spinal nerve carries both motor and sensory fibers, all spinal nerves are mixed nerves.

Shortly after the dorsal and ventral roots fuse to form the spinal nerve, it splits into three branches: a **dorsal ramus**, a **ventral ramus**, and a small **meningeal branch**. The dorsal rami serve the skin, joints, and musculature of the posterior trunk. The meningeal branches reenter the vertebral canal to innervate spinal structures. The larger ventral rami travel anteriorly to supply the muscles of the upper and lower limbs, the anterior thorax and abdomen, and part of the back. The distribution of the ventral rami is illustrated in Figure 8.25.

The ventral rami of the thoracic spinal nerves travel anteriorly as 11 separate pairs of **intercostal nerves** that innervate the intercostal muscles, the abdominal muscles, and the skin of the chest and abdomen. The ventral rami of the cervical, lumbar, and sacral nerves combine to form four large **plexuses**, or networks, of nerves: the **cervical**, **brachial**, **lumbar**, and **sacral plexuses**. The major nerves of the cervical, brachial, thoracic, lumbar, and sacral plexuses are as follows:

1. **Cervical plexuses.** The **cervical plexuses** consist of the ventral rami of C_1–C_4 with a small contribution from C_5. Their branches serve the skin of the head and the neck and certain neck muscles. Their major branch is the **phrenic** (FREN-ik; C_3–C_5) **nerve**, which serves the diaphragm, the main muscle for breathing.

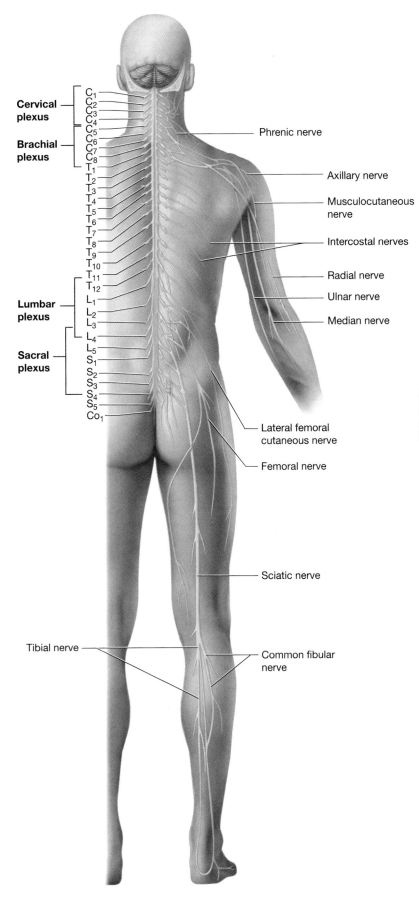

FIGURE **8.25** Nerve plexuses and ventral rami of the spinal nerves

2. **Brachial plexuses.** The complicated-looking brachial plexuses consist of the ventral rami of C_5–T_1 (Figure 8.26). Several nerves originate from the brachial plexuses, including the following:

a. **Axillary nerve.** The axillary nerve serves structures near the axilla (armpit), including the deltoid and teres minor muscles and the skin around this region.

b. **Musculocutaneous nerve.** The musculocutaneous (mus-kyoo-loh-kyoo-TAY-nee-us) nerve is located in the lateral arm and serves the anterior arm muscles (such as the biceps brachii) and the skin of the lateral forearm.

c. **Radial nerve.** The radial nerve is located in the posterior arm. It serves the posterior arm muscles and the forearm extensors as well as the skin in the lateral hand.

d. **Ulnar nerve.** The ulnar nerve, which you likely know as the "funny bone nerve," begins posteriorly but then crosses over to the anterior side of the arm as it curves around the medial epicondyle of the humerus. At this point the nerve is superficial and is easily injured when you smack your elbow on something. The ulnar nerve supplies certain forearm flexors, most of the intrinsic muscles of the hand, and the skin over the medial hand.

e. **Median nerve.** The median nerve travels approximately down the middle of the arm and forearm. It supplies most of the forearm flexors, certain intrinsic hand muscles, and the skin over the anterior and lateral hand. As the median nerve enters the wrist, it travels under a band of connective tissue called the *flexor retinaculum*. Occasionally the median nerve becomes trapped and inflamed under the flexor retinaculum, which results in *carpal tunnel syndrome*.

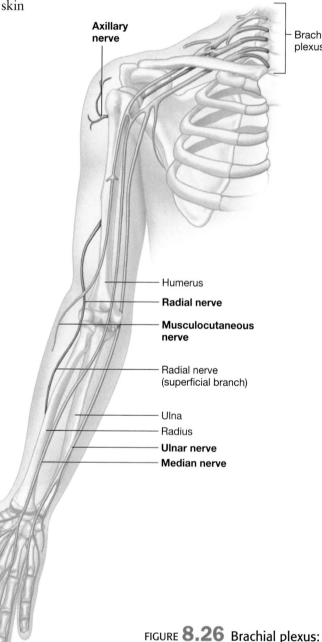

Axillary nerve

Brachial plexus

Humerus

Radial nerve

Musculocutaneous nerve

Radial nerve (superficial branch)

Ulna

Radius

Ulnar nerve

Median nerve

FIGURE **8.26** Brachial plexus: major nerves of the upper limb

8

3. **Lumbar plexuses.** Each lumbar plexus consists of the ventral rami of L_1–L_4 with a small contribution from T_{12} (Figure 8.27A). The largest nerve of this plexus is the **femoral nerve,** which provides motor innervation to most of the anterior thigh muscles and sensory innervation to the skin of the anterior and medial thigh, the leg, and the foot.

4. **Sacral plexuses.** The sacral plexuses form from ventral rami of L_4–S_4 (Figure 8.27B). Their largest nerves, and indeed the largest nerves in the body, are the **sciatic (sye-A-tik) nerves.** The sciatic nerve travels in the posterior thigh, where it splits into two branches: the **tibial nerve** and the **common fibular (peroneal) nerve.** The tibial nerve provides motor innervation to the posterior muscles of the thigh, posterior leg, and foot, and sensory innervation to the posterior leg and foot. The common fibular nerve provides motor and sensory innervation to the anterolateral leg and the foot.

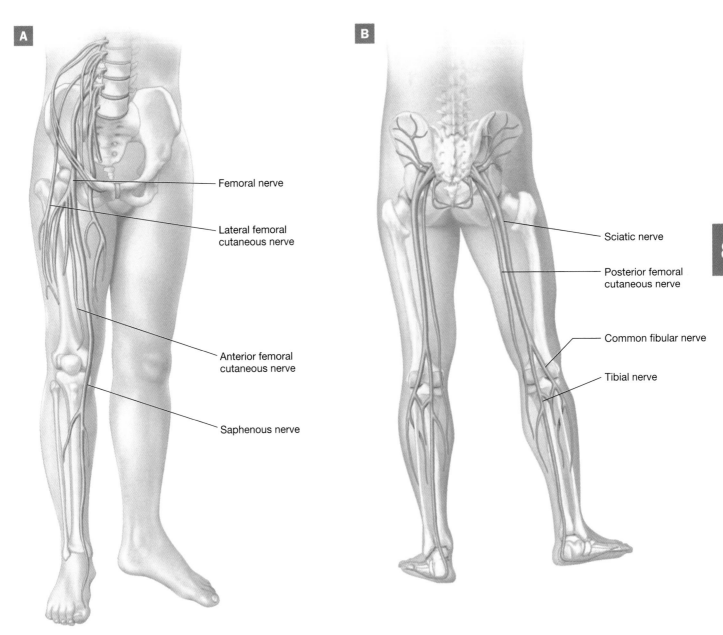

FIGURE **8.27** Nerve plexuses: (**A**) lumbar plexus; (**B**) sacral plexus

Identify the following nerves and nerve plexuses on models and diagrams, using your textbook and this unit for reference. As you examine the anatomical models and diagrams, record on the model inventory in Table 8.6 the name of the model and the structures you were able to identify.

1. Cervical plexus
   a. Phrenic nerve
2. Brachial plexus
   a. Axillary nerve
   b. Radial nerve
   c. Musculocutaneous nerve
   d. Ulnar nerve
   e. Median nerve
3. Thoracic (intercostal) nerves
4. Lumbar plexus
   a. Femoral nerve
5. Sacral plexus
   a. Sciatic nerve
      (1) Tibial nerve
      (2) Common fibular (peroneal) nerve

TABLE **8.6** Model Inventory for Cranial Nerve and Spinal Nerve Anatomy

Model/Diagram	Structures Identified

Procedure 2 Testing Spinal Reflexes

A **reflex** is an involuntary, predictable motor response to a stimulus. The pathway through which information travels, shown below and in Figure 8.28, is called a **reflex arc**:

sensory receptor detects the stimulus → sensory neurons bring the stimulus to the CNS → the CNS processes and integrates the information → the CNS sends its output via motor neurons to an effector → the effector performs the triggered action

The human body has many different reflex arcs, one of the simplest being the **stretch reflex**. Stretch reflexes are important in maintaining posture and balance and are initiated when a muscle is stretched. The stretch is detected by **muscle spindles**, specialized stretch receptors in the muscles, and this information is sent via sensory neurons to the CNS. The CNS then sends impulses down the motor neurons to the muscle that trigger a muscle contraction to counter the stretch.

You can demonstrate the stretch reflex easily: Sit down with your knees bent and relaxed, and palpate (feel) the musculature of your posterior thigh. How do the muscles feel (taut or soft)? Now stand up, and bend over to touch your toes. Palpate the muscles of your posterior thigh again. How do they

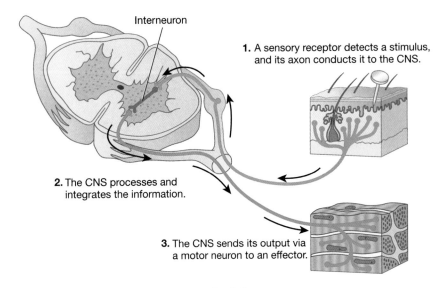

1. A sensory receptor detects a stimulus, and its axon conducts it to the CNS.

2. The CNS processes and integrates the information.

3. The CNS sends its output via a motor neuron to an effector.

FIGURE **8.28** Reflex arc

feel? The reason they feel different in this position is that you stretched the hamstring muscles when you bent over to touch your toes. This triggered a stretch reflex that resulted in shortening (or tightening) of those muscles.

Technically, this reflex can be carried out without the help of the cerebral cortex and can be mediated solely by the spinal cord. We will see shortly, however, that the cortex is involved in even the simplest example of a stretch reflex—the patellar tendon (knee-jerk) reflex, shown in Figure 8.29.

1 Have your lab partner sit in a chair with his or her legs dangling freely.

2 Palpate your partner's patellar tendon between the tibial tuberosity and the patella.

3 Tap this area with the flat end of a reflex hammer (sometimes a few taps are necessary to hit the right spot). What is the result?

_____

_____

_____

_____

_____

_____

_____

_____

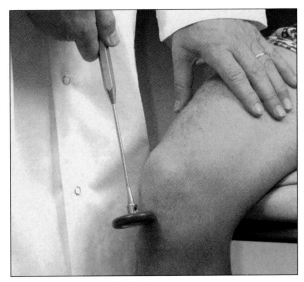

FIGURE **8.29** Patellar reflex

4 Now give your partner a difficult math problem to work (long division with decimals usually does the trick). As your partner works the problem, tap the tendon again. Is this response different from the original response? If yes, how, and why?

_____

_____

_____

_____

_____

_____

8

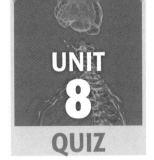

Name _____

Section _____ Date _____

1 Label the following structures on Figure 8.30.

❑ Axon
❑ Axon terminals
❑ Cell body
❑ Dendrites
❑ Telodendria

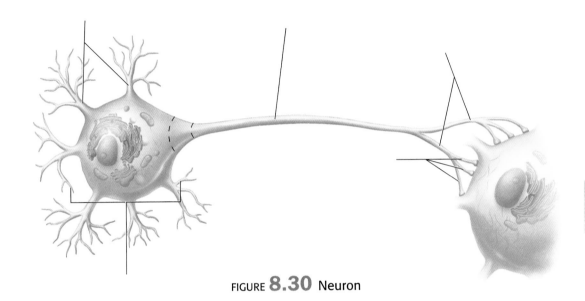

FIGURE **8.30** Neuron

2 *Matching:* Match the neuroglial cell with its correct function.

_____ Oligodendrocytes

_____ Astrocytes

_____ Microglial cells

_____ Schwann cells

_____ Satellite cells

_____ Ependymal cells

A. Create the myelin sheath in the PNS

B. Ciliated cells in the CNS that form and circulate cerebrospinal fluid

C. Surround the cell bodies of neurons in the PNS

D. Anchor neurons and blood vessels, maintain extracellular environment around neurons, assist in the formation of the blood-brain barrier

E. Phagocytic cells of the CNS

F. Form the myelin sheath in the CNS

3 What is the function of the myelin sheath?

_____

_____

4 Label the following parts of the brain in Figures 8.31 and 8.32.

- ❏ Cerebellum
- ❏ Corpus callosum
- ❏ Frontal lobe
- ❏ Hypothalamus
- ❏ Medulla oblongata
- ❏ Midbrain
- ❏ Occipital lobe
- ❏ Parietal lobe
- ❏ Pons
- ❏ Temporal lobe
- ❏ Thalamus

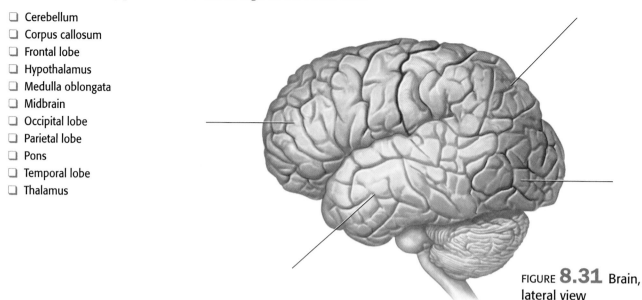

FIGURE **8.31** Brain, lateral view

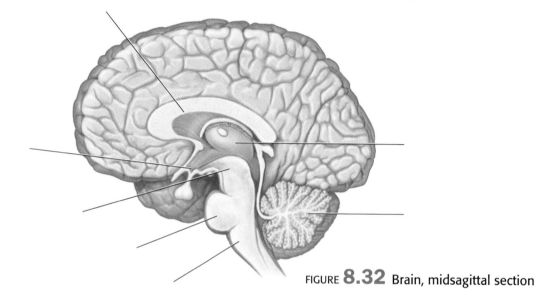

FIGURE **8.32** Brain, midsagittal section

5 Label the following parts of the spinal cord in Figure 8.33.

- ❏ Anterior horn
- ❏ Central canal
- ❏ Lateral horn
- ❏ Posterior horn
- ❏ Spinal arachnoid mater
- ❏ Spinal dura mater

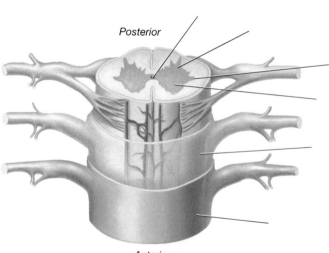

Posterior

Anterior

FIGURE **8.33** Spinal cord, transverse section

8

6 Which of the following is *not* one of the four main regions of the brain?

a. Cerebral hemispheres

b. Brainstem

c. Cerebral aqueduct

d. Cerebellum

e. Diencephalon

7 *Fill in the blanks:* The spinal cord extends from the _____ of the occipital bone to the

_____ vertebra. It terminates as the _____ and gives off a bundle

of nerve roots called the _____.

8 *Matching:* Match the cranial nerve with its main functions.

_____ CN I

_____ CN II

_____ CN III

_____ CN IV

_____ CN V

_____ CN VI

_____ CN VII

_____ CN VIII

_____ CN IX

_____ CN X

_____ CN XI

_____ CN XII

A. Sensory to the face, motor to the muscles of mastication

B. Motor to the trapezius and sternocleidomastoid muscles

C. Hearing and equilibrium

D. Olfaction (smell)

E. Motor to the muscles of swallowing; taste to the posterior one-third of the tongue

F. Motor to one-sixth of the extraocular muscles (superior oblique muscle)

G. Motor to the tongue

H. Vision

I. Motor to the muscles of facial expression, taste to the anterior two-thirds of the tongue

J. Motor to four-sixths of the extraocular muscles, dilates the pupil, opens the eye, changes the shape of the lens

K. Motor to the muscles of swallowing and speaking, motor to the thoracic and abdominal viscera

L. Motor to one-sixth of the extraocular muscles (lateral rectus muscle)

8

9 The receptor that detects the stretch in a stretch reflex is called a(an)

a. mitotic spindle.

b. muscle spindle.

c. capsular receptor.

d. efferent neuron.

10 Multiple sclerosis is a *demyelinating* disease, in which the patient's immune system attacks and destroys the cells that form the myelin sheath in the central nervous system. What types of symptoms would you expect from such a disease? Why? Would Schwann cells or oligodendrocytes be affected?

_____

_____

_____

_____

11 Label the following nerves and plexuses on Figure 8.34.
- ❏ Brachial plexus
- ❏ Cervical plexus
- ❏ Femoral nerve
- ❏ Lumbar plexus
- ❏ Median nerve
- ❏ Musculocutaneous nerve
- ❏ Radial nerve
- ❏ Sacral plexus
- ❏ Sciatic nerve
- ❏ Ulnar nerve

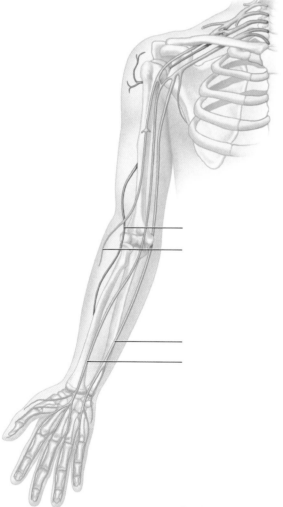

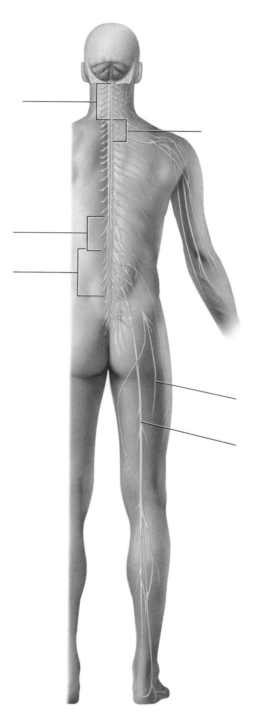

FIGURE **8.34** Nerve plexuses and the ventral rami of the spinal nerves

12 Predict the effects of injuries to the following areas:

   a Cerebral cortex _____

   _____

   b Brainstem _____

   _____

   c Cerebellum _____

   _____

   d Hypothalamus _____

   _____

13 A common way to deliver anesthesia for surgery and childbirth is to inject the anesthetic agent into the epidural space (*epidural anesthesia*). A possible complication of this procedure is a tear in the dura mater that causes CSF to leak out of the central nervous system. Why would a loss of cerebrospinal fluid be problematic? What symptoms do you predict with this condition? (*Hint*: Think about the function of cerebrospinal fluid.)

8

_____

_____

_____

_____

_____

_____

_____

14 Damage to which cranial nerve(s) might produce the following results?

   a Inability to move the tongue _____

   b Inability to taste _____

   c Inability to move the eyes in any direction _____

   d Inability to shrug the shoulders _____

   e Inability to swallow _____

General and Special Senses

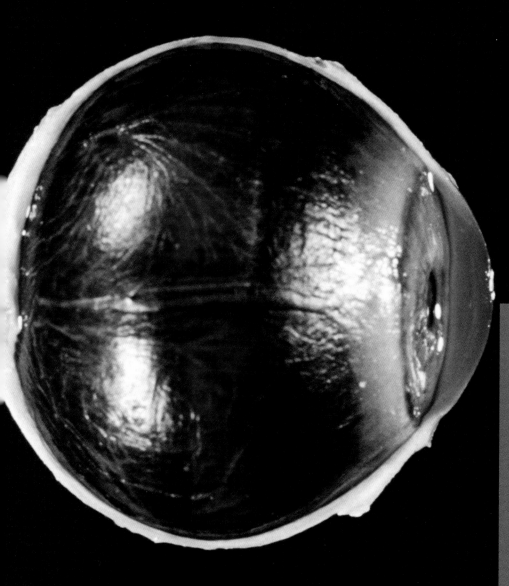

OBJECTIVES

Once you have completed this unit, you should be able to:

1. Describe and identify structures of the eye.

2. Compare and contrast the functions of the rods and cones.

3. Describe and identify structures of the ear.

4. Perform tests of hearing and equilibrium.

5. Identify structures of the olfactory and taste senses.

6. Determine the relative concentration of cutaneous sensory receptors in different regions of the body.

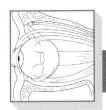

Name _____ Section _____ Date _____

PRE-LAB EXERCISES

Complete the following exercises prior to coming to lab, using your textbook and lab manual for reference.

Pre-Lab Exercise **9-1**

✎ Key Terms

You should be familiar with the following terms before coming to lab.

Term	Definition
Structures of the Eye	
Conjunctiva	
Lacrimal gland	
Sclera	
Cornea	
Iris	
Pupil	
Lens	
Choroid	
Retina	
Structures of the Ear	
Auricle	
External auditory canal	

Tympanic membrane _____

_____

Auditory ossicles _____

_____

Pharyngotympanic tube _____

_____

Vestibule _____

_____

Semicircular canals _____

_____

Cochlea _____

_____

Structures of Taste and Smell

Chemosenses _____

_____

Olfactory epithelium _____

_____

Tongue papillae _____

_____

Pre-Lab Exercise 9-2
Anatomy of the Eye

Label and color the structures of the eye depicted in Figure 9.1 with the following terms from Exercise 9-1. Use your text and Exercise 9-1 in this unit for reference.

Fibrous Tunic
- ❏ Sclera
- ❏ Cornea

Vascular Tunic (Uvea)
- ❏ Choroid
- ❏ Ciliary body
- ❏ Iris
- ❏ Pupil

- ❏ Lens

Sensory Tunic
- ❏ Retina

- ❏ Optic nerve (cranial nerve II)
- ❏ Anterior cavity
- ❏ Posterior cavity
- ❏ Conjunctiva

9

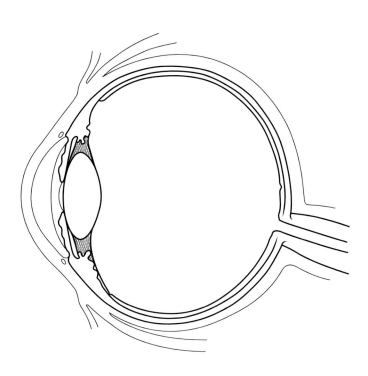

FIGURE **9.1** Eyeball, sagittal section

Label and color the structures of the ear in Figure 9.2 with the following terms from Exercise 9-2. Use your text and Exercise 9-2 in this unit for reference.

- ❏ Outer ear
  - ❏ Auricle (pinna)
  - ❏ External auditory canal
- ❏ Middle ear
  - ❏ Tympanic membrane
  - ❏ Ossicles

- ❏ Malleus
- ❏ Incus
- ❏ Stapes
- ❏ Pharyngotympanic tube

- ❏ Inner ear
  - ❏ Vestibule
  - ❏ Semicircular canals
  - ❏ Cochlea
  - ❏ Vestibulocochlear nerve (cranial nerve VIII)

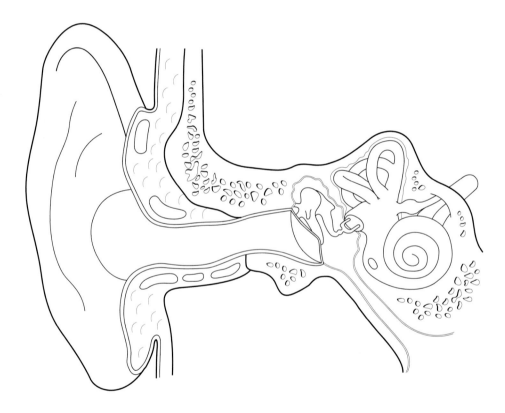

FIGURE **9.2** Ear

EXERCISES

Sensation is broadly defined as the detection of changes in the internal and external environments. Sensation may be conscious or subconscious, depending on the destination of the sensory information. For example, certain blood vessels have receptors that detect blood pressure. This information is taken to the brainstem, which makes changes as necessary to ensure blood pressure remains relatively constant. This information never makes it to the cerebral cortex, so you are not consciously aware of it. However, information eventually taken to the cerebral cortex for integration and interpretation (e.g., the taste of your food or the level of light in a room) is something of which you are consciously aware. This is called **perception**, and it is the focus of this unit.

The following exercises ask you to examine the anatomy and physiology of the **special senses**: vision, hearing and equilibrium, taste, and smell. You also will examine the **general senses** in this unit, which include touch, pain, and temperature.

Exercise **9-1**

Anatomy of the Eye and Vision

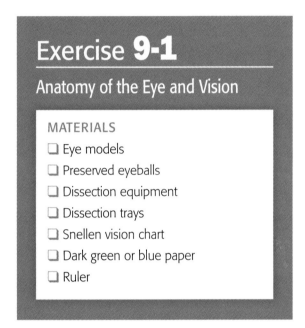

MATERIALS
- ❏ Eye models
- ❏ Preserved eyeballs
- ❏ Dissection equipment
- ❏ Dissection trays
- ❏ Snellen vision chart
- ❏ Dark green or blue paper
- ❏ Ruler

The eye is a complex organ consisting of three components:

1. External structures, such as the **eyelids** (Figure 9.3),
2. Accessory structures, such as the **lacrimal** (LAK-rim-ul) **gland** (Figure 9.3), and
3. The **eyeball** (Figure 9.4).

Many of the external and accessory structures of the eye protect the delicate eyeball.

Anteriorly, the eye is covered by the accessory structures known as the **palpebrae** (pal-PEE-bray), or eyelids. The internal surface of the eyelids and much of the anterior eyeball are covered with a thin mucous membrane called the **conjunctiva** (kahn-junk-TEE-vuh). Another accessory structure of the eye is the **lacrimal apparatus**, which produces and drains tears. The lacrimal apparatus consists of the **lacrimal gland**, located in the superolateral orbit, and the ducts that drain the tears it produces. The other major accessory structures are the **extraocular muscles**, which move the eyeball.

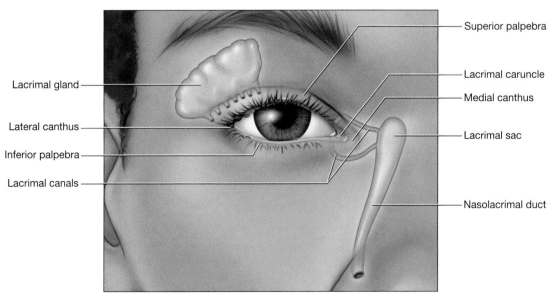

FIGURE **9.3** External and accessory structures of the eye

The eyeball itself is a hollow organ with three distinct tunics, or tissue layers (Figure 9.4):

1. **Fibrous tunic.** The outermost layer of the eyeball consists mostly of dense irregular connective tissue. It is avascular (lacks a blood supply) and consists of two parts:
   a. **Cornea.** The clear cornea makes up the anterior one-sixth of the fibrous tunic and is one of the refractory media of the eyeball (it bends light coming into the eye).
   b. **Sclera.** The sclera (**SKLAIR-uh**) is the white part of the eyeball, which makes up the posterior five-sixths of the fibrous tunic. It is white because of numerous collagen fibers that contribute to its thickness and toughness (in the same way a joint capsule or a ligament is tough and white).

2. **Vascular tunic.** Also called the **uvea** (**YOO-vee-uh**), the vascular tunic carries most of the blood supply to the tissues of the eye. It is composed of three main parts:
   a. **Iris.** The pigmented iris is the most anterior portion of the uvea. It consists of muscle fibers arranged around an opening called the **pupil**. As the fibers contract, the pupil either constricts or dilates.
   b. **Ciliary body.** The ciliary body is located at the anterior aspect of the eye. It is made chiefly of the **ciliary muscle,** which controls the shape of the lens. The muscle attaches to the lens via small **suspensory ligaments**.
   c. **Choroid.** The highly vascular choroid makes up the posterior part of the vascular tunic. The choroid is brown in color to prevent light scattering in the eye.

3. **Sensory tunic.** This layer consists of the **retina** and the **optic nerve.** The retina is a thin, delicate structure that contains **photoreceptors** called **rods** and **cones**.
   a. **Rods.** Rods are scattered throughout the retina and are responsible for vision in dim light and for peripheral vision.
   b. **Cones.** Cones are concentrated at the posterior portion of the retina and are found in highest numbers in an area called the **macula lutea** (**MAK-yoo-luh LOO-tee-uh**). At the center of the macula lutea is the **fovea centralis** (**FOH-vee-uh sen-TRAL-iz**), which contains only cones. Cones are responsible for color and high-acuity (sharp) vision in bright light.

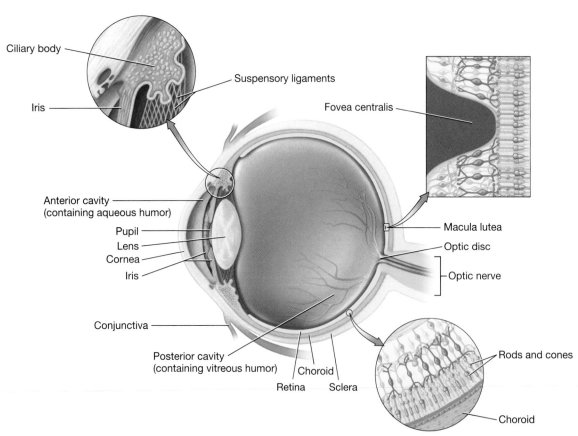

FIGURE **9.4** Eyeball, sagittal section

Note that there are no rods or cones at the posteriormost aspect of the eyeball where the optic nerve leaves the eyeball. This location is called the **optic disc,** or blind spot.

Another component of the eyeball is the **lens,** which allows for precise focusing of light on the retina. The lens divides the eyeball into the **anterior** and **posterior cavities** (sometimes called the anterior and posterior segments). The anterior cavity is filled with a watery fluid called **aqueous humor,** and the posterior cavity contains a thicker fluid called **vitreous humor.** Both help to refract light onto the retina.

Procedure **1** Model Inventory for the Eye

Identify the following structures of the eye and the eyeball on models and diagrams using your textbook and this unit for reference. As you examine the anatomical models and diagrams, record on the model inventory in Table 9.1 the name of the model and the structures you were able to identify.

Eyeball

1. Fibrous tunic
   a. Sclera
   b. Cornea
2. Vascular tunic (uvea)
   a. Choroid
   b. Ciliary body
   c. Suspensory ligaments
   d. Iris
   e. Pupil
3. Lens

4. Sensory tunic
   a. Retina
   b. Optic disc
   c. Macula lutea
   d. Fovea centralis
5. Optic nerve (cranial nerve II)
6. Anterior cavity
   a. Aqueous humor
7. Posterior cavity
   a. Vitreous humor

Accessory Structures

1. Palpebrae
2. Lacrimal apparatus
   a. Lacrimal gland
   b. Lacrimal canal
   c. Nasolacrimal duct
3. Conjunctiva

TABLE **9.1** Model Inventory for the Eye

Model/Diagram	Structures Identified

Procedure 2 Eyeball Dissection

In this exercise you will examine the structures of the eyeball on a fresh or preserved eyeball. I promise eyeball dissection isn't as gross as it sounds!

1 Examine the external anatomy of the eyeball (Figure 9.5), and record below the structures you can identify.

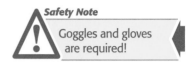
_____

_____

_____

_____

_____

_____

2 Use scissors to remove the adipose tissue surrounding the eyeball. Identify the optic nerve.

3 Hold the eyeball at its anterior and posterior poles, and use a sharp scalpel or scissors to make an incision in the frontal plane. Watch out, as aqueous humor and vitreous humor are likely to spill everywhere.

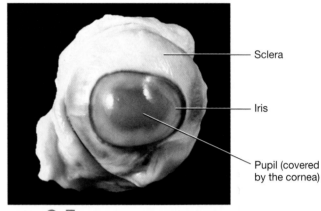

FIGURE **9.5** Anterior view of an eyeball

4 Complete the incision, and separate the anterior and posterior portions of the eyeball (Figure 9.6). Take care to preserve the fragile retina—the thin, delicate yellow-tinted inner layer.

5 List the structures you can identify in the anterior half of the eyeball (Figure 9.7):

_____

_____

_____

_____

_____

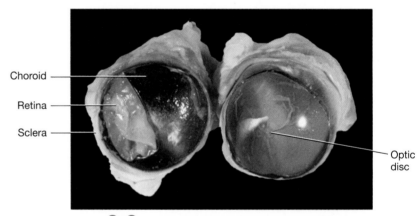

FIGURE **9.6** Frontal section of an eyeball showing the tunics

6 List the structures you can identify in the posterior half of the eyeball:

_____

_____

_____

_____

_____

_____

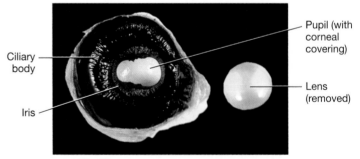

FIGURE **9.7** Posterior view of the anterior portion of an eyeball and lens

Procedure 3 Comparing the Distribution of Rods and Cones

We discussed earlier the unequal distribution of the photoreceptors in the retina. In this procedure you will see (no pun intended) firsthand the differences in vision produced by the rods and the vision produced by the cones.

1 On a small sheet of paper, write the phrase "Anatomy is fun" in your regular-size print.

2 Hold this piece of paper about 25 cm (10 inches) directly in front of your lab partner's eyes, and have your lab partner read the phrase.

   a Can your partner read the phrase clearly?_____

   b Which photoreceptors are producing the image? _____

3 Now write a second phrase on the paper, and don't tell your partner what the phrase says. Hold the paper about 10 inches from your partner's peripheral vision field. Have him or her continue to stare forward and attempt to read what you have written.

   a Can your partner read the phrase clearly?_____

   b Which photoreceptors are producing the image? _____

4 For the next test, dim the lights in the room. Have your partner stand 20 feet in front of a Snellen eye chart and read the chart. You should stand next to the chart to verify that the letters your partner reads are correct. This indicates your partner's vision relative to someone with perfect vision. For example, a person with 20/40 vision can see at 20 feet what someone with perfect vision could see at 40 feet. Record the number of the smallest line he or she can read without errors (e.g., 20/40).

   Visual acuity: _____

5 With the lights still dimmed, and your partner standing in the same place, hold a piece of dark green or dark blue paper over the Snellen chart. Ask your partner to identify the color of the paper you are holding:

   Paper color: _____

6 Repeat the above processes with the lights illuminated:

   Visual acuity:_____

   Paper color: _____

7 In which scenario were visual acuity and color vision better? Explain your findings.

_____

_____

_____

_____

_____

9

Exercise 9-2

Anatomy of the Ear, Hearing, and Equilibrium

MATERIALS

❑ Ear models

❑ Tuning fork (500–1,000 Hz)

❑ Chalk

The ear contains structures both for hearing and equilibrium (balance). It is divided into three regions: the outer, middle, and inner ear (Figure 9.8).

1. **Outer ear.** The outer ear begins with the **auricle** (OHR-ik-ul), or *pinna*, a shell-shaped structure composed of elastic cartilage that surrounds the opening to the **external auditory canal.** The external auditory canal extends about 2.5 cm into the temporal bone, where it ends in the **tympanic membrane**, a thin, flexible sheet of tissue that separates the outer ear from the middle ear.

2. **Middle ear.** The middle ear is a small air-filled cavity within the temporal bone that houses tiny bones called the **auditory ossicles**—the **malleus** (MAL-ee-us; hammer), **incus** (INK-us; anvil), and **stapes** (STAY-peez; stirrup). The ossicles transmit vibrations from the tympanic membrane to the inner ear through a structure called the **oval window.** An additional structure in the middle ear is the **pharyngotympanic** (fair-in-go-tim-PAN-ik) **tube,** which connects the middle ear to the pharynx (throat) and equalizes pressure in the middle ear.

3. **Inner ear.** The inner ear contains the sense organs for hearing and equilibrium. It consists of cavities collectively called the **bony labyrinth** that contain a series of membranes called the **membranous labyrinth.** The bony labyrinth has three regions:

    a. **Vestibule.** The vestibule is an egg-shaped bony cavity that houses two structures of the membranous labyrinth responsible for equilibrium or balance—the **saccule** (SAK-yool) and the **utricle** (YOO-trih-kul).

    b. **Semicircular canals.** Situated at right angles to one another, the semicircular canals house the membranous **semicircular ducts** and the **ampulla**, which work together with the organs of the vestibule to maintain equilibrium. Their orientation allows them to sense rotational movements of the head and body.

    c. **Cochlea.** The cochlea is a spiral bony canal that contains the membranous **organ of Corti**, whose specialized **hair cells** transmit sound impulses.

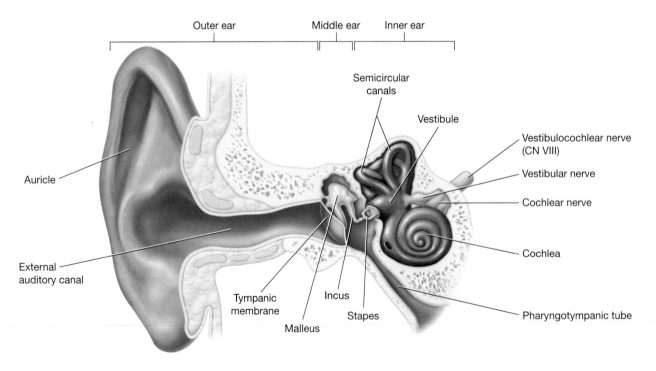

FIGURE **9.8** Anatomy of the ear

Procedure 1 Model Inventory for the Ear

Identify the following structures of the ear on models and diagrams, using your textbook and this unit for reference. As you examine the anatomical models and diagrams, record on the model inventory in Table 9.2 the name of the model and the structures you were able to identify.

1. Outer ear
   a. Auricle (pinna)
   b. External auditory canal
2. Middle ear
   a. Tympanic membrane
   b. Ossicles
      (1) Malleus
      (2) Incus
      (3) Stapes
   c. Oval window
   d. Pharyngotympanic tube

3. Inner ear
   a. Vestibule
   b. Semicircular canals
   c. Cochlea
   d. Vestibulocochlear nerve (cranial nerve VIII)

TABLE **9.2** Model Inventory for the Ear

Model/Diagram	Structures Identified

Hearing Acuity

There are two possible types of hearing loss:

1. **Conductive hearing loss** results from interference of sound conduction through the outer and/or middle ear.

2. **Sensorineural hearing loss** results from damage to the inner ear or the vestibulocochlear nerve.

Two clinical tests can help a health-care professional determine if hearing loss is conductive or sensorineural—the Weber test and the Rinne test. Both tests use tuning forks that vibrate at specific frequencies when struck. The tuning forks are placed directly on the bones of the skull to evaluate bone conduction—the ability to hear the vibrations transmitted through the bone. The forks are then held near the ear, not touching bone, to evaluate air conduction—the ability to hear the vibrations transmitted through the air.

Procedure 2 Weber Test

1 Obtain a tuning fork with a frequency of 500–1,000 Hz (cycles per second).

2 Hold the tuning fork by the base, and strike it lightly with a mallet, or tap it on the edge of the table. The fork should begin ringing softly. If it is ringing too loudly, grasp the tines to stop it from ringing, and try again.

3 Place the base of the vibrating tuning fork on the midline of your partner's head, as shown in Figure 9.9.

4 Ask your partner if the sound is heard better in one ear or if the sound is heard equally in both ears. If the sound is heard better in one ear, this is called lateralization.

   a Was the sound lateralized? If yes, to which ear? _____

5 To illustrate what it would sound like if the sound were lateralized, have your partner place his or her finger in one ear. Repeat the test.

   a In which ear was the sound heard better? _____

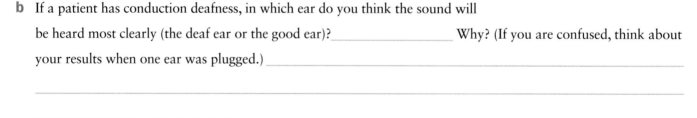

FIGURE **9.9** Weber test

   b If a patient has conduction deafness, in which ear do you think the sound will be heard most clearly (the deaf ear or the good ear)?_____ Why? (If you are confused, think about your results when one ear was plugged.) _____

_____

_____

   c If a patient has sensorineural deafness, in which ear do you think the sound will be best heard?

_____

Procedure 3 Rinne Test

1 Strike the tuning fork lightly to start it ringing, as shown in Figure 9.10.

2 Place the base of the tuning fork on your partner's mastoid process.

3 Time the interval during which your partner can hear the sound. Your partner will have to tell you when he or she can no longer hear the ringing.

Time interval in seconds: _____

4 After your partner can no longer hear the ringing, quickly move the still-vibrating tuning fork 1–2 cm lateral to the external auditory canal (the fork should not be touching your partner at this point).

FIGURE **9.10** Rinne test

5 Time the interval from the point when you moved the tuning fork in front of the external auditory canal to when your partner can no longer hear the sound.

Time interval in seconds: _____

   a Which situation tested bone conduction? _____

   b Which situation tested air conduction? _____

6 Typically, the air-conducted sound is heard twice as long as the bone-conducted sound. For example, if the bone-conducted sound was heard for 15 seconds, the air-conducted sound should be heard for 30 seconds.

   a Were your results normal? _____

   b What type of deafness is present if the bone-conducted sound is heard longer than the air-conducted sound?

9

Equilibrium

A common and simple test of equilibrium is the **Romberg test,** in which the person is asked to stand still, first with the eyes open and then with the eyes closed. Under normal conditions, the vestibular apparatus should be able to maintain equilibrium in the absence of visual input. If the vestibular apparatus is impaired, however, the brain relies on visual cues to maintain balance.

Procedure 4 Romberg Test

1 Have your partner stand erect in front of a chalkboard with feet together and arms at the sides.

2 Use chalk to draw lines on the board on either side of your partner's torso. These lines are for your reference in the next part.

3 Have your partner stand in front of the chalkboard for one minute, staring forward with his or her eyes open. Use the lines on either side of his or her torso to note how much he or she sways as she stands. Below, record the amount of side-to-side swaying (i.e., minimal or significant):

_____

4 Now have your partner stand in the same position for one minute with his or her eyes closed. Again note the amount of side-to-side swaying, using the chalk lines for reference.

a Was the amount of swaying more or less with his/her eyes closed? _____

b Why do you think this is so? _____

_____

_____

_____

c What do you predict would be the result for a person with an impaired vestibular apparatus? Explain.

_____

_____

_____

_____

Exercise 9-3

Olfactory and Taste Senses

MATERIALS
❏ Head and neck models
❏ Tongue model

Both olfaction and taste are sometimes referred to as the **chemosenses**, because they both rely on chemoreceptors to relay information about the environment to the brain. The chemoreceptors of the olfactory sense are located in a small patch in the roof of the nasal cavity called the **olfactory epithelium** (Figure 9.11). The olfactory epithelium contains bipolar neurons called **olfactory receptor cells**. Their axons penetrate the holes in the cribriform plate to synapse on the olfactory bulb, which then sends the impulses down the axons of the olfactory tract to the olfactory cortex.

Taste receptors are located in **taste buds** on projections from the tongue called **papillae** (Figure 9.12). Of the four types of papillae—**filiform, fungiform, foliate,** and **circumvallate**—all but filiform papillae contain taste buds. Fungiform papillae are scattered over the surface of the tongue, whereas the large circumvallate papillae are located at the posterior aspect of the tongue, arranged in a V shape.

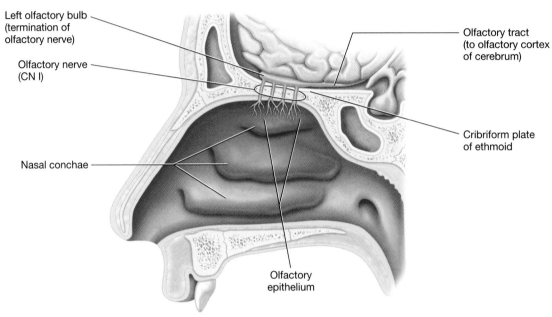

Left olfactory bulb (termination of olfactory nerve)

Olfactory nerve (CN I)

Nasal conchae

Olfactory epithelium

Olfactory tract (to olfactory cortex of cerebrum)

Cribriform plate of ethmoid

FIGURE **9.11** Nasal cavity and olfactory epithelium

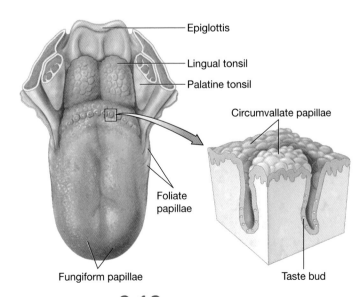

Epiglottis

Lingual tonsil

Palatine tonsil

Circumvallate papillae

Foliate papillae

Fungiform papillae

Taste bud

FIGURE **9.12** Surface of the tongue

9

Procedure 1 Model Inventory for Olfaction and Taste

Identify the following structures of the olfactory and taste senses on anatomical models and charts. As you examine the anatomical models and diagrams, record on the model inventory in Table 9.3 the name of the model and the structures you were able to identify.

Olfaction

1. Nasal cavity
   a. Nasal conchae
   b. Nasal septum
2. Olfactory epithelium
   a. Olfactory receptor cells
3. Olfactory bulbs
4. Olfactory tracts
5. Cribriform plate

Taste

1. Papillae
   a. Fungiform papillae
   b. Circumvallate papillae
   c. Foliate papillae
2. Taste buds

TABLE **9.3** Model Inventory for Olfaction and Taste

Model/Diagram	Structures Identified

Exercise 9-4

The General Senses: Cutaneous Sensation

MATERIALS

❏ Water-soluble marking pens (two colors)
❏ Ruler
❏ 2 wooden applicator sticks (or toothpicks)

Sensory receptors in the skin respond to different stimuli, including temperature, touch, and pain. These receptors are not distributed throughout the skin equally; instead, they are concentrated in certain regions of the body. The following experiments will allow you to determine the relative distribution of the receptors for touch in the skin by performing two tests: the error of localization and two-point discrimination.

Error of Localization

Every region of the skin corresponds to an area of the somatosensory association area in the cerebral cortex. Some regions are better represented than others and, therefore, are capable of localizing stimuli with greater precision than are less well-represented areas. The **error of localization** (also called tactile localization) tests the ability to determine the location of the skin touched and demonstrates how well represented each region of the skin is in the cerebral cortex.

Procedure 1 Testing Error of Localization

1 Have your partner sit with his or her eyes closed.

2 Use a water-soluble marking pen to place a mark on your partner's anterior forearm.

3 Using a different color of marker, have your partner, still with his or her eyes closed, place a mark as close as possible to where he or she believes the original spot is located.

4 Use a ruler to measure the distance between the two points in millimeters. This is your error of localization.

5 Repeat this procedure for each of the following locations:

   a Anterior thigh
   b Face
   c Palm of hand
   d Fingertip

6 Record your data in Table 9.4.

TABLE **9.4** Error of Localization

Location	Error of Localization (mm)
Anterior forearm	
Anterior thigh	
Face	
Palm of hand	
Fingertip	

Two-Point Discrimination

The **two-point discrimination test** assesses the ability to perceive the number of stimuli ("points") placed on the skin. Areas that have a higher density of touch receptors are better able to distinguish between multiple stimuli than those with fewer touch receptors.

Procedure 2 Testing Two-Point Discrimination

1 Have your partner close his or her eyes.

2 Place the ends of two wooden applicator sticks close together (they should be nearly touching) on your partner's skin on the anterior forearm. Ask your partner how many points he or she can discriminate—one or two.

3 If he or she can sense only one point, move the sticks farther apart. Repeat this procedure until your partner can distinguish two separate points touching his or her skin.

4 Use a ruler to measure the distance between the two sticks in millimeters. This is your two-point discrimination.

5 Repeat this procedure for each of the following locations:

  a Anterior thigh

  b Face (around the lips and/or eyes)

  c Vertebral region

  d Fingertip

6 Record your data in Table 9.5.

TABLE **9.5** Two-Point Discrimination

Location	Two-Point Discrimination (mm)
Anterior forearm	
Anterior thigh	
Face	
Vertebral region	
Fingertip	

7 What results did you expect for each test? Explain.

_____

_____

_____

_____

_____

8 Did your observations agree with your expectations? Interpret your results.

_____

_____

_____

_____

_____

_____

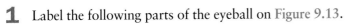

UNIT
9
QUIZ

1 Label the following parts of the eyeball on Figure 9.13.

❑ Choroid
❑ Cornea
❑ Iris
❑ Lens
❑ Optic nerve
❑ Posterior cavity
❑ Retina
❑ Sclera

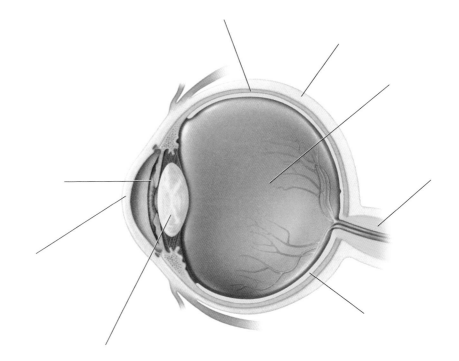

FIGURE **9.13** Eyeball, sagittal section

2 The lacrimal gland is located in the _____ and produces _____.

a. superolateral orbit; mucus
b. inferomedial orbit; tears
c. superolateral orbit; tears
d. inferomedial orbit; mucus

3 The rods are responsible for _____, whereas the cones are responsible for _____.

a. peripheral and dim light vision; high-acuity color vision
b. high-acuity color vision; peripheral and dim light vision
c. peripheral and color vision; high-acuity and dim light vision
d. high-acuity and dim light vision; peripheral and color vision

4 Label the following parts of the ear on Figure 9.14.

- ☐ Auricle
- ☐ Cochlea
- ☐ External auditory canal
- ☐ Incus

- ☐ Malleus
- ☐ Pharyngotympanic tube
- ☐ Semicircular canals
- ☐ Stapes

- ☐ Tympanic membrane
- ☐ Vestibule
- ☐ Vestibulocochlear nerve

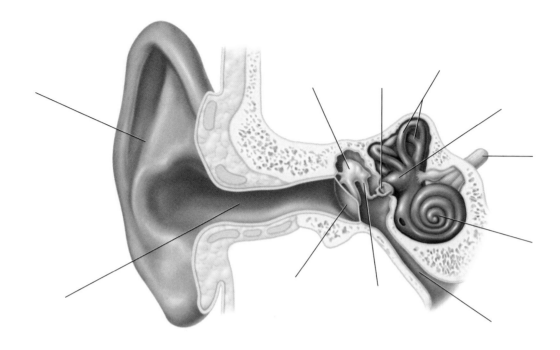

FIGURE **9.14** Anatomy of the ear

5 The auditory ossicles transmit vibrations from the _____ to the _____.
- a. auricle; malleus
- b. tympanic membrane; inner ear
- c. tympanic membrane; middle ear
- d. auricle; inner ear

6 The structures of the cochlea are responsible for _____, whereas the structures of the vestibule and semicircular canals are responsible for _____.
- a. equilibrium; balance
- b. equilibrium; hearing
- c. hearing; equilibrium
- d. hearing; audition

7 The receptors for smell are located in the
- a. gustatory mucosa.
- b. olfactory epithelium.
- c. olfactory fossa.
- d. squamous epithelium.

9

8 Taste buds are located on the

   a. filiform, fungiform, and circumvallate papillae.

   b. filiform, fungiform, and foliate papillae.

   c. filiform and circumvallate papillae only.

   d. fungiform, foliate, and circumvallate papillae.

9 You would expect the error of localization and the two-point discrimination threshold to be lowest on the

   a. back.

   b. forearm.

   c. fingertip.

   d. thigh.

10 The disease *macular degeneration* is characterized by a gradual loss of vision as a result of degeneration of the macula lutea. Considering the type of cells located in the macula lutea, which type of vision do you think a sufferer of macular degeneration would lose? Why?

11 How would the signs and symptoms differ from those in question 10 in a condition that caused degeneration of rods?

12 Explain why infectious *otitis media* (inflammation of the middle ear) may result in a simultaneous *pharyngitis* (inflammation of the throat).

9

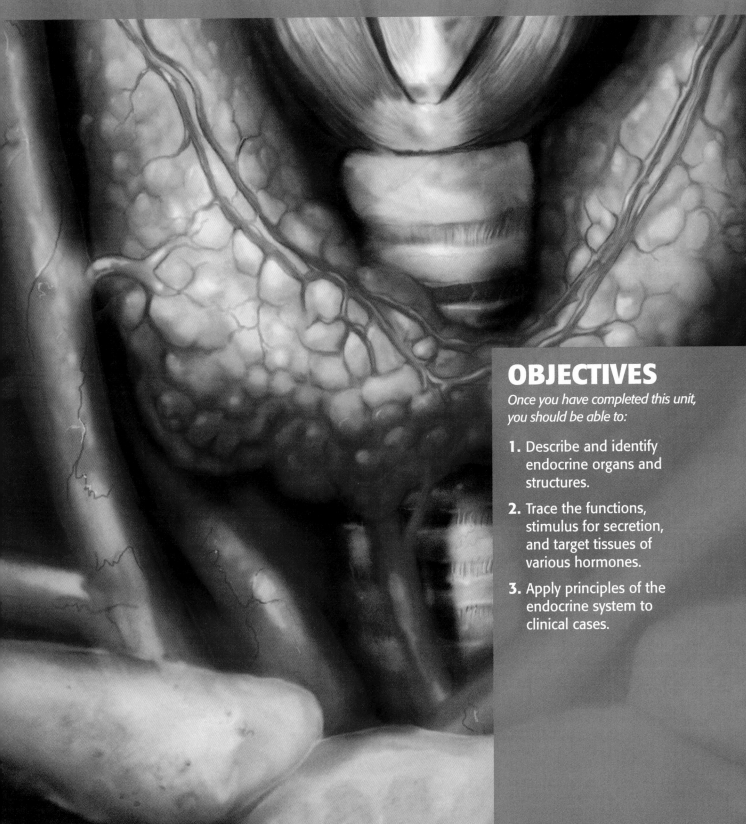

Endocrine System

OBJECTIVES

Once you have completed this unit, you should be able to:

1. Describe and identify endocrine organs and structures.

2. Trace the functions, stimulus for secretion, and target tissues of various hormones.

3. Apply principles of the endocrine system to clinical cases.

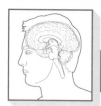

Name _____ Section _____ Date _____

PRE-LAB EXERCISES

Complete the following exercises prior to coming to lab, using your textbook and lab manual for reference.

Pre-Lab Exercise **10-1**

 Key Terms

You should be familiar with the following terms before coming to lab. Please note that key hormones are covered in Pre-Lab Exercise 10-3 (p. 250).

Term	Definition
General Terms	
Endocrine organ (gland)	
Hormone	
Target tissue	
Negative feedback	
Endocrine Organs	
Hypothalamus	
Anterior pituitary	
Posterior pituitary	
Thyroid gland	
Parathyroid glands	
Pineal gland	
Pancreas	
Adrenal gland	

10

Name _____ Section _____ Date _____

Ovaries _____

_____

Testes _____

_____

Pre-Lab Exercise 10-2
Endocrine System Anatomy

Label and color the structures of the endocrine system depicted in Figure 10.1 with the following terms from Exercise 10-1.
Use your text and Exercise 10-1 in this unit for reference.

❏ Hypothalamus
❏ Pituitary gland
   ❏ Anterior pituitary
   ❏ Posterior pituitary
❏ Pineal gland
❏ Thyroid gland
   ❏ Isthmus
   ❏ Right and left lobes
❏ Parathyroid glands
❏ Thymus gland
❏ Adrenal glands
   ❏ Adrenal cortex
   ❏ Adrenal medulla
❏ Pancreas
   ❏ Pancreatic islets
❏ Ovaries
❏ Testes

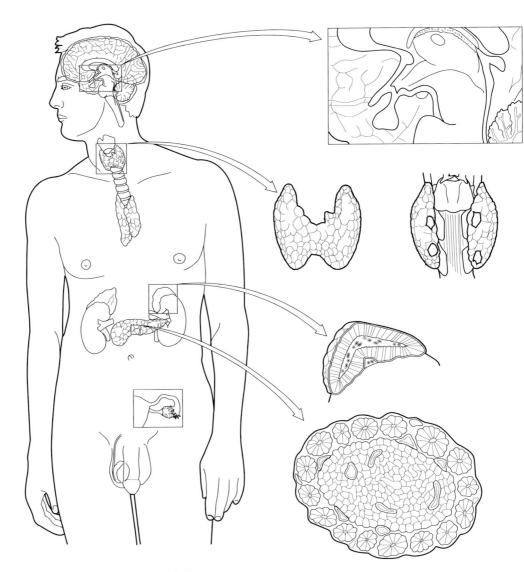

FIGURE **10.1** Endocrine system

Pre-Lab Exercise 10-3

Hormones: Target Tissues and Effects

Complete Table 10.1 with the organ that secretes each hormone, the stimulus for that hormone's secretion, and the hormone's target tissue.

TABLE **10.1** Properties of Hormones

Hormone	Organ That Secretes the Hormone	Stimulus for Secretion	Target Tissue
Antidiuretic hormone			
Oxytocin			
Thyroid-stimulating hormone			
Adrenocorticotropic hormone			
Growth hormone			
Thyroxine and triiodothyronine (T4 and T3)			
Parathyroid hormone			
Cortisol			
Aldosterone			
Insulin			
Glucagon			

EXERCISES

The **endocrine system** is a diverse group of ductless glands that plays a major role in maintaining the body's homeostasis along with the nervous system. Although these two systems both work toward the same goal, you will notice that the methods by which they do so differ. The cells of the nervous system work via action potentials (nerve impulses) and release **neurotransmitters** that directly affect target cells. The effects are nearly immediate, but they are very short-lived. In contrast, the cells of the endocrine system work via secretion of **hormones**—chemicals secreted into the bloodstream that typically act on distant targets. The effects of hormones are not immediate, but they are longer lasting than those of nerve impulses.

In general, hormones function to regulate the processes of other cells, including inducing the production of enzymes or other hormones, changing the metabolic rate of the cell, and altering permeability of the plasma membranes. You might think of hormones as the "middle managers" of the body, because they communicate the messages from their "bosses" (the endocrine glands) and tell other cells what to do. The primary function of some endocrine glands (e.g., the thyroid and anterior pituitary glands) is to secrete hormones. Others, however, secrete hormones as a secondary function, examples of which are the heart (atrial natriuretic peptide), adipose tissue (leptin), the kidneys (erythropoietin), and the stomach (gastrin).

This unit introduces you to the anatomy and physiology of the endocrine organs and hormones. To close out this unit, you will play "endocrine detective" and try to solve three "endocrine mysteries" involving a cast of characters you will see again in later units.

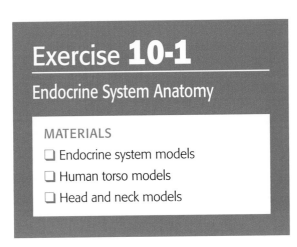

Exercise **10-1**

Endocrine System Anatomy

MATERIALS
- ❑ Endocrine system models
- ❑ Human torso models
- ❑ Head and neck models

The 10 organs in the body that have hormone secretion as a primary function are the hypothalamus, the pituitary gland, the pineal gland, the thyroid gland, the parathyroid glands, the thymus, the adrenal gland, the pancreas, and the ovaries or testes (Figure 10.2).

1. **Hypothalamus.** The hypothalamus, the inferior part of the diencephalon, can be likened to the endocrine system's chief executive officer (CEO). It releases hormones that inhibit and stimulate secretion—called **inhibiting** and **releasing hormones,** respectively—from the anterior pituitary gland. The anterior pituitary in turn releases hormones that stimulate other endocrine and exocrine glands in the body. In addition to inhibiting and releasing hormones, the hypothalamus makes the hormone **oxytocin,** which triggers contraction of the uterus and milk ejection from the mammary gland, and **antidiuretic hormone (ADH),** which causes water retention from the kidneys.

2. **Pituitary gland.** Note in Figure 10.2 that the pituitary gland is actually two separate structures:

   a. The **anterior pituitary gland** is composed of glandular epithelium and secretes a variety of hormones that affect other tissues in the body. These hormones include **thyroid-stimulating hormone (TSH),** which stimulates growth of and secretion from the thyroid; **growth hormone (GH),** which increases the rate of cell division and protein synthesis in all tissues; **prolactin,** which stimulates milk production from mammary glands; **adrenocorticotropic (a-DREE-noh-kohr-tih-koh-TROH-pik) hormone (ACTH),** which stimulates secretion from the adrenal cortex; and two reproductive hormones, **luteinizing (LOO-tee-nye-zing) hormone** and **follicle (FAH-lih-kul)-stimulating hormone** that affect primarily the testes and ovaries.

   b. The other component of the pituitary gland is the **posterior pituitary,** actually composed of nervous tissue rather than glandular tissue. In fact, the posterior pituitary doesn't produce any hormones at all and functions merely as a place for storing the oxytocin and ADH produced by the hypothalamus.

3. **Pineal gland.** Recall from Unit 8 (p. 196) that the tiny pineal gland is located in the posterior and superior diencephalon. It secretes the hormone **melatonin** in response to decreased light levels, which acts on the reticular formation of the brainstem to trigger sleep.

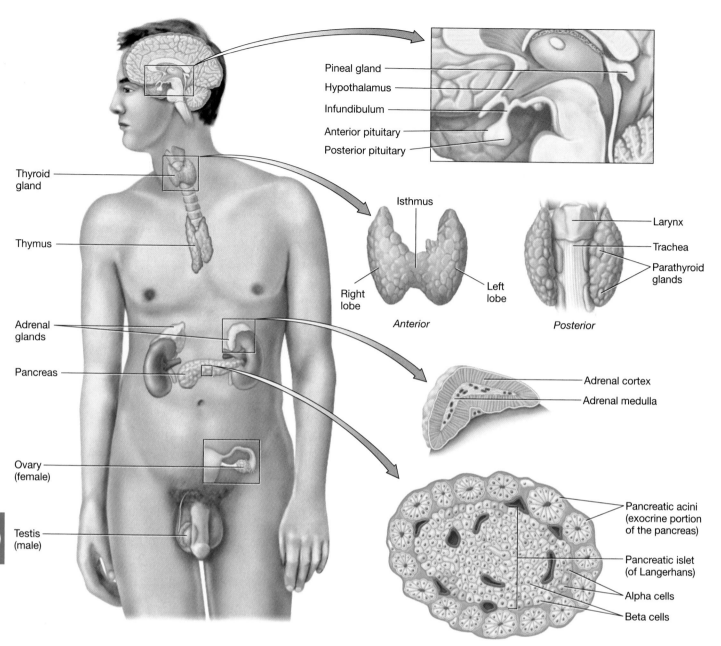

FIGURE **10.2** Endocrine system

4. **Thyroid gland**. The thyroid gland, located in the anterior and inferior neck superficial to the larynx, is composed of hollow spheres called **thyroid follicles**. The cells that line the thyroid follicles are simple cuboidal cells called **follicle cells**, and they surround a gelatinous, iodine-rich substance called **colloid**. The follicle cells respond to TSH from the anterior pituitary by secreting a chemical into the colloid that reacts with iodine to produce two different hormones: **thyroxine (thy-ROX-in), or T4**, which has four iodine molecules, and **triiodothyronine (try-eye-oh-doh-THY-roh-neen), or T3**, which has three iodine molecules. T3 is the most active of the two hormones and acts on essentially all cells in the body to increase the metabolic rate, increase protein synthesis, and regulate the heart rate and blood pressure, among other things. About 10 times as much T4 is produced as T3, and the body converts T4 to T3 when T3 levels in the blood drop.

5. **Parathyroid glands**. As you can see in Figure 10.2, the small parathyroid glands are located on the posterior surface of the thyroid gland. They secrete the hormone **parathyroid hormone (PTH)**, which maintains calcium ion homeostasis. PTH is secreted in response to decreased levels of calcium ions in the blood, and it triggers osteoclast activity and resorption of bone tissue, increased calcium ion absorption from the gut, and increased calcium ion reabsorption from the kidneys.

6. **Thymus.** The thymus gland sits in the superior mediastinum. It is largest and most active in infancy and early childhood, during which it secretes hormones that stimulate the development of blood cells called T lymphocytes within the thymus. In adults most of the thymic tissue is gradually replaced by fat and other connective tissue.

7. **Adrenal glands.** The adrenal glands sit atop the superior pole of each kidney. Like the pituitary gland, the adrenal gland is actually two separate glands.

   a. The superficial region consists of glandular tissue called the **adrenal cortex,** and it secretes **steroid hormones** in response to stimulation by ACTH and other factors. The outermost zone of the adrenal cortex secretes steroids that regulate fluid and electrolyte homeostasis, such as **aldosterone** (al-DAHS-tur-ohn). The middle zone of the adrenal cortex secretes steroids that regulate the stress response, blood glucose, fluid homeostasis, and inflammation, such as **cortisol** (KOHR-tih-sahl). The innermost zone secretes cortisol-like steroids and others that affect the gonads and other tissues.

   b. The deep region of the adrenal gland, called the **adrenal medulla,** consists of modified sympathetic neurons that secrete **epinephrine** and **norepinephrine** in response to stimulation from the sympathetic nervous system.

8. **Pancreas.** The pancreas has both endocrine and exocrine functions. The endocrine functions are carried out by cells in small, round "islands" called **pancreatic islets.** The cells within the pancreatic islets secrete the hormones **insulin** and **glucagon,** which play a major role in regulating blood sugar levels. Insulin triggers the uptake of glucose by cells, which decreases blood glucose, and glucagon triggers the release of stored glucose from the liver, which increases blood glucose. Note that glucagon and insulin have opposite actions and so are known as **antagonists.**

9. **Testes.** The testes are the male reproductive organs that produce sperm cells, the male gametes. Cells within the testes called **interstitial** (in-tur-STISH-ul) **cells** (or **Leydig cells**) produce a steroid hormone called **testosterone.** This hormone promotes the production of sperm cells and the development of male secondary sex characteristics such as a deeper voice, greater bone and muscle mass, and facial hair.

10. **Ovaries.** The ovaries are the female reproductive organs that produce ooctyes, the female gametes. The ovaries produce steroid hormones called **estrogens** and **progesterone.** Estrogens play a role in the development of oocytes; female secondary sex characteristics, such as breast development and the development of subcutaneous fat stores; and a variety of other processes. Progesterone has myriad effects that prepare the body for pregnancy.

Let's now examine these structures on models and charts. Note that human torso models are typically a good place to start when studying the endocrine system, because most of the organs are easy to find. The one exception is the thymus; many torsos and models do not show this structure because it is fairly inactive in adults.

Procedure 1 Model Inventory of the Endocrine System

Identify the following structures of the endocrine system on models and diagrams, using your textbook and this unit for reference. As you examine the anatomical models and diagrams, record on the model inventory in Table 10.2 the name of the model and the structures you were able to identify.

Endocrine Glands

1. Hypothalamus
2. Pituitary gland
   a. Anterior pituitary
   b. Posterior pituitary
3. Pineal gland
4. Thyroid gland
   a. Isthmus
   b. Right and left lobes

5. Parathyroid glands
6. Thymus gland
7. Adrenal glands
   a. Adrenal cortex
   b. Adrenal medulla
8. Pancreas
   a. Pancreatic islets

9. Ovaries
10. Testes

TABLE 10.2 Model Inventory for the Endocrine System

Model/Diagram	Structures Identified

Exercise 10-2

Time to Trace:
Negative Feedback Loops

Earlier in this unit we pointed out that each hormone has its own stimulus for secretion. The stimulus for secretion is generally a disturbance of homeostasis, such as a change in body temperature, a change in the concentration of blood glucose or electrolytes, or a stressor. The hormone's response is to act on distant target cells to cause changes that restore homeostasis. When homeostasis is restored, the concentration of the hormone and activity of the glands declines. This type of response is called a **negative feedback loop**.

In this exercise you will be tracing a hormone's negative feedback loop from the initial homeostatic disturbance through the hormone's effects on its target cells to restore homeostasis. Following is an example:

Stimulus: Blood glucose falls → Response: the pancreas releases glucagon, and glucagon levels in the blood rise → Effect: glucagon causes glycogenolysis by the liver, and blood glucose levels rise → Negative feedback: glucagon levels in the blood decline → End

Some of the negative feedback loops are slightly more complex because they involve multiple organs, such as the following:

Stimulus: body temperature and/or metabolic rate drops → Response 1: thyrotropin-releasing hormone is released from the hypothalamus → Response 2: thyroid-stimulating hormone is released from the anterior pituitary → Response 3: T3 and T4 are produced and released from the thyroid gland, and T3 and T4 concentrations rise in the blood → Effect: T3 increases the metabolic rate of cells and heat production, and body temperature and metabolic rate return to normal → Negative feedback step 1: levels of thyrotropin-releasing hormone in the blood decrease → Negative feedback step 2: levels of thyroid-stimulating hormone in the blood decrease → Negative feedback step 3: levels of T3 and T4 in the blood decrease → End

Now it's your turn! Complete the negative feedback loops that follow, using the examples as a guide. Refer to Pre-Lab Exercise 10-3 and your textbook for help with the hormones and their actions.

1 Stimulus: the concentration of the blood increases (i.e., the amount of water in the blood decreases) → Response: the hypothala-

mus releases _____ and stores it in the _____ → Response 2:

the _____ releases _____, and its level in the blood increases → Effect: the concentration

of the blood _____ → Negative feedback: levels of _____ in the blood

_____ End

2 Stimulus: blood glucose increases → Response: the pancreas releases _____, and _____

levels in the blood rise → Effect: _____ causes _____,

and blood glucose levels _____ → Negative feedback: levels of _____

in the blood _____ End

3 Stimulus: blood calcium ion concentration decreases → Response: the parathyroid glands release _____

and _____ levels in the blood _____ →

Effect: _____ causes _____

and the concentration of calcium ions in the blood _____ → Negative feedback: levels

of _____ in the blood _____ End

Exercise 10-3

Endocrine "Mystery Cases"

In this exercise you will be playing the role of "endocrine detective" to solve endocrine disease mysteries. In each case you will have a victim who has suddenly fallen ill with a mysterious malady. You will be presented a set of "witnesses," each of whom will give you a clue as to the nature of the illness. Other clues will come from samples you send off to the lab for analysis. You will solve the mystery by providing the victim a diagnosis. You may wish to use your textbook for assistance with these cases.

Case 1: The Cold Colonel

You are called upon to visit the ailing Col. Lemon. Before you see him, you speak with three witnesses who were with him when he fell ill.

Witness Statements

- *Ms. Magenta*: "Col. Lemon has been hot-blooded for as long as I've known him. But I noticed that he couldn't seem to keep warm. He kept complaining about being cold. . . ."

- *Mr. Olive*: "Just between you and me, I've noticed that the old chap has put on quite a bit of weight lately."

- *Professor Purple*: "The colonel and I used to go on major expeditions together. Now he just doesn't seem to have the energy to do much of anything."

What are your initial thoughts about the witnesses' statements? Does one hormone come to mind that may be the cause?

You see the colonel and collect some blood to send off to the lab. The analysis comes back as follows:

T3 (triiodothyronine): 0.03 ng/dl (normal: 0.2–0.5 ng/dl)

T4 (thyroxine): 1.1 µg/dl (normal: 4–7 µg/dl)

TSH (thyroid-stimulating hormone): 86 mU/l (normal: 0.3–4.0 mU/l)

Analyze the Results

Why do you think the T3 and T4 are low and the TSH is elevated? (*Hint:* Think about negative feedback loops.)

Based upon the witness statements and the laboratory analysis, what is your final diagnosis?

10

Case 2: The Parched Professor

Your next call is to the aid of Professor Purple. Three witnesses are present from whom to take statements.

Witness Statements

■ *Mr. Olive*: "I swear I saw him drink a full glass of water every half an hour today. He kept saying how thirsty he was!"

■ *Mrs. Blanc*: "He must be going to the . . . well, you know, the little boys' room, two or three times every hour!"

■ *Ms. Feather*: "He's been saying lately that his mouth is dry and that he feels weak. Personally, I think he's just not following a healthy diet! He should be drinking some of my herbal teas!"

Based upon the witnesses' statements, what are your initial thoughts? Does one hormone come to mind that could produce these effects?

You interview Professor Purple and collect blood and urine specimens to be sent off to the lab for analysis. The lab reports that the urine osmolality is 150 mOsm/kg, which means the urine is overly dilute (too *much* water in the urine). The blood osmolality is 300 mOsm/kg, meaning the blood is overly concentrated (too *little* water in the blood). The lab also reports that his blood glucose is completely *normal*. What is the significance of these clues?

Analyze the Results

Based upon the witness statements and the laboratory analysis, what is your final diagnosis? (*Hint:* Think of the hormone that is supposed to trigger water retention from the kidneys. Is there a disease where this hormone is deficient?)

UNIT 10
QUIZ

1 Label Figure 10.3 with the terms below.
- ❏ Adrenal gland
- ❏ Anterior pituitary
- ❏ Hypothalamus
- ❏ Ovary
- ❏ Pancreas
- ❏ Parathyroid glands
- ❏ Posterior pituitary
- ❏ Testis
- ❏ Thyroid gland

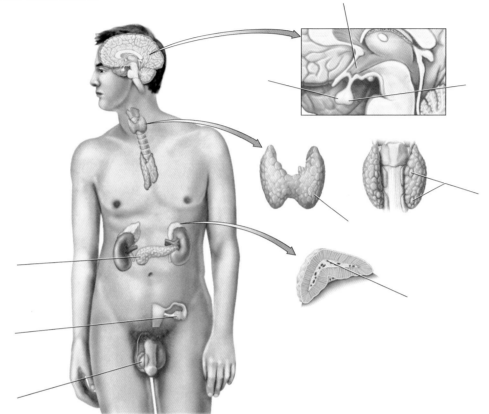

FIGURE **10.3** Endocrine system

2 *Fill in the blanks:* The nervous system works through secretion of _____, whereas the endocrine system works via secretion of _____.

3 Which of the following is not a function of the hypothalamus?
  a. Produces antidiuretic hormone and oxytocin
  b. Stimulates production and release of hormones from the anterior pituitary
  c. Stimulates production and release of hormones from the posterior pituitary
  d. Inhibits the production and release of hormones from the anterior pituitary

4 Which of the following sets of hormones are antagonists?
  a. T3 and T4
  b. Glucagon and insulin
  c. Epinephrine and cortisol
  d. Growth hormone and thyroxine

5 *Matching:* Match the following endocrine organs with the hormone(s) each secretes.

_____ Adrenal medulla

_____ Thyroid gland

_____ Pancreas

_____ Pineal gland

_____ Parathyroid glands

_____ Adrenal cortex

_____ Anterior pituitary

A. Parathyroid hormone

B. Insulin and glucagon

C. Steroid hormones

D. Epinephrine and norepinephrine

E. Thyroxine and triiodothyronine

F. Thyroid-stimulating hormone, growth hormone

G. Melatonin

6 Which of the following is *not* true regarding endocrine organ histology?

a. The thyroid gland consists of rings of simple cuboidal follicle cells surrounding colloid.

b. The pancreas has an exocrine portion consisting of pancreatic islets and an endocrine portion consisting of acinar cells.

c. The adrenal cortex has three zones of cells that secrete three different types of hormones.

d. The adrenal medulla is modified nervous tissue of the sympathetic nervous system.

7 What is a negative feedback loop? Cite an example of a negative feedback loop in the endocrine system.

_____

_____

_____

_____

_____

8 List the stimulus for secretion for each of the following hormones (note that some hormones are stimulated by other hormones):

a Glucagon _____

b Parathyroid hormone _____

c Thyroxine and triiodothyronine (T4 and T3) _____

d Cortisol _____

e Antidiuretic hormone _____

10

9 List the target tissue and effects of each of the following hormones:

a Insulin: _____

_____

_____

b Adrenocorticotropic hormone (ACTH): _____

_____

_____

c Growth hormone: _____

_____

_____

d Oxytocin: _____

_____

_____

10 How are the endocrine system and nervous system similar? How do they differ?

_____

_____

_____

_____

_____

_____

11 Explain why an increase in thyroid hormone generally leads to a decrease in thyroid-stimulating hormone (TSH).

_____

_____

_____

_____

_____

_____

12 Tumors of the parathyroid gland often result in secretion of excess parathyroid hormone. Considering the function of this hormone, predict the effects of such a tumor.

_____

_____

_____

_____

_____

_____

_____

10

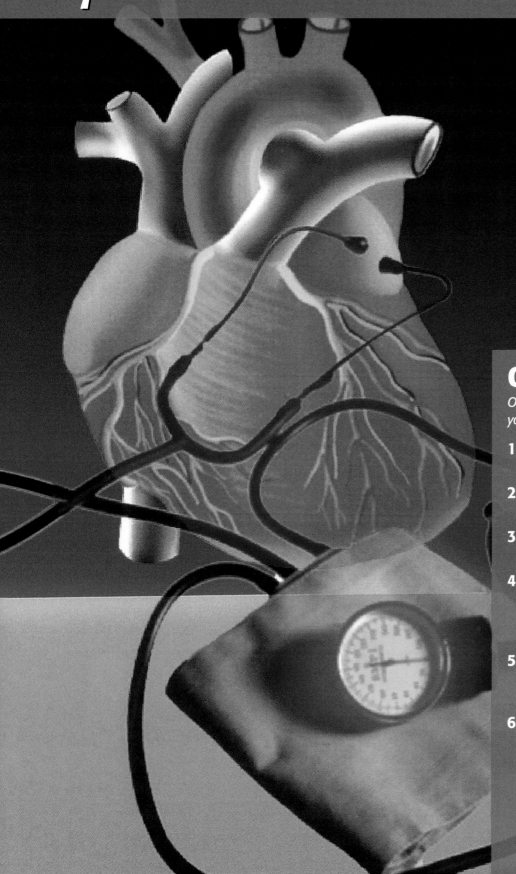

Cardiovascular System

OBJECTIVES

Once you have completed this unit, you should be able to:

1. Describe and identify structures of the heart.

2. Trace the pathway of blood flow through the heart.

3. Describe and identify selected arteries and veins.

4. Describe and demonstrate common physical examination tests of the heart and blood vessels.

5. Measure blood pressure using a stethoscope and a sphygmomanometer.

6. Describe the waves and intervals on an ECG, and perform basic ECG interpretation.

Name _____ Section _____ Date _____

PRE-LAB EXERCISES

Complete the following exercises prior to coming to lab, using your textbook and lab manual for reference.

Pre-Lab Exercise **11-1**

✎ Key Terms

You should be familiar with the following terms before coming to lab.

Term	Definition
Layers of the Heart Wall	
Pericardium	
Pericardial cavity	
Myocardium	
Endocardium	
Structures of the Heart	
Atria (right and left)	
Ventricles (right and left)	
Tricuspid valve	
Mitral (bicuspid) valve	
Pulmonary valve	
Aortic valve	
Great Vessels	
Superior vena cava	

11

Inferior vena cava _____

Pulmonary trunk _____

Pulmonary veins _____

Aorta _____

Cardiovascular Physiology

S1 _____

S2 _____

Pulse point _____

Systolic pressure _____

Diastolic pressure _____

Electrocardiogram _____

11

Pre-Lab Exercise **11-2**

Anatomy of the Heart

Label and color the two views of the heart in Figure 11.1 with the following terms from Exercise 11-1. Use your text and Exercise 11-1 in this unit for reference.

❑ Right atrium
❑ Left atrium

Structures of the Ventricles
❑ Right ventricle
❑ Left ventricle
❑ Interventricular septum
❑ Chordae tendineae
❑ Papillary muscles

Atrioventricular Valves
❑ Tricuspid valve
❑ Mitral valve

Semilunar Valves
❑ Pulmonary valve
❑ Aortic valve

Great Vessels
❑ Superior vena cava
❑ Inferior vena cava
❑ Pulmonary trunk
❑ Pulmonary veins
❑ Aorta

Coronary Arteries
❑ Right coronary artery
❑ Anterior interventricular artery

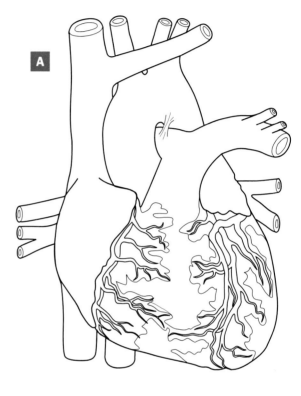

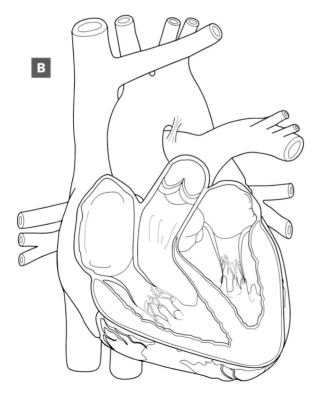

FIGURE **11.1** Heart: (**A**) anterior view; (**B**) frontal section

Pre-Lab Exercise 11-3

Pathway of Blood Flow through the Heart

Answer the following questions about the pathway of blood flow through the heart. Use your textbook and Exercise 11-1 in this unit for reference.

1. Regarding veins:

   a. Where do veins carry blood? _____

   b. Is this blood generally oxygenated or deoxygenated? _____

   c. Does this rule have any exceptions? If yes, where? _____

2. Regarding arteries:

   a. Where do arteries carry blood? _____

   b. Is this blood generally oxygenated or deoxygenated? _____

   c. Does this rule have any exceptions? If yes, where? _____

3. Where does each atrium pump blood when it contracts?

   a. Right atrium: _____

   b. Left atrium: _____

4. Where does each ventricle pump blood when it contracts?

   a. Right ventricle: _____

   b. Left ventricle: _____

Pre-Lab Exercise 11-4

Arterial Anatomy

Label the arterial diagrams depicted in Figure 11.2A–B with the following terms from Exercise 11-2. Use your text and Exercise 11-2 in this unit for reference. Note that these diagrams are presented in color to facilitate identification of the vessels.

Arteries of the Trunk

- ❑ Aorta
  - ❑ Ascending aorta
  - ❑ Aortic arch
  - ❑ Abdominal aorta
- ❑ Brachiocephalic artery
- ❑ Celiac trunk
  - ❑ Splenic artery
  - ❑ Left gastric artery
  - ❑ Common hepatic artery
- ❑ Superior mesenteric artery
- ❑ Renal artery
- ❑ Inferior mesenteric artery
- ❑ Common iliac artery

Arteries of the Head and Neck

- ❑ Common carotid artery
- ❑ Vertebral artery

Arteries of the Upper Limbs

- ❑ Subclavian artery
- ❑ Axillary artery
- ❑ Brachial artery
- ❑ Radial artery
- ❑ Ulnar artery

Arteries of the Lower Limbs

- ❑ External iliac artery
- ❑ Femoral artery
- ❑ Popliteal artery
  - ❑ Anterior tibial artery
    - ❑ (1) Dorsalis pedis artery
  - ❑ Posterior tibial artery

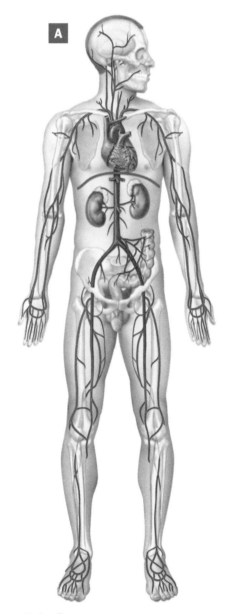

A

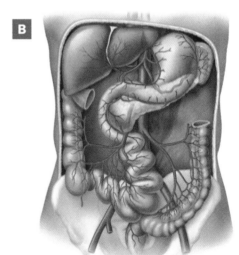

B

FIGURE **11.2** Major arteries: (**A**) of the body; (**B**) of the abdomen

11

Label the venous diagrams depicted in Figure 11.3A–B with the following terms from Exercise 11-3. Use your text and Exercise 11-3 in this unit for reference. Note that these diagrams are presented in color to facilitate identification of the vessels.

Veins of the Trunk
❏ Superior vena cava
❏ Inferior vena cava
❏ Brachiocephalic vein
❏ Hepatic portal vein
❏ Superior mesenteric vein
❏ Inferior mesenteric vein
❏ Renal vein
❏ Common iliac vein

Veins of the Head and Neck
❏ Internal jugular vein
❏ Vertebral vein

Veins of the Upper Limbs
❏ Ulnar vein
❏ Radial vein
❏ Median cubital vein
❏ Brachial vein
❏ Basilic vein
❏ Cephalic vein
❏ Axillary vein
❏ Subclavian vein

Veins of the Lower Limbs
❏ Great saphenous vein
❏ Femoral vein
❏ External iliac vein

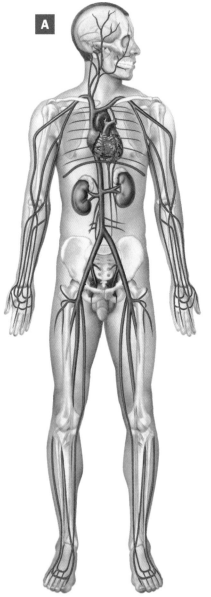

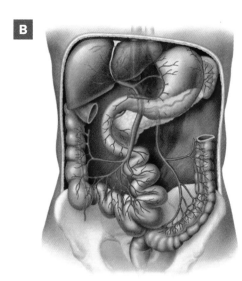

FIGURE **11.3** Major veins: (**A**) of the body; (**B**) of the abdomen

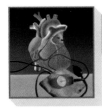

EXERCISES

The cardiovascular system transports oxygen, nutrients, wastes, other solutes, and cells throughout the body in the blood. The heart is the remarkable organ that drives this transport, tirelessly beating more than 100,000 times per day to pump more than 8,000 liters of blood around the body.

Blood is delivered to and from the heart by a series of organs known as **blood vessels**. The blood vessels are a closed system of tubes that carries blood around the body. The heart pumps blood away from the heart through a series of **arteries**. Arteries branch as they pass through organs and tissues to form progressively smaller vessels until they branch into tiny **capillary beds,** where gas, nutrient, and waste exchange take place. The blood is drained from the capillaries via a series of **veins** that returns the blood to the heart.

The three major circuits of blood flow in the body are

1. the **systemic circuit,** which delivers oxygenated blood to most organs and tissues in the body,

2. the **coronary circuit,** which delivers oxygenated blood to the heart, and

3. the **pulmonary circuit,** which delivers deoxygenated blood to the lungs.

In this unit we examine the anatomy and physiology of this remarkable system. In the upcoming exercises, you will identify the parts of the heart and the body's major blood vessels and trace various pathways of blood flow through the body. In the final exercise you will investigate cardiovascular physiology by performing common clinical tests.

Exercise **11-1**

Anatomy of the Heart

MATERIALS
- ❏ Heart models
- ❏ Preserved heart
- ❏ Dissection equipment
- ❏ Dissection tray
- ❏ Water-soluble marking pen
- ❏ Laminated outline of the heart and lungs

The heart lies in the mediastinum and is, on average, about the size of a fist (Figure 11.4). Its **apex** points down and to the left, and its **base** is its flattened posterosuperior surface. The heart is surrounded by a double-layered membrane called the **pericardium (pair-ih-KAR-dee-um).** The outermost layer of the pericardium, called the **fibrous pericardium,** anchors the heart to surrounding structures. It is made of dense irregular connective tissue that is not very distensible, which helps to prevent the heart from overfilling.

The inner layer, called the **serous pericardium,** is itself composed of two layers. The outer portion, called the **parietal pericardium,** is fused to the fibrous pericardium. The inner portion is attached to the heart muscle and is called the **visceral pericardium,** or the **epicardium.** Between the parietal and visceral layers we find a thin layer of serous fluid that occupies a narrow space called the **pericardial cavity.** The fluid within the pericardial cavity helps the heart to beat without friction.

The heart itself is an organ that consists of three tissue layers:

1. **Epicardium.** The epicardium, or visceral pericardium, is considered the outermost layer of the heart wall. It consists of a layer of epithelial tissue and loose connective tissue.

2. **Myocardium.** The middle myocardium (my-oh-KAR-dee-um) is the actual muscle of the heart. It consists of cardiac muscle tissue and its fibrous skeleton.

3. **Endocardium.** The innermost endocardium is a type of simple squamous epithelium called **endothelium.** It is continuous with the endothelium lining all blood vessels in the body.

As you can see in Figure 11.5, the heart consists of four hollow chambers: two **atria (AY-tree-uh),** which receive blood

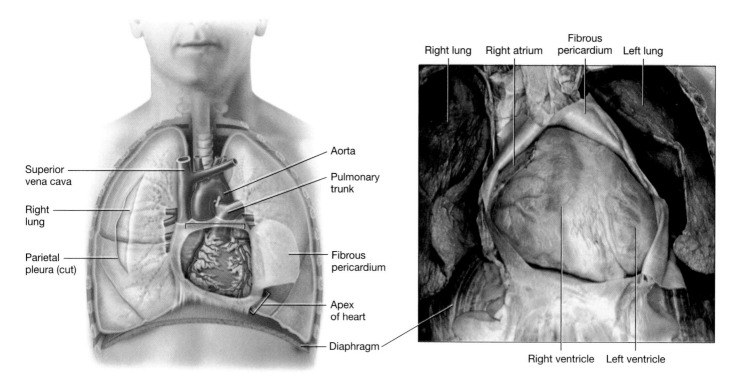

Figure **11.4** Thoracic cavity

from the body's **veins,** and two **ventricles,** which eject blood into the body's **arteries.** In between the atria is a thin wall called the **interatrial septum.** The much thicker **interventricular septum** separates the two ventricles. The heart's four chambers include the:

1. **Right atrium.** The right atrium is the superior right chamber. It receives deoxygenated blood from the body's main veins—the **superior vena cava** (VEE-nah KAY-vuh), the **inferior vena cava,** and the **coronary sinus.**

2. **Right ventricle.** The right ventricle is a large chamber inferior to the right atrium, from which it receives deoxygenated blood. It ejects blood into a vessel called the **pulmonary trunk.** The pulmonary trunk branches into the **right** and **left pulmonary arteries,** which deliver deoxygenated blood to the lungs through the **pulmonary circuit.** Within the pulmonary circuit gases are exchanged and the blood becomes oxygenated.

3. **Left atrium.** The superior left chamber is the left atrium. It receives oxygenated blood returning from the pulmonary circuit via four **pulmonary veins.**

4. **Left ventricle.** The left ventricle receives oxygenated blood from the left atrium and pumps it into the largest artery in the systemic circuit, the **aorta** (ay-OHR-tuh). The aorta then branches repeatedly to deliver the oxygenated blood to the body's cells. Note that the left ventricle is considerably thicker than the right ventricle, which reflects the fact that the pressure is much higher in the systemic circuit than it is in the pulmonary circuit. The higher pressure requires the left ventricle to pump harder, and so its structure is altered to better perform its function.

Between the atria and ventricles and the ventricles and their vessels are **valves** that prevent the blood from flowing backward in the heart. The valves between the chambers are called **atrioventricular valves.** The three-cusped **tricuspid valve** is between the right atrium and

HINTS & TIPS

Red or Blue?

On anatomical models, vessels that carry oxygenated blood are red, whereas those that carry deoxygenated blood are blue. Systemic arteries carry oxygenated blood to the body's cells and so are red on anatomical models. Systemic veins, on the other hand, carry deoxygenated blood back to the right atrium and so are blue. But be sure to remember that the reverse is true in the pulmonary circuit: The pulmonary arteries carry deoxygenated blood to the lungs, and the pulmonary veins carry oxygenated blood to the heart. So, in the pulmonary circuit, the arteries are blue and the veins are red.

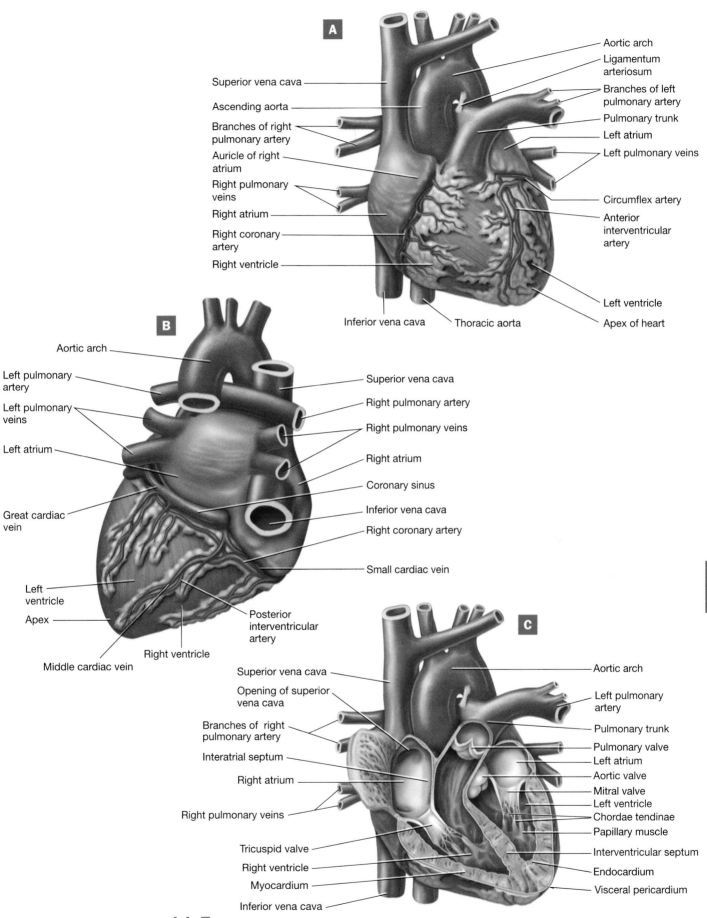

Figure **11.5** Heart: (**A**) anterior view; (**B**) posterior view; (**C**) frontal section

11

right ventricle, and the two-cusped **mitral (MY-trul)**, or **bicuspid, valve** is between the left atrium and left ventricle. Each cusp of the atrioventricular valves is attached to muscles within the ventricular wall called **papillary muscles** by collagenous "strings" called **chordae tendineae (KORD-ee TEN-din-ee)**. When the ventricles contract, the papillary muscles pull the chordae tendineae taut, which puts tension on the cusps and prevents them from bulging up into the atria, a condition called **prolapse**.

The valves between the ventricles and their arteries are called **semilunar valves**. The **pulmonary valve** lies between the right ventricle and the pulmonary trunk, and the **aortic valve** lies between the left ventricle and the aorta. Note that there are no chordae tendineae or papillary muscles attached to the semilunar valves.

The final structures you will examine in this lab period are the vessels of the **coronary circulation**. The **coronary arteries** branch off the base of the aorta and bring oxygenated blood to the cells of the myocardium, and they are drained by a set of **cardiac veins**. The first coronary artery, the **right coronary artery**, travels in the right coronary sulcus, which serves part of the right atrium and right ventricle and the posterior heart. The other coronary artery is the **left coronary artery**, which branches shortly after it forms into the **anterior interventricular artery** (also known as the **left anterior descending artery**), which travels along the interventricular septum to supply the anterior heart, and the **circumflex artery**, which travels in the left coronary sulcus to supply the left atrium and posterior left ventricle. When a coronary artery is blocked, the reduced blood flow to the myocardium can result in hypoxic injury and death to the tissue, a condition termed **myocardial infarction** (commonly called a heart attack).

The anatomy of the cardiac veins often varies from person to person, but the following three main veins generally are present:

1. **small cardiac vein**, which drains the inferolateral heart,

2. **middle cardiac vein**, which drains the posterior heart, and

3. **great cardiac vein**, which drains most of the left side of the heart.

All three veins drain into the large **coronary sinus**, located on the posterior right atrium. The coronary sinus drains into the right atrium.

Procedure **1** Model Inventory for the Heart

Identify the following structures of the heart on models and diagrams, using your textbook and this unit for reference. As you examine the anatomical models and diagrams, record on the model inventory in Table 11.1 the name of the model and the structures you were able to identify.

11

1. General structures
   a. Mediastinum
      (1) Pericardial cavity
   b. Pericardium
      (1) Fibrous pericardium
      (2) Parietal pericardium
      (3) Visceral pericardium (epicardium)
   c. Myocardium
   d. Endocardium
   e. Apex of the heart
   f. Base of the heart
2. Right atrium
   a. Opening of the superior vena cava
   b. Opening of the inferior vena cava
   c. Opening of the coronary sinus
   d. Right auricle
   e. Interatrial septum

3. Left atrium
   a. Opening of the pulmonary veins
   b. Left auricle
   c. Interatrial septum
4. Structures of the ventricles
   a. Right ventricle
   b. Left ventricle
   c. Interventricular septum
   d. Chordae tendineae
   e. Papillary muscles
5. Atrioventricular valves
   a. Tricuspid valve
   b. Mitral valve
6. Semilunar valves
   a. Pulmonary valve
   b. Aortic valve

7. Great vessels
   a. Superior vena cava
   b. Inferior vena cava
   c. Pulmonary trunk
   d. Right and left pulmonary arteries
   e. Pulmonary veins
   f. Aorta
8. Coronary arteries
   a. Right coronary artery
   b. Left coronary artery
   c. Anterior interventricular artery
   d. Circumflex artery
9. Cardiac veins
   a. Small cardiac vein
   b. Middle cardiac vein
   c. Great cardiac vein
   d. Coronary sinus

TABLE **11.1** Model Inventory for the Heart

Model	Structures Identified

11

Procedure 2 Heart Dissection

You will now examine a preserved heart or a fresh heart, likely from a sheep or a cow. Follow the procedure below to find the structures indicated.

1 Orient yourself by first determining the superior aspect and the inferior aspect of the heart. The superior aspect of the heart is the broad end, and the inferior aspect (apex) is the pointy tip. Now orient yourself to the anterior and posterior sides. The easiest way to do this is to locate the pulmonary trunk—the vessel directly in the middle of the anterior side. Find the side from which the pulmonary trunk originates, and you will be on the anterior side, which you can see in Figure 11.6. Structures to locate at this time are the

❑ parietal pericardium (may not be attached),

❑ visceral pericardium (shiny layer over the surface of the heart),

❑ aorta,

❑ pulmonary trunk,

❑ superior vena cava,

❑ inferior vena cava,

❑ pulmonary veins,

❑ ventricles, and

❑ atria.

Finding the coronary vessels tends to be difficult because the superficial surface of the heart is covered with adipose tissue. To see the coronary vessels, carefully dissect the adipose tissue.

2 Locate the superior vena cava. Insert scissors or a scalpel into the superior vena cava, and cut down into the right atrium. Before moving on to step 3, note the structure of the tricuspid valve, and draw it below. How many flaps do you see? What is the function of this valve?

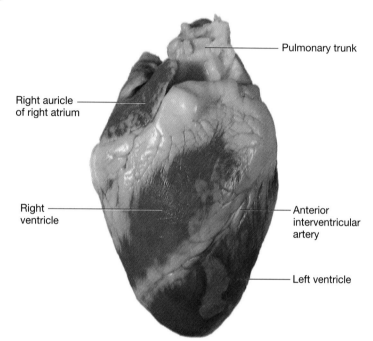

Figure 11.6 Anterior view of a sheep heart

3 After the right atrium is exposed, continue the cut down into the right ventricle, shown in Figure 11.7. Structures to locate at this time include the

- ❏ tricuspid valve,
- ❏ chordae tendineae,
- ❏ papillary muscles,
- ❏ myocardium, and
- ❏ endocardium (shiny layer on the inside of the heart).

4 Insert the scissors into the pulmonary trunk. Note the structure of the pulmonary valve, and draw it below. How does it differ structurally from the tricuspid valve? What is the function of this valve?

_____

_____

_____

_____

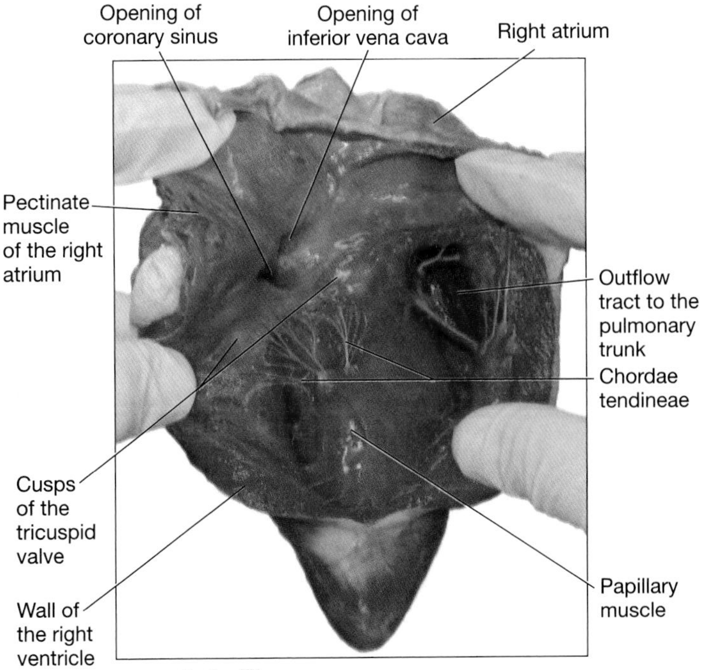

Figure **11.7** Right ventricle of a sheep heart

5 Insert the scissors into a pulmonary vein. Cut down into the left atrium. Note the structure of the mitral valve, and draw it below. What is the function of this valve? How does its structure differ from that of the pulmonary and tricuspid valves?

_____

_____

_____

_____

11

6 Continue the cut into the left ventricle. Note the thickness of the left ventricle, as shown in Figure 11.8. How does it compare with the thickness of the right ventricle? Why is there a difference?

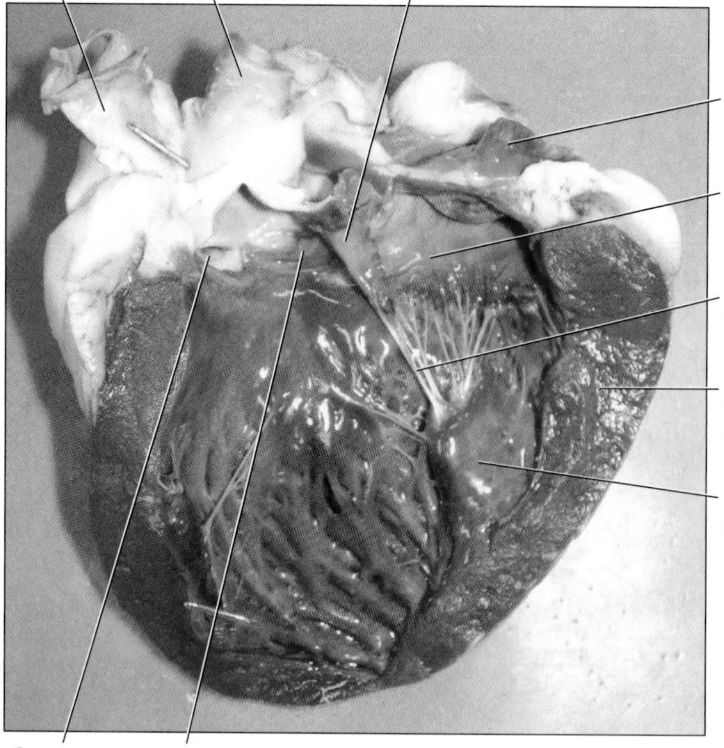

_____

_____

_____

_____

_____

_____

_____

_____

_____

_____

_____

_____

Figure **11.8** Left ventricle of a sheep heart

7 Insert the scissors into the aorta. Extend the cut until you can see the aortic valve. Draw the aortic valve below. Is it structurally more similar to the pulmonary valve or the mitral valve? What is the function of this valve?

_____

_____

8 Your instructor may wish you to identify other structures on the heart. List any additional structures below.

_____

_____

_____

Procedure **3** Tracing Blood through the Heart

Use water-soluble markers and a laminated outline of the heart to trace the pathway of blood as it flows through the heart and pulmonary circulation. Use a blue marker to indicate areas that contain deoxygenated blood and a red marker to indicate areas that contain oxygenated blood. If no laminated outline is available, use colored pencils and Figure 11.9.

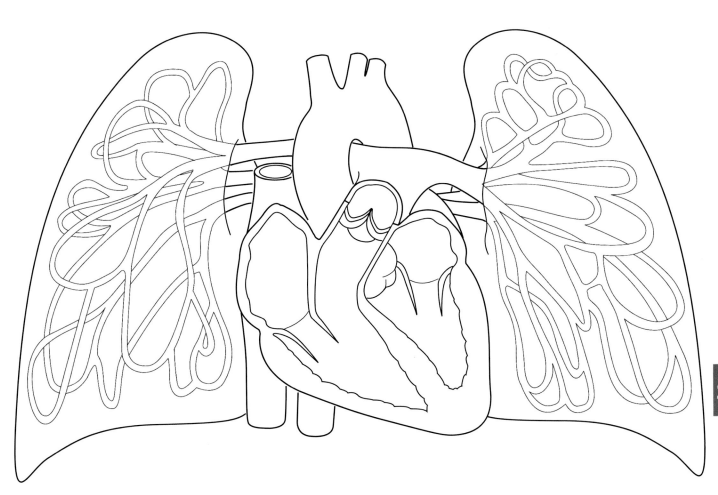

Figure **11.9** Heart, lungs, and pulmonary circulation

11

Exercise 11-2

Major Arteries of the Body

MATERIALS

- ❑ Blood vessel models:
  - ❑ Human torsos
  - ❑ Brain
  - ❑ Head and neck
  - ❑ Abdomen
  - ❑ Upper limb
  - ❑ Lower limb

The systemic arterial circuit begins with the largest artery in the body, the aorta. The aorta originates from the left ventricle as the **ascending aorta**, which ascends until it curves around to form the **aortic arch**. The aortic arch has three major branches:

1. **Brachiocephalic artery.** The first branch is the brachiocephalic (bray-kee-oh-sef-AL-ik) artery, which travels superiorly and to the right. Near the clavicle it splits into two branches—the **right subclavian (sub-KLAY-vee-un) artery** and the **right common carotid (kuh-RAH-tid) artery** (Figure 11.10). The right subclavian artery travels to the upper limb and becomes the **axillary artery** near the axilla. In the arm, the axillary artery becomes the **brachial artery**, which branches into the **radial artery** and the **ulnar artery**. The right common carotid artery travels to the neck, where it splits into the **internal carotid artery**, which supplies the brain, and the **external carotid artery**, which supplies the face and the scalp.

2. **Left common carotid artery.** The second branch is the left common carotid artery. Like the right common carotid artery, the left common carotid artery splits into internal and external carotid arteries in the neck.

3. **Left subclavian artery.** The final branch off of the aortic arch is the left subclavian artery, which supplies the left upper limb. The branches and names of the left subclavian artery are the same as those of the right subclavian artery.

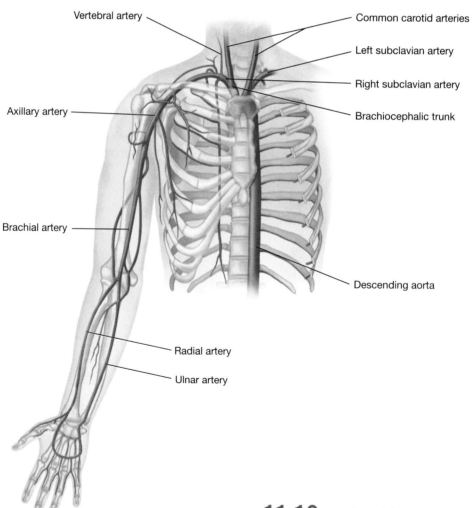

Vertebral artery

Common carotid arteries

Left subclavian artery

Right subclavian artery

Brachiocephalic trunk

Axillary artery

Brachial artery

Descending aorta

Radial artery

Ulnar artery

FIGURE 11.10 Arteries of the right arm and thorax

11

The arterial supply of the brain comes primarily from the internal carotid arteries and the **vertebral arteries**. At the base of the brainstem, the two vertebral arteries fuse to form the **basilar** (BAY-sih-lur) **artery** (Figure 11.11). After the internal carotid arteries and basilar artery enter the brain, they contribute to a structure called the **cerebral arterial circle** (also called the **circle of Willis**). This circle is composed of branches of these vessels and a set of **anterior** and **posterior communicating arteries**. These vessels are connected to provide alternate routes of circulation to the brain if one of the arteries supplying the brain becomes blocked. From the cerebral arterial circle stem the **anterior**, **middle**, and **posterior cerebral arteries**, which supply the lobes of the cerebrum.

As the aortic arch turns inferiorly, it becomes the **thoracic aorta**. The thoracic aorta descends through the thoracic cavity posterior to the heart, after which it passes through the diaphragm to become the **abdominal aorta**. The major branches of the abdominal aorta, shown in Figure 11.12, include the following:

1. **Celiac trunk**. The short, stubby celiac (SEE-lee-ak) trunk is the first branch off of the abdominal aorta. It splits almost immediately into the **common hepatic artery**, the **splenic artery**, and the **left gastric artery**.

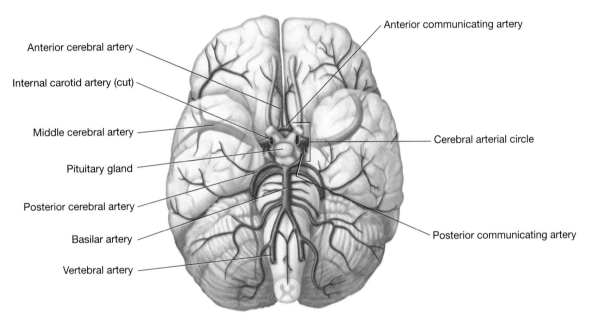

FIGURE **11.11** Arteries of the brain, inferior view

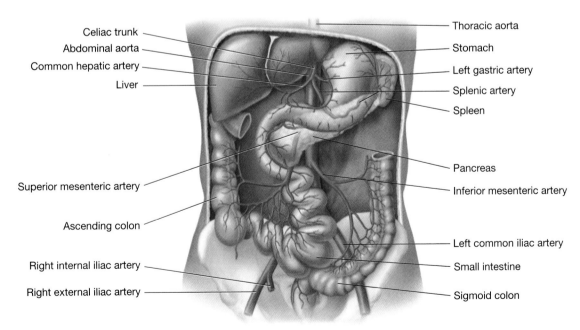

FIGURE **11.12** Arteries of the abdomen

2. **Renal arteries.** Inferior to the celiac trunk we find the two renal (REE-nul) arteries, which serve the kidneys. Note that the renal arteries are not illustrated in Figure 11.12, but they are visible in Figure 11.13.

3. **Superior mesenteric artery.** Right around the renal arteries is another branch called the superior mesenteric artery, which supplies the small and much of the large intestine.

4. **Inferior mesenteric artery.** The last large branch off of the abdominal aorta is the inferior mesenteric artery, which supplies the remainder of the large intestine.

The abdominal aorta terminates by splitting into the two **common iliac (il-EE-ak) arteries,** which themselves split into an **internal iliac artery** and an **external iliac artery** (Figure 11.13). The internal iliac artery supplies structures of the pelvis, and the external iliac artery passes deep to the inguinal ligament to enter the thigh, where it becomes the **femoral artery.** The femoral artery continues to the area around the popliteal fossa (the posterior knee), where it becomes the **popliteal artery.** Shortly thereafter, the popliteal artery divides into its two main branches: the **anterior tibial artery,** which continues in the foot as the **dorsalis pedis (dohr-SAL-iz PEE-diz) artery,** and the **posterior tibial artery.**

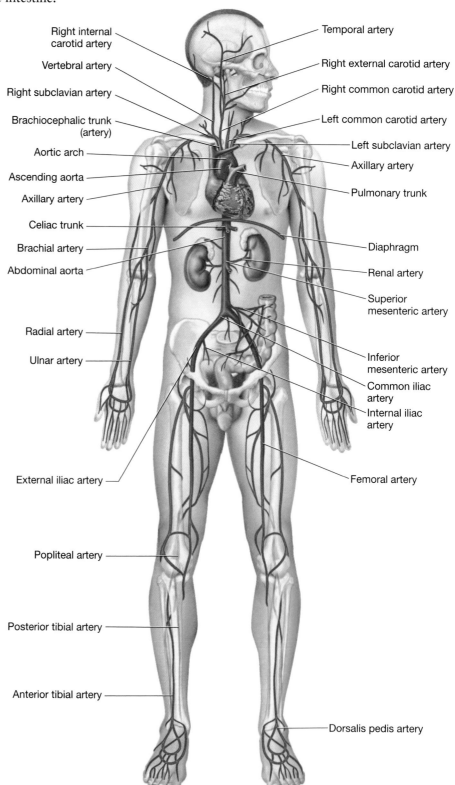

FIGURE **11.13** Major arteries of the body

Procedure 1 Model Inventory for Arteries

Identify the following arteries on models and diagrams, using your textbook and this unit for reference. As you examine the anatomical models and diagrams, record on the model inventory in Table 11.2 the name of the model and the structures you were able to identify.

Arteries of the Trunk

1. Aorta
   a. Ascending aorta
   b. Aortic arch
   c. Thoracic (descending) aorta
   d. Abdominal aorta
2. Brachiocephalic artery
3. Celiac trunk
   a. Splenic artery
   b. Left gastric artery
   c. Common hepatic artery
4. Superior mesenteric artery
5. Renal artery
6. Inferior mesenteric artery
7. Common iliac artery
   a. Internal iliac artery

Arteries of the Head and Neck

1. Common carotid artery
   a. External carotid artery
   b. Internal carotid artery
2. Vertebral artery
3. Basilar artery
4. Cerebral arterial circle
5. Anterior cerebral artery
6. Middle cerebral artery
7. Posterior cerebral artery

Arteries of the Upper Limbs

1. Subclavian artery
2. Axillary artery
3. Brachial artery
4. Radial artery
5. Ulnar artery

Arteries of the Lower Limbs

1. External iliac artery
2. Femoral artery
3. Popliteal artery
   a. Anterior tibial artery
      (1) Dorsalis pedis artery
   b. Posterior tibial artery

TABLE **11.2** Model Inventory for Arteries

Model/Diagram	Structures Identified

11

MATERIALS

- ❏ Blood vessel models:
  - ❏ Human torsos
  - ❏ Brain
  - ❏ Head and neck
  - ❏ Abdomen
  - ❏ Upper limb
  - ❏ Lower limb
  - ❏ Dural sinuses

Arteries of the systemic circuit deliver oxygen and nutrient-rich blood to capillary beds, where gases, nutrients, and wastes are exchanged. The oxygen-poor, carbon dioxide–rich blood is then drained from the capillary beds by a series of veins. The two largest veins in the body are the superior vena cava, which drains the structures superior to the diaphragm, and the inferior vena cava, which drains the structures inferior to the diaphragm.

The head and the neck are drained primarily by the **internal** and **external jugular veins** (Figure 11.14). The much smaller external jugular vein drains the face and the scalp, and the larger internal jugular vein, which travels in a sheath with the common carotid artery, drains the brain. Note, however, that venous blood from the brain does not simply drain into one vein and exit the head. Instead, it drains into spaces between the two layers of the dura mater called the **dural sinuses** (Figure 11.15), which in turn drain into the internal jugular vein.

Veins draining blood from the organs of the abdomen are named largely in parallel with the arteries that serve the organs: The **renal veins** drain the kidneys (Figure 11.16), the **splenic vein** drains the spleen, the **gastric veins** drain the stomach, the **superior mesenteric vein** drains the small intestine and much of the large intestine, and the **inferior mesenteric vein** drains the remainder of the large intestine. Although the renal vein empties into the inferior vena cava, the blood from the latter four veins does not drain into the inferior vena cava directly. Instead, note in Figure 11.17 that each vein drains into a common vein called the **hepatic portal vein**. Here, the nutrient-rich blood filters through the liver, where it is processed and detoxified. In this way, everything we ingest (except lipids, which we discuss in Unit 14) must travel through the liver before entering the systemic circulation. After the blood has filtered through the hepatic portal system, it exits via **hepatic veins** and drains into the inferior vena cava.

11

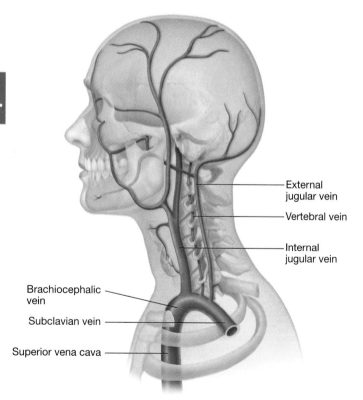

FIGURE **11.14** Veins of left superficial aspect of head and neck

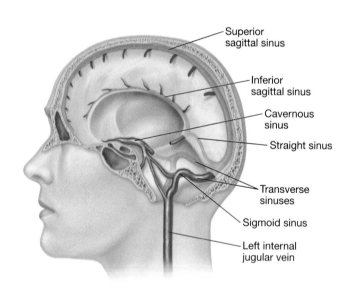

FIGURE **11.15** Dural sinuses of brain

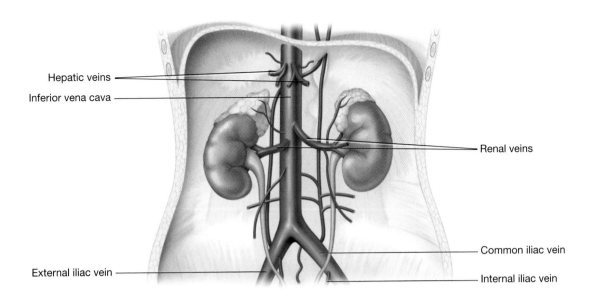

Hepatic veins

Inferior vena cava

Renal veins

Common iliac vein

External iliac vein

Internal iliac vein

FIGURE **11.16** Veins draining the abdominal area (excluding the hepatic portal system)

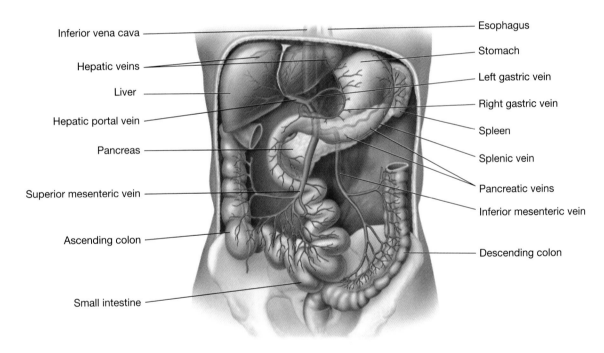

Inferior vena cava

Hepatic veins

Liver

Hepatic portal vein

Pancreas

Superior mesenteric vein

Ascending colon

Small intestine

Esophagus

Stomach

Left gastric vein

Right gastric vein

Spleen

Splenic vein

Pancreatic veins

Inferior mesenteric vein

Descending colon

FIGURE **11.17** Veins of the abdomen and the hepatic portal system

Blood from the deep structures of the upper limb is drained by the **radial** and **ulnar veins**, both of which parallel the bones for which they are named (Figure 11.18). These two veins merge in the arm to form the **brachial vein**, which becomes the **axillary vein** in the axilla. Near the clavicle, the axillary vein becomes the **subclavian vein**, which drains into the **brachiocephalic vein** and finally into the superior vena cava. The superficial structures of the upper limb are drained by the **cephalic vein** on the lateral side and the **basilic vein** on the medial side. Note in Figure 11.18 that the cephalic vein and the basilic vein are united in the antecubital fossa by the **median cubital vein**. This is a frequent site for withdrawing blood with a syringe.

The deep structures of the lower limb are drained by the **femoral vein**, which becomes the **external iliac vein** after it passes into the pelvis (Figure 11.19). The external iliac vein merges with the **internal iliac vein**, which drains pelvic structures, forming the **common iliac vein**. The two common iliac veins unite to form the inferior vena cava near the superior part of the pelvis. The largest superficial vein of the lower limb is the **great saphenous (SAF-in-us) vein**, which drains the medial leg and thigh and empties into the femoral vein.

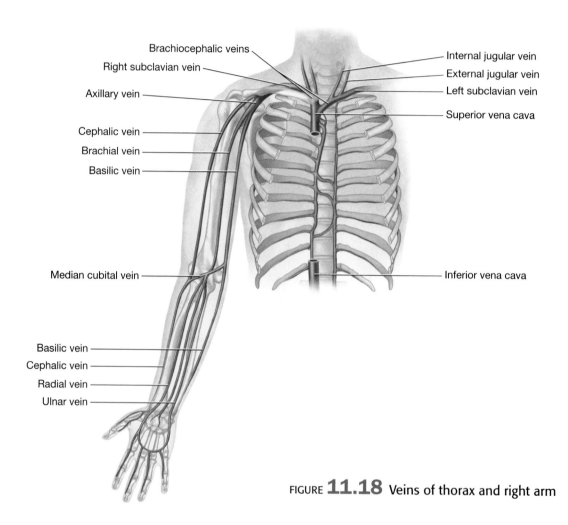

FIGURE **11.18** Veins of thorax and right arm

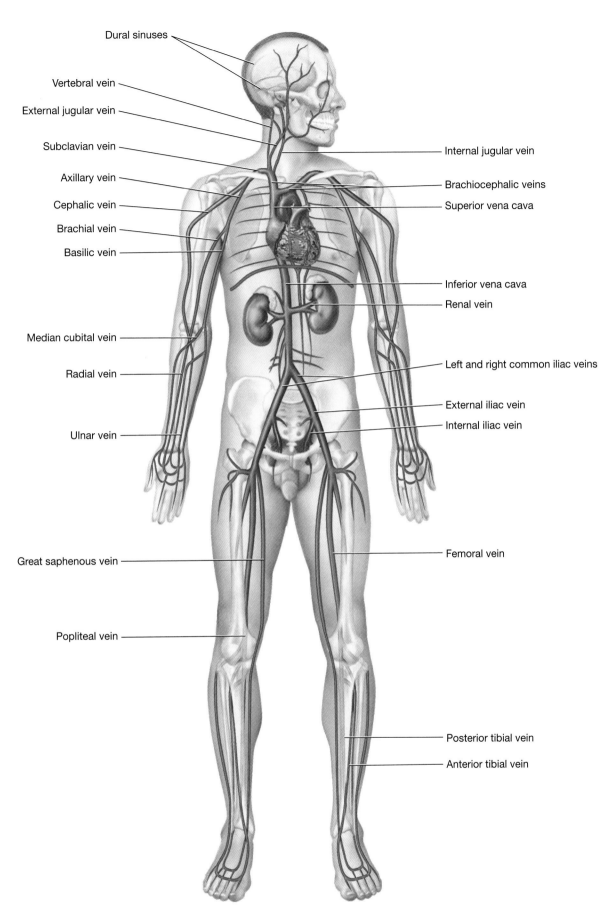

Dural sinuses

Vertebral vein

External jugular vein

Subclavian vein

Axillary vein

Cephalic vein

Brachial vein

Basilic vein

Median cubital vein

Radial vein

Ulnar vein

Great saphenous vein

Popliteal vein

Internal jugular vein

Brachiocephalic veins

Superior vena cava

Inferior vena cava

Renal vein

Left and right common iliac veins

External iliac vein

Internal iliac vein

Femoral vein

Posterior tibial vein

Anterior tibial vein

FIGURE **11.19** Major veins of the body

11

Procedure 1 Model Inventory for Veins

Identify the following veins on models and diagrams, using your textbook and this unit for reference. As you examine the anatomical models and diagrams, record on the model inventory in Table 11.3 the name of the model and the structures you were able to identify.

Veins of the Trunk
1. Superior vena cava
2. Inferior vena cava
3. Brachiocephalic vein
4. Hepatic veins
5. Hepatic portal vein
6. Splenic vein
7. Superior mesenteric vein
8. Inferior mesenteric vein
9. Gastric vein
10. Renal vein
11. Internal iliac vein
12. Common iliac vein

Veins of the Head and Neck
1. Dural sinuses
2. Internal jugular vein
3. External jugular vein
4. Vertebral vein

Veins of the Upper Limbs
1. Ulnar vein
2. Radial vein
3. Median cubital vein
4. Brachial vein
5. Basilic vein
6. Cephalic vein
7. Axillary vein
8. Subclavian vein

Veins of the Lower Limbs
1. Great saphenous vein
2. Femoral vein
3. External iliac vein

11

TABLE **11.3** Model Inventory for Veins

Model	Structures Identified

11

Exercise 11-4

Time to Trace!

MATERIALS
❏ Laminated outline of the human body
❏ Water-soluble marking pen

In this exercise you will trace the blood flow through various places in the body. As you trace, keep the following hints in mind:

▌ Don't forget about the hepatic portal system! Remember that most venous blood coming from the abdominal organs has to go through the hepatic portal vein and the hepatic portal system before it can enter the general circulation.

▌ If you start in a vein, you have to go through the entire venous system and through the heart before you can get back to the arterial system.

▌ If you start in an artery, you have to go through the entire arterial system and then through a *capillary bed* before you can go through the venous system. You can't go backward through the arterial system—that's cheating!

▌ If you start in an artery and end in an artery, you likely will have to go through the arterial circuit, through a capillary bed, through the venous circuit, back to the heart and lungs, and *then* reenter the arterial circuit. Whew!

▌ Following is an example in which we have started in the right popliteal vein and ended in the left internal carotid artery:

Start: right popliteal vein → right femoral vein → right external iliac vein → right common iliac vein → inferior vena

cava → right atrium → tricuspid valve → right ventricle → pulmonary valve → pulmonary artery → lungs →

pulmonary veins →left atrium → mitral valve → left ventricle → aortic valve → ascending aorta → aortic arch → left

common carotid artery → left internal carotid artery → End

Wasn't that easy?

11

Procedure 1 Tracing Blood-Flow Patterns

Trace the path of blood flow through the following circuits, using the example on page 290 for reference. It is helpful to draw the pathway on a laminated outline of the human body, and label each vessel as you trace. If a laminated outline is not available, use Figures 11.20–11.22 instead.

1 *Start:* Right radial vein
   End: Right renal artery

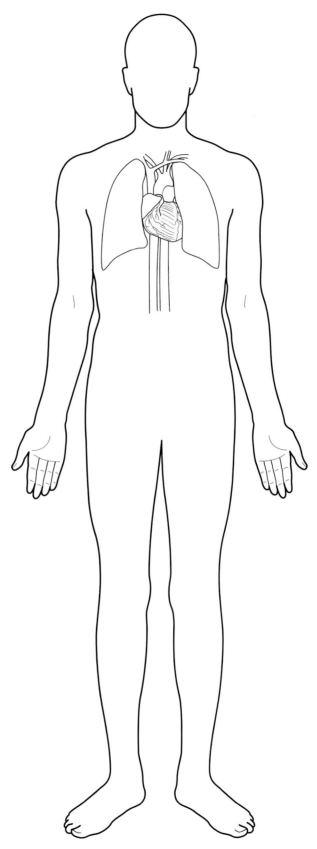

FIGURE **11.20** Outline of the human body

11

2 *Start:* Superior mesenteric vein

    End: Superior mesenteric artery

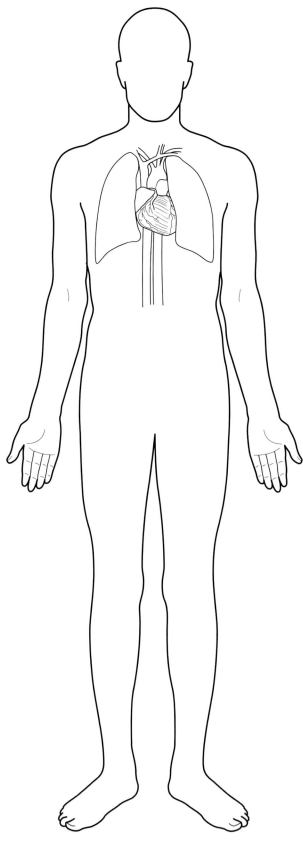

FIGURE **11.21** Outline of the human body

3 *Start:* Left coronary artery
   End: Dorsalis pedis artery

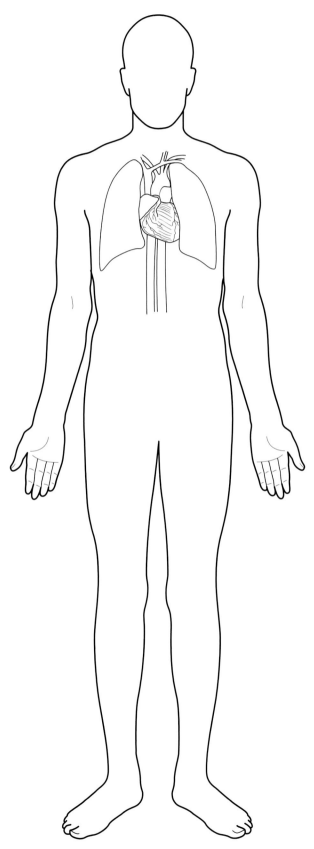

FIGURE **11.22** Outline of the human body

Exercise 11-5

Heart and Vascular Examination

MATERIALS
- ❑ Stethoscope
- ❑ Alcohol and cotton ball

Examination of the heart and blood vessels is an important part of every physical examination. The process of listening to heart sounds is known as **auscultation** (aw-skul-TAY-shun). The two main sounds you hear when you listen to the heart are produced by the closing of valves at certain points during the cardiac cycle. The first heart sound is known as **S1**, and it is caused by closure of the mitral and tricuspid valves. The second heart sound, **S2**, is caused by closure of the aortic and pulmonary valves.

Heart sounds are typically auscultated in four areas, each of which is named for the valve best heard at that specific location. The position of each area is described relative to the sternum and the spaces between the ribs, known as *intercostal spaces*. The first intercostal space is located between the first and second rib, roughly below the clavicle. From the clavicle you can count down to consecutive spaces to auscultate in the appropriate areas. The four areas are as follows (Figure 11.23):

1. **Aortic area.** This is the area where the sounds of the aortic valve are best heard. It is located in the second intercostal space at the right sternal border.

2. **Pulmonic area.** The pulmonic valve is best heard over the second intercostal space at the left sternal border.

3. **Tricuspid area.** The sounds produced by the tricuspid valve are best heard over the fourth intercostal space at the left sternal border.

4. **Mitral area.** The mitral area is located in the fifth intercostal space at the left midclavicular line (draw an imaginary line down the middle of the clavicle, roughly in line with the nipple).

The following variables are checked during heart auscultation:

▌ **Heart rate.** The heart rate refers to the number of heartbeats per minute.

▌ **Heart rhythm.** The heart's rhythm refers to the pattern and regularity with which it beats.

▌ **Additional heart sounds.** Sometimes sounds in addition to S1 and S2 are heard that could be a sign of pathology. These sounds are called **S3**, which occurs just after S2, and **S4**, which occurs just prior to S1.

▌ **Heart murmur.** A heart murmur is a clicking or "swooshing" noise heard between the heart sounds. Murmurs are caused by a valve leaking, called **regurgitation**, or by a valve that has lost its pliability, called **stenosis**.

Heart sounds are auscultated with a stethoscope, which you will use in this unit. Most stethoscopes contain the following parts (Figure 11.24):

▌ **Earpieces** are gently inserted into the external auditory canal and allow you to auscultate the heart sounds.

▌ The **diaphragm** is the broad, flat side of the end of the stethoscope. It is used to auscultate higher-pitched sounds and is the side used most often in auscultation of heart sounds.

▌ The **bell** is the concave, smaller side of the end of the stethoscope. It is used to auscultate lower-pitched sounds.

Note that sounds are not audible through both the bell and the diaphragm at the same time. Typically, the end can be flipped from

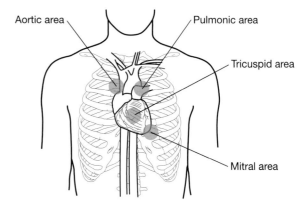

FIGURE **11.23** Areas of auscultation

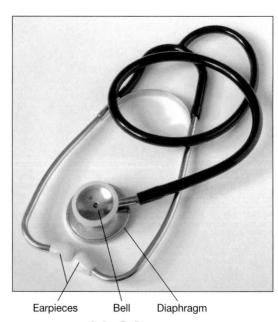

FIGURE **11.24** Stethoscope

one side to the next. Before auscultating with either side, lightly tap the end to ensure that you can hear sound through it. Note also that the ends of some stethoscopes have only one side—the diaphragm. In this case, placing light pressure on the end as you are auscultating yields sounds associated with the diaphragm, whereas placing heavier pressure yields sounds associated with the bell.

Procedure 1 Heart Auscultation

1 Obtain a stethoscope, and clean the earpieces and diaphragm with alcohol and cotton balls.

2 Place the earpieces in your ears, and gently tap the diaphragm to ensure that it is on the proper side. If it is not, flip it to the other side.

3 Lightly place the diaphragm on your partner's chest in the aortic area. (*Note:* You may wish to have your lab partner place the stethoscope on his or her chest under the shirt, because the sounds are heard best on bare skin.)

4 Auscultate several cardiac cycles, and determine which sound is S1 and which sound is S2. Measure your partner's heart rate, and determine if the rhythm is regular. In addition, check for heart murmurs and extra heart sounds.

5 Record your results in Table 11.4.

6 Move on to the next area, and repeat.

TABLE **11.4** Heart Auscultation Results

Area	Rate	Rhythm	Extra Heart Sounds? (yes/no)	Murmurs Present? (yes/no)
Aortic area				
Pulmonic area				
Tricuspid area				
Mitral area				

Procedure 2 Pulse Palpation

Pulse palpation is the process of feeling the pulse with the fingertips. It is performed to assess rate, rhythm, and regularity of the heartbeat and to assess the arterial circulation to different parts of the body. The pulses commonly measured are those found at the radial, ulnar, brachial, carotid, temporal, femoral, popliteal, posterior tibial, and dorsalis pedis arteries, shown in Figure 11.25.

When pulses are palpated, they are **graded** according to a standard scale. This allows health-care professionals to communicate about a patient unambiguously and to assess the progress or deterioration of a patient's condition. The scale utilizes the following four grades:

Grade 0/4: The pulse is absent.
Grade 1/4: The pulse is barely or only lightly palpable.
Grade 2/4: The pulse is normal.
Grade 3/4: The pulse is quite strong.
Grade 4/4: The pulse is bounding and visible through the skin.

Note that this scale has no negative numbers or decimal numbers (e.g., you would not use –1/4 or 2.5/4). In a healthy person most pulses are grade 2/4, although occasionally a pulse is weak or absent. This is simply normal anatomical variation and does not signify pathology. Students often mistakenly grade any strong pulse (such as the carotid pulse) as 4/4. If a pulse were truly 4/4, however, this would be a sign of extremely high blood pressure in that artery.

The following procedure asks you to palpate certain pulses on your lab partner (we will not be palpating each pulse illustrated in Figure 11.25). Please note before you begin that you should never assess both of your lab partner's carotid arteries at the same time. This might initiate the **baroreceptor reflex**, in which the parasympathetic nervous system triggers a reflexive and often dramatic drop in blood pressure and heart rate. This could cause your lab partner to momentarily lose consciousness.

1 Wash your hands prior to palpating your lab partner's pulses.

2 On a model or diagram, locate the artery you are palpating.

3 Lightly place your index finger and middle finger over the artery. You may increase the pressure slightly, but be careful not to press too hard, because you could cut off blood flow through the artery and also could mistake the pulse in your fingertips for your partner's pulse. If you are unsure if the pulse is yours or your partner's, feel the lab table. If the lab table "has a pulse," you are feeling the pulse in your own fingertips.

4 Palpate *only* one side (right or left) at a time, especially in the carotid artery.

5 Grade your partner's pulses according to the 0/4 to 4/4 scale, and record the results in Table 11.5.

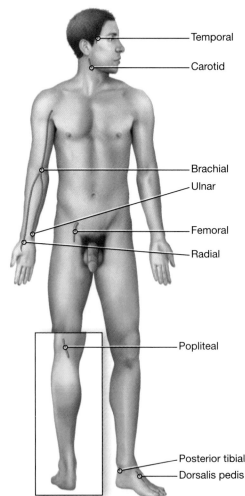

FIGURE **11.25** Common pulse points

TABLE **11.5** Pulse Points Grades

Artery	Right-Side Grade	Left-Side Grade
Carotid		
Temporal		
Brachial		
Radial		
Ulnar		
Dorsalis pedis		
Posterior tibial		

Exercise 11-6

Blood Pressure

MATERIALS

❑ Sphygmomanometer
❑ Stethoscope
❑ Alcohol and cotton ball
❑ Bucket of ice water

Blood pressure is defined as the pressure exerted by the blood on the walls of the blood vessels. It is determined by the following three factors:

1. **Cardiac output.** Cardiac output is the amount of blood each ventricle pumps in one minute. It is a product of **stroke volume,** or the amount pumped with each beat, and heart rate.

2. **Peripheral resistance.** Resistance is defined as any impedance to blood flow encountered in the blood vessels. It is determined largely by the degree of **vasoconstriction** or **vasodilation** in the systemic circulation. Vasoconstriction increases peripheral resistance, and vasodilation has the opposite effect.

3. **Blood volume.** The amount of blood found in the blood vessels at any given time is known as the blood volume. It is greatly influenced by overall fluid volume and is largely controlled by the kidneys and hormones of the endocrine system.

Note that cardiac output and peripheral resistance are factors that can be altered quickly to change blood pressure. Alterations to blood volume, however, occur relatively slowly and generally require two to three days to have a noticeable effect.

Arterial blood pressure is measured clinically and experimentally using instruments called a **sphygmomanometer** (sfig-mah-man-AHM-et-ur) and a stethoscope. This procedure yields two pressure readings:

1. **Systolic pressure.** The pressure in the arteries during ventricular systole, the period of time during which the ventricles contract, is known as the systolic (sis-TAH-lik) pressure. This is the larger of the two readings, averaging between 100 and 120 mmHg.

2. **Diastolic pressure.** The pressure in the arteries during ventricular diastole, the period of time during which the ventricles relax, is the diastolic (dy-uh-STAH-lik) pressure. This is the smaller of the two readings, averaging between 60 and 80 mmHg.

Arterial blood pressure is measured by placing the cuff of the sphygmomanometer around the upper arm. When the cuff is inflated, it compresses the brachial artery and cuts off blood flow. When the pressure is released to the level of the systolic arterial pressure, blood flow through the brachial artery resumes but becomes rough. This results in sounds known as **sounds of Korotkoff,** which may be auscultated with a stethoscope.

Procedure 1 Measuring Blood Pressure

Practice is necessary to develop the skills to accurately measure arterial blood pressure. Following are the steps you may use to practice using the sphygmomanometer and stethoscope together. All readings should be taken with your lab partner seated and relaxed.

1 Obtain a stethoscope and sphygmomanometer of the appropriate size (about 80% of the circumference of the arm).

2 Clean the earpieces and diaphragm as in Exercise 11-5.

3 Wrap the cuff around your partner's arm. It should not be noticeably tight, but it should stay in place when you are not holding it. It should be about 1½ inches proximal to the antecubital fossa (the anterior part of the elbow).

4 Place the diaphragm of your stethoscope over the brachial artery. You should *not* hear anything at this point.

5 Support your partner's arm by cradling it in your arm, or have your partner rest his or her arm on the lab table.

6 Locate the screw of the sphygmomanometer near the bulb, and close it by turning it clockwise. Inflate the cuff by squeezing the bulb several times. Pay attention to the level of pressure you are applying by watching the pressure gauge. You should not inflate it beyond about 30 mmHg above your partner's normal systolic pressure (for most people, this is no higher than 180 mmHg). Your lab partner will not likely be happy with you if you inflate it above about 200 mmHg, because this can be uncomfortable.

7 Slowly open the screw by turning it counterclockwise. Watch the pressure gauge, and listen to the brachial artery with your stethoscope.

8 Eventually you will see the needle on the pressure gauge begin to bounce; at about the same time, you will begin to hear the pulse in the brachial artery. Record the pressure at which this first happens as the *systolic pressure*.

9 Continue to listen, and watch the gauge until you can no longer hear the pulse. At this point, the needle on the gauge will stop rhythmically bouncing. Record the pressure at which this happens as the *diastolic pressure*. The numbers should be recorded as a fraction (e.g., 110/70, where 110 is the systolic pressure and 70 is the diastolic pressure).

Practice Reading 1: _____

Practice Reading 2: _____

Procedure 2 Measuring the Effects of the Autonomic Nervous System on Blood Pressure and Heart Rate

The autonomic nervous system (ANS) exerts a great deal of control over blood pressure through its influence on cardiac output, peripheral resistance, and blood volume. This exercise limits us to measuring only its effects on cardiac output and peripheral resistance (unless you want to stay in lab for the next two days and measure urine output—but I'm guessing you don't want to do that).

> **⚠ Safety Note**
> Students with health problems or known cardiovascular disorders should not engage in this activity.

1 Have your lab partner remain seated and relaxed for three minutes. After three minutes, measure your partner's blood pressure and heart rate.

2 Have your partner place one of his or her hands into a bucket of ice water.

3 Repeat the blood pressure and pulse measurements with your partner's hand still in the ice water. (*Note:* Be kind to your partner and do this quickly!)

4 Have your partner remove his or her hand from the ice water.

5 Wait five minutes, then repeat the blood pressure and pulse measurements. Record your results in Table 11.6.

6 Interpret your results:

  a Which situation(s) represented activation of the sympathetic nervous system?

  _____

  b Which situation(s) represented activation of the parasympathetic nervous system?

  _____

TABLE **11.6** Blood Pressure and Pulse Readings: Ice-Water Experiment

Test Situation	Blood Pressure	Pulse Rate
At rest		
After immersing in ice water		
5 minutes after removing from ice water		

Exercise 11-7

The Electrocardiogram

The **electrocardiogram**, or **ECG**, is a recording of the electrical activity of the heart. Electrical activity is recorded by placing *electrodes* on the surface of the skin that record the changes in electrical activity. The changes in electrical activity are visible on the ECG as **waves**. Note that if there is no *net* change in electrical activity, the line on the ECG is flat. However, even when the ECG is flat between waves, the cells of the heart are in some phase of an action potential.

A standard ECG recording is shown in Figure 11.26. Notice that it consists of five waves, each of which represents the depolarization or repolarization of different parts of the heart.

- **P wave.** The initial P wave shows the depolarization of the cells of the right and left atria. It is fairly small because of the small number of cells in the atria.

- **QRS complex.** The next set of waves is called collectively the QRS complex, which represents the depolarization of the right and left ventricles. The first wave is the **Q wave**, a downward deflection, the next is the **R wave**, a large upward deflection, and the last is the **S wave**, the final downward deflection. The large size of the QRS complex compared with the P wave results from the large number of ventricular cells.

- **T wave.** The small T wave is usually the final wave, and it shows the repolarization of the right and left ventricles.

The waves aren't the only important landmarks of the ECG. In addition, we consider the periods between the waves, which show the spread of electrical activity through the heart and phases of the myocardial cells' action potentials. One important period is the **R-R interval**, or the period of time between two R waves. This interval represents the duration of the generation and spread of an action potential through the heart. It can also be used to determine the heart rate, which we will discuss shortly. Another period we examine is the **P-R interval**, defined as the period from the beginning of the P wave to the beginning of the R wave. During the P-R interval, the depolarization from the SA node spreads through the atria to the ventricles via the AV node.

The **S-T segment** is between the end of the S wave and the beginning of the T wave. This period is recorded during the ventricles' plateau phase. Recall that there is no net change in electrical activity during this phase, and for this reason, the S-T segment is generally flat. The final period we discuss is the **Q-T interval**, the time from the beginning of the Q wave to the end of the T wave. During the Q-T interval, the ventricular cells are depolarizing and repolarizing.

The normal pattern seen on an ECG is known as a **normal sinus rhythm**, which means that the SA node is pacing the heart at a rate between 60 and 100 beats per minute. Any deviation from the normal sinus rhythm is known as a **dysrhythmia** (dis-RITH-mee-uh).

An electrocardiograph records the tracing at a standard speed of 25 mm/second. This allows us to determine precisely the heart rate and the duration of the intervals we discussed. As you can see in Figure 11.26, each small box on the ECG tracing measures 0.04s, and each large box measures 0.20s. Five large boxes together measure one second. Determining the duration of most intervals is simple—just count the small or large boxes, and add the seconds together. Calculating the heart rate is equally simple: count the number of large boxes, and divide 300 by this number. For example, if you count 4.2 boxes: 300/4.2 = 71 beats per minute. The normal values for the periods we discussed are given in Table 11.7.

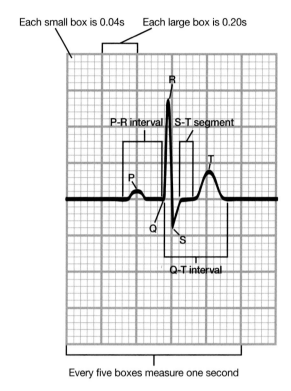

Each small box is 0.04s   Each large box is 0.20s

Every five boxes measure one second

FIGURE **11.26** Standard ECG recording

TABLE **11.7** Normal Values for ECG Periods

Period	Normal Value
Heart rate	60–100 beats per minute
R-R interval	0.60–1.0s
P-R interval	0.12–0.20s
Q-T interval	0.42–0.44s
QRS complex duration	Less than or equal to 0.12s

11

1 Obtain three glass tubes
2 Obtain a bottle of 5 DL...
3 In each tube, place 2 ml of...
4 Add one-fourth of one...
5 Add one-fourth of one...
6 Add one-fourth of one...
7 Allow the tubes to sit for...
8 Measure the pH of the...

Procedure 1 Interpreting an ECG

You will now perform some basic ECG interpretation. Following are two tracings for which you will calculate the heart rate and determine the duration of key periods of the ECG.

1 Identify and label the P wave, QRS complex, T wave, P-R interval, R-R interval, and Q-T interval on Tracings 1 and 2 in Figure 11.27.

Tracing 1

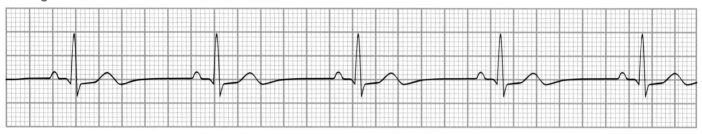

Tracing 2

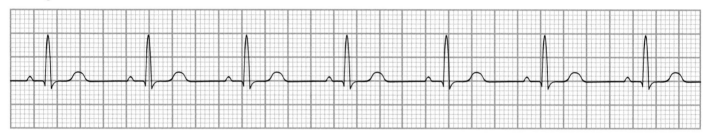

FIGURE **11.27** ECG tracings

2 Calculate the heart rate for each tracing. Are the values normal or abnormal?

Heart Rate Tracing 1: _____

Heart Rate Tracing 2: _____

3 Determine the R-R interval, QRS duration, P-R interval, and Q-T interval for each tracing, and record the values in Table 11.8.

TABLE **11.8** Values for ECG Periods

Value	Tracing 1	Tracing 2
R-R interval		
QRS duration		
P-R interval		
Q-T interval		

11

1 Label the following parts of the heart on Figure 11.28.

- ❏ Anterior interventricular artery
- ❏ Aorta
- ❏ Circumflex artery
- ❏ Inferior vena cava
- ❏ Pulmonary trunk
- ❏ Pulmonary veins
- ❏ Right coronary artery
- ❏ Superior vena cava

Figure **11.28** Heart, anterior view

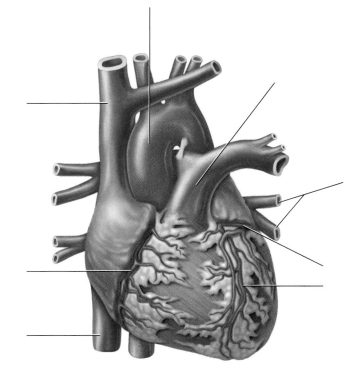

11

2 Label the following parts of the heart on Figure 11.29.

- ❏ Aortic valve
- ❏ Left atrium
- ❏ Left ventricle
- ❏ Mitral valve
- ❏ Pulmonary valve
- ❏ Right atrium
- ❏ Right ventricle
- ❏ Tricuspid valve

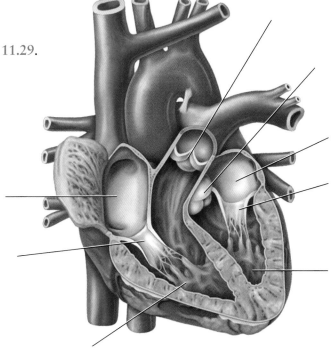

Figure **11.29** Heart, frontal section

3 The pulmonary and aortic valves are known as the

   a. atrioventricular (AV) valves.

   b. semilunar valves.

   c. coronary valves.

   d. chordae tendineae.

4 The right and left coronary arteries are the first branches off the

   a. aorta.

   b. superior vena cava.

   c. pulmonary trunk.

   d. pulmonary veins.

5 High pressure in the systemic and pulmonary circuits often results in *ventricular hypertrophy*, in which the ventricle enlarges to pump against greater force. Which side(s) of the heart would be affected by high pressure in the pulmonary circuit? Which side(s) of the heart would be affected by high pressure in the systemic circuit? Explain.

_____

_____

_____

_____

_____

_____

6 The cerebral arterial circle (circle of Willis):

   a. provides alternate routes of blood flow in the brain.

   b. supplies the face and the scalp.

   c. provides alternate routes of blood flow in the liver.

   d. supplies the myocardium.

7 The venous blood of the brain drains into a set of _____ before draining into a vein.

   a. coronary arteries

   b. cerebral veins

   c. dural sinuses

   d. paranasal sinuses

8 Label the following arteries in Figures 11.30 and 11.31.

Figure 11.30

- ❏ Brachial artery
- ❏ Femoral artery
- ❏ Left common carotid artery
- ❏ Posterior tibial artery
- ❏ Radial artery
- ❏ Renal artery
- ❏ Right subclavian artery
- ❏ Ulnar artery
- ❏ Vertebral artery

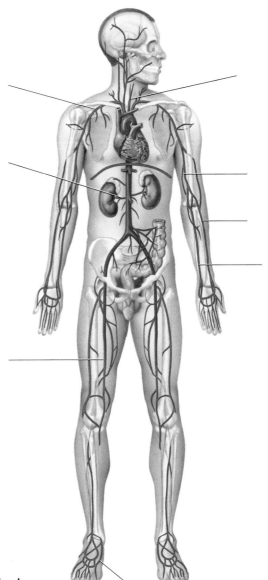

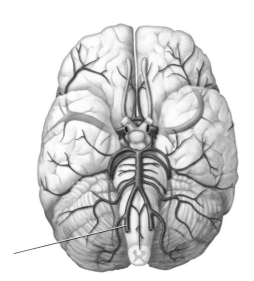

FIGURE **11.30** Major arteries of the body

Figure 11.31

- ❏ Celiac trunk
- ❏ Common hepatic artery
- ❏ Inferior mesenteric artery
- ❏ Splenic artery
- ❏ Superior mesenteric artery

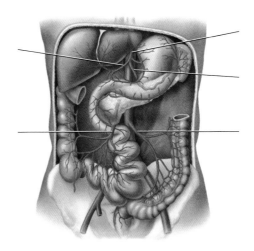

FIGURE **11.31** Arteries of the abdomen

9 Label the following veins on Figures 11.32 and 11.33.

Figure 11.32

❏ Brachiocephalic vein
❏ Cephalic vein
❏ Great saphenous vein
❏ Internal jugular vein
❏ Renal vein
❏ Subclavian vein
❏ Vertebral vein

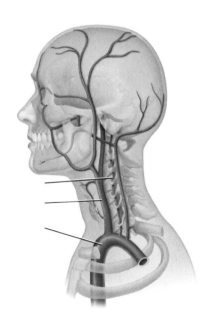

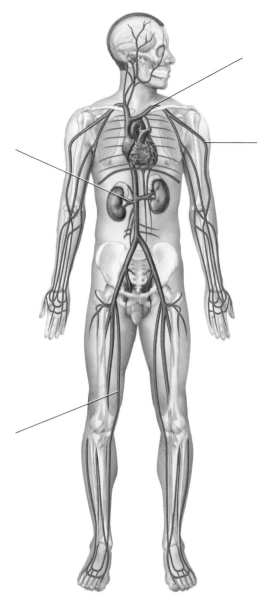

FIGURE **11.32** Major veins of the body

Figure 11.33

❏ Hepatic portal vein
❏ Inferior mesenteric vein
❏ Splenic vein
❏ Superior mesenteric vein

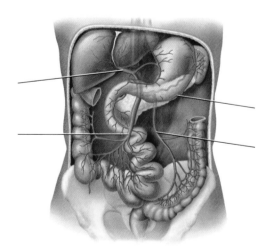

FIGURE **11.33** Veins of the abdomen and the hepatic portal system

10 In the surgical procedure called a bypass graft, a vessel is removed from a patient and used to make a vascular bridge that bypasses one of that patient's blocked arteries. A common vessel used for this procedure is the great saphenous vein. Why do you think a surgeon might use the great saphenous vein instead of the femoral vein or a large artery?

_____

_____

_____

_____

_____

_____

11 Which of the following is *not* a factor that determines blood pressure?
a. Cardiac output
b. Blood type
c. Peripheral resistance
d. Blood volume

12 *Fill in the blanks:* The _____ is the pressure in the arteries during ventricular systole and

averages about _____ . The _____ is the pressure in the arteries during

ventricular diastole and averages about _____ .

13 The QRS complex on an ECG represents:
a. depolarization of the atria.
b. repolarization of the atria.
c. depolarization of the ventricles.
d. repolarization of the ventricles.

14 Your patient has been admitted to the emergency room with an occupational injury from an industrial saw. He has lost a significant volume of blood. What effect has this blood loss likely had on his blood pressure, and why?

_____

_____

_____

_____

_____

Blood and Lymphatics

12

OBJECTIVES

Once you have completed this unit, you should be able to:

1. Identify the formed elements of blood.

2. Perform blood typing of the ABO and Rh blood groups using simulated blood.

3. Explain the basis for blood typing and matching for blood donation.

4. Determine your own blood type and the hemoglobin content of your blood.

5. Identify structures of the lymphatic system.

6. Trace the pathway of lymph as it is returned to the cardiovascular system.

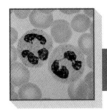

PRE-LAB EXERCISES

Complete the following exercises prior to coming to lab, using your textbook and lab manual for reference.

Pre-Lab Exercise **12-1**

✎ Key Terms

You should be familiar with the following terms before coming to lab.

Term	Definition
Formed Elements	
Erythrocyte	
Leukocyte	
Neutrophil	
Eosinophil	
Basophil	
Lymphocyte	
Monocyte	
Platelets	
Blood Typing	
Antigen	
Antiserum	
Antibody	

12

Blood Donation

Universal donor _____

_____

Universal recipient _____

_____

Lymphatic System Structures

Lymphatic capillary _____

_____

Lymph _____

_____

Spleen _____

_____

Thymus _____

_____

Tonsil _____

_____

Lymph node _____

_____

Pre-Lab Exercise 12-2

Formed Elements

In this unit we will identify the formed elements of blood on a peripheral blood smear. Each formed element has unique morphological characteristics and functions. Use your text and Exercise 12-1 in this unit to complete Table 12.1 with these functions and characteristics.

TABLE **12.1** Properties of Formed Elements

Formed Element	Nucleus Shape	Cytoplasm and/or Granule Color	Function	Prevalence
Erythrocyte				
Neutrophil				
Eosinophil				
Basophil				
Lymphocyte				
Monocyte				
Platelet				

12

Label and color the structures of the lymphatic system depicted in Figure 12.1 with the following terms from Exercise 12-6. Use your text and Exercise 12-6 in this unit for reference.

❏ Spleen
❏ Thymus

Lymph Vessels
   ❏ Thoracic duct
   ❏ Right lymphatic duct

Lymph Nodes
   ❏ Cervical lymph nodes
   ❏ Axillary lymph nodes
   ❏ Inguinal lymph nodes
   ❏ Intestinal lymph nodes

Tonsils
   ❏ Palatine tonsil
   ❏ Pharyngeal tonsil
   ❏ Lingual tonsil

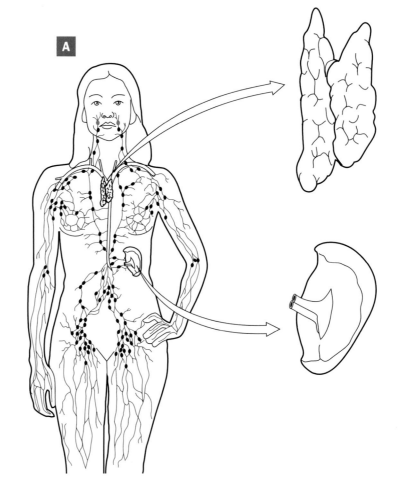

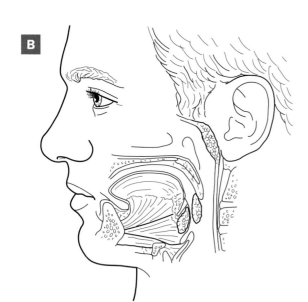

FIGURE **12.1** Lymphoid organs: (**A**) overview of the lymphatic organs and vessels; (**B**) tonsils

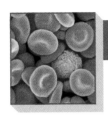

EXERCISES

You have already examined the vessels that make up the cardiovascular system, and in this unit you will study the fluid tissue located within those vessels: **blood**. Safety concerns often preclude the use of real blood in the laboratory, but we can still demonstrate important principles by viewing prepared microscope slides of blood cells and by using simulated blood to learn about blood typing. There is no real concern over blood-borne diseases with simulated blood, but do keep in mind that the simulated blood contains chemicals that may be hazardous. Therefore, use appropriate safety protocols when handling all materials in this lab.

Your study of blood will begin with an examination of the formed elements of blood on microscope slides. After this, you will play a murder mystery game in which you use simulated blood to apply blood-typing techniques in relation to blood donation. If your lab has the appropriate protocols for the use of real blood, you will also type your own blood and determine its hemoglobin content.

This unit also examines a topic closely related to the cardiovascular system and blood: the **lymphatic system**, which contains vessels and organs that filter blood and another type of fluid known as **lymph** (limf). As you will see, this system works closely with the cardiovascular system to maintain fluid homeostasis in the extracellular fluid. You will examine this and other functions of the lymphatic system in Exercise 12-6.

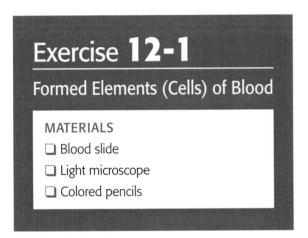

Exercise **12-1**

Formed Elements (Cells) of Blood

MATERIALS
- ❏ Blood slide
- ❏ Light microscope
- ❏ Colored pencils

Whole blood consists of two main components: **plasma**, the fluid portion of blood, and **formed elements**, the cellular portion of blood. Plasma accounts for about 55% of the volume of whole blood and consists primarily of water, proteins, and other solutes such as nutrients and ions. Formed elements account for about 45% of the volume of whole blood. Formed elements can be divided into three classes, each of which is shown in Figure 12.2.

1. **Erythrocytes.** Erythrocytes (e-RITH-roh-sytz), also known as **red blood cells,** are the most numerous formed elements. These cells carry oxygen around the body on an iron-containing molecule called **hemoglobin** (HEE-moh-gloh-bin). Erythrocytes are easily distinguished from the other formed elements by their red color and the fact that mature erythrocytes lack nuclei and most organelles.

2. **Leukocytes.** Leukocytes (LOO-koh-sytz), also known as **white blood cells,** play a role in the immune system. The two subclasses of leukocytes are based upon the presence or absence of granules in their cytoplasm.

    a. **Granulocytes.** As implied by their name, granulocytes (GRAN-yoo-loh-sytz) are cells containing cytoplasmic granules that are visible when stained. The three types of granulocytes stain differently when treated with the dyes hematoxylin and eosin and are named for the type of stain with which they interact.

    (1) **Neutrophils** (NOO-troh-filz) stain a light violet with a mixture of the basic (hematoxylin) and acidic (eosin) dyes. They are the most numerous type of leukocyte and have multilobed nuclei.

    (2) **Eosinophils** (ee-oh-SIN-oh-filz) interact strongly with the red dye eosin, and their granules stain bright red. They are far less numerous than neutrophils and tend to have bilobed nuclei.

    (3) **Basophils** (BAY-soh-filz) take up the dark purple basic stain hematoxylin, and their granules appear dark blue-purple. They tend to have bilobed nuclei, but their nuclei are often obscured by their dark granules. They are the least numerous of the leukocytes and will likely be the most difficult to find on your slide.

    b. **Agranulocytes.** The cells known as agranulocytes lack cytoplasmic granules. The two types of agranulocytes are:

    (1) **Lymphocytes** (LIMF-oh-sytz) tend to be smaller than granulocytes and have large, spherical nuclei. They are the second most numerous type of leukocyte.

12

(2) **Monocytes** (MAH-noh-sytz) are the largest of the leukocytes and have U-shaped or horseshoe-shaped nuclei. They are the third most numerous type of leukocyte.

3. **Platelets**. Note in Figure 12.2 that platelets aren't actually cells at all but are instead just small cellular fragments. As such, they lack nuclei and most organelles and are much smaller than the other formed elements. Platelets are involved in blood clotting.

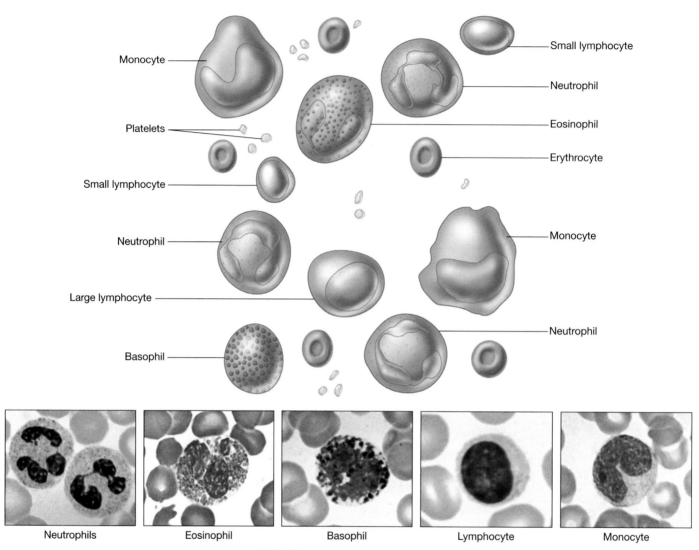

FIGURE **12.2** Formed elements of the blood

Procedure 1 Microscopy of a Peripheral Blood Smear

In this procedure, you will examine a blood slide called a **peripheral blood smear**. Examine the peripheral blood smear on high power, and scroll through to find each of the formed elements. Note that you may have to find a second slide to locate certain cells, because some types are more difficult to find (in particular the eosinophils and basophils). In the spaces provided, use colored pencils to draw and describe each formed element you locate.

1 Erythrocyte

2 Neutrophil

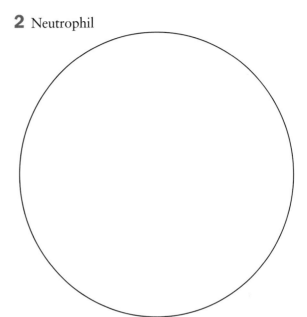

3 Eosinophil

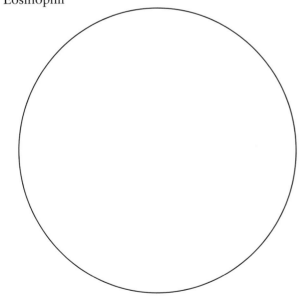

4 Basophil

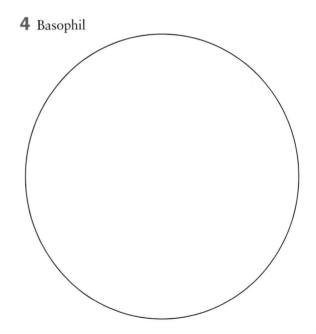

5 Monocyte

6 Lymphocyte

7 Platelets

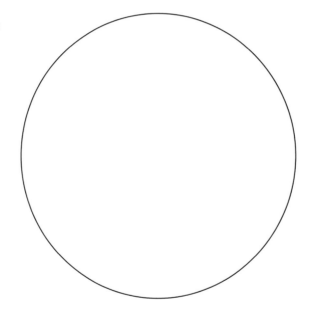

12

Exercise 12-2

ABO and Rh Blood Groups

MATERIALS

❑ Well plates

❑ Simulated blood types A−, B+, AB−, and O+

❑ Simulated antisera: anti-A, anti-B, anti-Rh

Blood typing is done by checking the blood for the presence or absence of specific glycoproteins called **antigens** (AN-tih-jenz) found on the cell surface. Two clinically relevant antigens are the **A antigen** and the **B antigen**. The blood type is named based upon which of the antigens is present.

- **Type A** blood has A antigens on the cell surface.
- **Type B** blood has B antigens on the cell surface.
- **Type AB** blood has both A and B antigens on the cell surface.
- **Type O** blood has neither A nor B antigens on the cell surface.

An additional clinically relevant antigen is the Rh antigen.

- Blood that has the Rh antigen is denoted as **Rh positive** (e.g., A+).

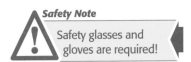

Safety Note

Safety glasses and gloves are required!

- Blood that lacks the Rh antigen is denoted as **Rh negative** (e.g., A−).

The prevalence of different blood types in the United States varies with different ethnic groups. In general, we can say that the most common type is O+, followed by A+ and then B+.

The antigens present on the surface of an erythrocyte can be determined by combining it with a solution called an **antiserum**. An antiserum is a solution that contains proteins from the immune system called **antibodies** that bind to specific antigens. When antibodies bind to antigens on erythrocytes, they cause **agglutination**, or clumping of the erythrocytes, in the sample. In this exercise we are using simulated blood, so you won't see agglutination unless your instructor sets up a demonstration or permits you to type your blood (which is in a later, optional procedure). The antisera used to determine the blood type of a sample are named according to the antigens they bind:

- **Anti-A antiserum** contains anti-A antibodies that bind to erythrocytes with A antigens.
- **Anti-B antiserum** contains anti-B antibodies that bind to erythrocytes with B antigens.
- **Anti-Rh antiserum** contains anti-Rh antibodies that bind to erythrocytes with Rh antigens.

Antigen-Antibody Reactions

This exercise allows you to examine the antigen-antibody reactions of known blood types. Each student group should take one well plate and one set of dropper bottles. The bottles are labeled A−, B+, AB−, and O+ to represent each of those blood types, and anti-A, anti-B, and anti-Rh to represent the different antisera. You can see what a positive reaction looks like in Figure 12.3. Notice that a positive reaction is indicated by the formation of a white, cloudy precipitate. So, for type A+, a positive reaction is seen in the wells to which anti-A and anti-Rh antisera were added, but there is no reaction in the well containing anti-B antiserum.

12

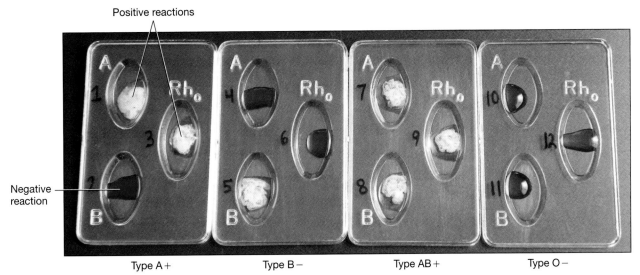

FIGURE 12.3 Reactions of simulated blood with simulated antisera

Procedure 1 Testing Simulated Blood

Use Figure 12.4 as a guide to placement of samples in the wells.

1 Label wells on the well plate as wells 1–12.

2 Drop two drops of type A − blood in well 1, well 2, and well 3.

3 Drop two drops of type B + blood in well 4, well 5, and well 6.

4 Drop two drops of type AB − blood in well 7, well 8, and well 9.

5 Drop two drops of type O + blood in well 10, well 11, and well 12.

6 Add two drops of the anti-A antiserum to wells 1, 4, 7, and 10.

7 Add two drops of the anti-B antiserum to wells 2, 5, 8, and 11.

8 Add two drops of the anti-Rh antiserum to wells 3, 6, 9, and 12.

9 Observe the samples for changes in color symbolizing the agglutination, or clumping, that would normally occur between antisera and specific blood types. Record your results in Table 12.2.

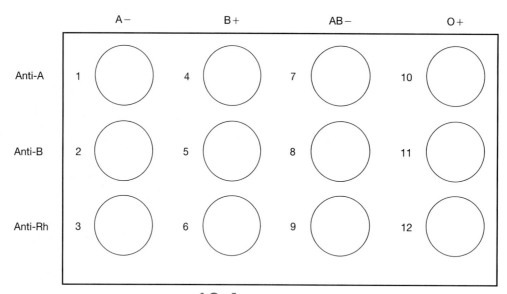

FIGURE **12.4** Well-plate diagram

TABLE **12.2** Blood-Typing Results

Blood Type	Reacted with Anti-A? (yes/no)	Reacted with Anti-B? (yes/no)	Reacted with Anti-Rh? (yes/no)	Antigens Present on Cell Surface
A −				
B +				
AB −				
O +				

Exercise 12-3

Murder Mystery Game

MATERIALS
❏ Well plate
❏ Simulated antisera: anti-A, anti-B, anti-Rh
❏ Murder mystery game

In this game you will be applying the blood-typing techniques you learned in Exercise 12-2 to solve a series of murder mysteries. Each of the following cases presents a victim, a murderer, three suspects, three possible murder rooms, and three possible murder weapons. Your job is to play the role of detective, and determine the identity of the murderer, which weapon he or she used, and in which room the crime was committed.

Procedure 1 Solving the Murder Mysteries

For each case a unique set of bottles is marked with a number that corresponds to the specific cases (i.e., the bottles are marked 1 for Case 1, 2 for Case 2, and 3 for Case 3). The murderer, rooms, and murder weapons are different for each case, but the cast of characters remains the same.

1 To begin the game, assemble groups of two or three students. Obtain a well plate, and choose one set of samples to test (e.g., the rooms from Case 1, the suspects from Case 2, or the weapons from Case 3).

2 Test the samples by placing drops of the sample in three separate wells. Add two drops of anti-A antiserum to the first well, add two drops of anti-B antiserum to the second well, and add two drops of anti-Rh antiserum to the third well. After you have tested each of the samples, return them to their proper places in the front of the lab.

3 Read and record the blood type by watching for a reaction with the antisera. Remember, this is simulated blood just as in Exercise 12-2. A positive reaction is denoted by a color change.

4 To determine the
  ▌ *Murderer*: Match the blood type of one of the *suspects* to that of the murderer.
  ▌ *Weapon and room*: Match the blood type of the *victim* to the blood types found in the rooms and on the weapon.

Case 1: Ms. Magenta

We enter the scene to find the dearly departed Ms. Magenta. Forensic analysis determines that there are two types of blood on the body. One blood type is Ms. Magenta's, and the other blood type is a trace amount left behind from the murderer.

Ms. Magenta's blood type: _____   **Murderer's blood type:** _____

We have three suspects:

1. *Mrs. Blanc* was being blackmailed by Ms. Magenta and Col. Lemon. They had discovered that Mrs. Blanc had murdered her late husband. Mrs. Blanc knew this would ruin her reputation at the country club.

2. *Col. Lemon* wanted to keep the blackmail money for himself and wanted Ms. Magenta out of the way.

3. *Mr. Olive* had been secretly in love with Ms. Magenta for years, and when he told her of his feelings, she rejected him harshly.

Mrs. Blanc's blood type: _____   **Col. Lemon's blood type:** _____

Mr. Olive's blood type: _____

We have three possible murder rooms:

Ballroom blood type: _____   **Library blood type:** _____

Den blood type: _____

12

We have three possible murder weapons:

  Candlestick blood type: _____   **Noose blood type:** _____

  Knife blood type: _____

Case 1: Conclusion

Ms. Magenta was killed by _____, in the _____,

with the _____.

Case 2: Col. Lemon

Our next victim is poor Col. Lemon. On his body we find his blood and also trace amounts of the blood of another person, presumably the murderer.

  Col. Lemon's blood type: _____   **Murderer's blood type:** _____

We have three potential suspects:

1. *Mrs. Blanc*. Now, with Ms. Magenta out of the way, Mrs. Blanc could easily rid herself of her problem by disposing of the only other person who knows her secret—Col. Lemon.
2. *Professor Purple* believed the colonel had stolen his groundbreaking research into collagen lip injections.
3. *Mr. Olive* couldn't stand the colonel because of his close relationship with Ms. Magenta.

  Mrs. Blanc's blood type: _____   **Professor Purple's blood type:** _____

  Mr. Olive's blood type: _____

We have blood in three different rooms:

  Hall blood type: _____   **Kitchen blood type:** _____

  Billiards room blood type: _____

Forensics found blood on three different weapons:

  Copper pipe blood type: _____   **Hammer blood type:** _____

  Revolver blood type: _____

Case 2: Conclusion

Col. Lemon was killed by _____, in the _____,

with the _____.

12

Case 3: Mr. Olive

Our next (and hopefully last) victim is Mr. Olive. Analysis demonstrates two blood types: one belonging to Mr. Olive, and trace amounts of another belonging to the murderer.

Mr. Olive's blood type: _____   **Murderer's blood type:** _____

We have three potential suspects:

1. *Ms. Feather* had always secretly loved Mr. Olive, but he spurned her advances in favor of Ms. Magenta.

2. *Mrs. Blanc* was worried that Mr. Olive knew her secret, and she wanted him out of the way.

3. *Professor Purple* discovered that Mr. Olive—not Col. Lemon—had actually stolen the collagen lip implant research. Whoops!

Ms. Feather's blood type: _____   **Mrs. Blanc's blood type:** _____

Professor Purple's blood type: _____

Blood was found in three rooms:

Lounge blood type: _____   **Dining room blood type:** _____

Greenhouse blood type: _____

We have three potential murder weapons:

Noose blood type: _____   **Hammer blood type:** _____

Revolver blood type: _____

Case 3: Conclusion

Mr. Olive was killed by _____, in the _____,

with the _____.

Exercise 12-4

Blood Donation

Blood transfusion, the infusion of a recipient with a donor's blood, is a commonly performed medical procedure. Before a recipient is given a blood transfusion, the medical team must first learn the patient's blood type and then find a suitable, or "matching," donor. This is necessary because of the A, B, and Rh antigens on the surface of the donor erythrocytes and the presence of preformed antibodies in the recipient's blood. If a donor's blood has antigens the recipient's immune system recognizes as foreign, the recipient's antibodies will agglutinate the foreign erythrocytes, and the immune system will destroy them, a process known as **hemolysis (hee-MAH-lih-sis).** This is called a **transfusion reaction,** and it is a medical emergency that can lead to kidney failure and death.

To ensure that a transfusion reaction does not occur, we must make sure the donor blood does not have antigens the recipient's immune system will recognize as foreign. Our immune systems produce antibodies to any antigen *not* present on the surface of our own cells.

- People with type A blood have A antigens and so produce anti-B antibodies.

- People with type B blood have B antigens and so produce anti-A antibodies.

- People with type O blood have neither A nor B antigens and so produce anti-A and anti-B antibodies.

- People with type AB blood have both A and B antigens and so produce neither anti-A nor anti-B antibodies.

If you're wondering about the Rh factor, wait just a moment—we're getting there. Let's do an example with the ABO blood groups first:

Patient 1 has type B blood, which means that he has anti-A antibodies. What will happen if we give him blood from a donor with:

- **Type A blood?** There are A antigens on these erythrocytes, and his anti-A antibodies would agglutinate them. ✕

- **Type B blood?** Patient 1's anti-A antibodies would have no effect on the B antigens on these erythrocytes, so this blood is safe. ✓

- **Type O blood?** There are no antigens on these donor erythrocytes, so Patient 1's anti-A antibodies would have no effect on them, and this blood is safe. ✓

- **Type AB blood?** There are both A and B antigens on these erythrocytes, and Patient 1's anti-A antibodies would agglutinate the erythrocytes. ✕

Now that's easy, isn't it?

Next let's address the Rh factor. The blood of an Rh-negative person does *not* contain preformed antibodies to the Rh antigen. If an Rh-negative person is exposed to the Rh antigen, however, he or she *does* produce anti-Rh antibodies. In an emergency setting, it is generally not possible to determine if an Rh-negative person has been exposed to the Rh antigen, so health-care professionals err on the side of caution and assume that the person has anti-Rh antibodies. For the sake of simplicity, we will assume the same thing in this exercise. So, for our purposes:

- People with Rh-positive blood *do not* produce anti-Rh antibodies.

- People with Rh-negative blood *do* produce anti-Rh antibodies.

Let's do one more example, taking into account the Rh factor this time:

Patient 2 has A− blood, which means that she has anti-B and anti-Rh antibodies. What will happen if we give her blood from a donor with:

- **Type A+ blood?** There are A and Rh antigens on these erythrocytes, and her anti-Rh antibodies would agglutinate them. ✕

- **Type B− blood?** There are B antigens on these erythrocytes, and her anti-B antibodies would agglutinate them. ✕

- **Type O− blood?** There are no antigens on these erythrocytes, so Patient 2's anti-B and anti-Rh antibodies would have no effect on them, and this blood is safe. ✓

- **Type AB+ blood?** There are A, B, and Rh antigens on these erythrocytes, and Patient 2's anti-B and anti-Rh antibodies would agglutinate them. ✕

12

Procedure 1 Blood-Type Matching Practice

Use the information above and your text to fill in Table 12.3.

TABLE **12.3** Blood Donation

Blood Type	Antigens Present	Antibodies Present	Can Donate Safely to Which Blood Types?	Can Receive Safely from Which Blood Types?
A+				
A−				
B+				
B−				
AB+				
AB−				
O+				
O−				

You should notice something from Table 12.3: AB+ blood can receive from any blood type, and O− blood can donate to any blood type. This is because AB+ blood has all three antigens but no antibodies to these antigens, which is why it is often called the **universal recipient**. But Type O− has none of the three antigens for a recipient's antibodies to bind, so it can be donated to any blood type. For this reason, type O− is often called the **universal donor**.

Procedure 2 Type Matching for Transfusions

Gasp! It turns out that Ms. Magenta, Col. Lemon, and Mr. Olive all survived their injuries! But they have lost blood and are in need of blood transfusions. All of the suspects have had a sudden change of heart and have offered to help the three victims by donating blood. Your job is to determine who among the suspects could safely donate blood to whom. You do not need to retest each person's blood type because you may use your results from Exercise 12-3 (p. 319).

HINTS & TIPS

Remember—when trying to work out who can donate blood to whom, you are concerned with the recipient's antibodies and the donor's antigens. So first work out which antibodies the recipient has, then make sure the recipient's antibodies won't bind any antigens on the donor's erythrocytes.

Recipient 1: Ms. Magenta

Ms. Magenta's blood type: _____

Donors:

Ms. Feather's blood type: _____

Mrs. Blanc's blood type: _____

Professor Purple's blood type: _____

Who could safely donate blood to Ms. Magenta? _____

Who could not safely donate blood to Ms. Magenta? _____

Recipient 2: Col. Lemon

Col. Lemon's blood type: _____

Donors:

Ms. Feather's blood type: _____

Mrs. Blanc's blood type: _____

Professor Purple's blood type: _____

Who could safely donate blood to Col. Lemon? _____

Who could not safely donate blood to Col. Lemon? _____

Recipient 3: Mr. Olive

Mr. Olive's blood type: _____

Donors:

Ms. Feather's blood type: _____

Mrs. Blanc's blood type: _____

Professor Purple's blood type: _____

Who could safely donate blood to Mr. Olive? _____

Who could not safely donate blood to Mr. Olive? _____

Exercise 12-5

Typing and Examining Your Own Blood

MATERIALS

- ❏ Lancet
- ❏ Alcohol wipes
- ❏ Anti-A, anti-B, and anti-Rh antisera
- ❏ Blank microscope slide
- ❏ Sharpie pen
- ❏ Toothpicks
- ❏ Tallquist paper and scale
- ❏ Dissection microscope or magnifying glass

If your lab has the appropriate equipment and biohazard disposal means, your instructor may permit you to type and examine your own blood in this optional exercise. Working with blood is actually very safe provided you follow some basic procedures outlined here:

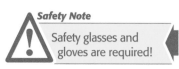

Safety Note

Safety glasses and gloves are required!

1. Wash your hands with soap and water before starting and after completing the procedures.

2. Prepare your work area by placing a disposable absorbent liner on the lab table.

3. Wear gloves and safety glasses when handling all materials for this lab.

4. Handle only your own lab materials to avoid coming into contact with blood other than your own.

5. Dispose of all lancets and microscope slides in the designated sharps container only.

6. Dispose of all nonsharp materials (disposable pads, gloves, alcohol wipes, and any other materials you have used) in the designated red biohazard bag.

7. When you are finished with the procedures, clean your work area with the disinfectant solution provided by your lab instructor.

In the following procedures, you will determine your blood type and measure the approximate hemoglobin content of your blood. Note that these exercises involve lancing your own finger to stimulate bleeding. If you have any medical conditions that render this activity unsafe, discuss this with your lab instructor.

Procedure 1 Determining Your Blood Type

The process of determining the blood type of real blood is similar to the process you performed earlier with simulated blood: You use three blood samples and apply three different antisera to look for a reaction. The reaction between real blood antigens and antibodies is more subtle than in the simulated blood; in particular, the reaction with Rh antigens and the anti-Rh antibodies can be difficult to see. You may wish to examine your samples under a magnifying glass to more clearly see the reaction.

1 Obtain a blank microscope slide, and draw three circles on it with a Sharpie pen. Label the circles A, B, and Rh.

2 Wash your hands, and prepare your work area with a disposable absorbent liner.

3 Place a glove on one hand, and prepare one finger of your ungloved hand by cleaning it with an alcohol wipe.

4 Use a fresh lancet to lance the finger you just cleaned. Dispose of the used lancet in the sharps bin.

5 Squeeze your finger to stimulate bleeding, and squeeze a small drop of blood onto each of the three circles on the slide.

6 Place a drop of anti-A antiserum in the circle marked A, anti-B in the circle marked B, and anti-Rh in the circle marked Rh.

7 Use three toothpicks, one for each circle, to gently mix the blood with the antisera. You must use a different toothpick for each circle to avoid cross-contamination. Watch carefully for a reaction, using a dissection microscope or magnifying glass if needed (be sure to hold a magnifying glass in your gloved hand to avoid coming into contact with blood from your classmates).

12

8 Determine your blood type based upon the reactions with the antisera. Remember, if the blood reacts with an antiserum, that antigen is present. For example, if your blood reacts with anti-B antiserum and anti-Rh antiserum, the B and Rh antigens are present, and the blood type is B + .

Record your blood type here: _____

9 Dispose of your microscope slide in the sharps bin when you have completed the blood-typing procedure.

Procedure 2 Determining the Hemoglobin Content of Your Blood

As you learned in Exercise 12-1 (p. 313), erythrocytes are filled with the protein hemoglobin, which binds and transports oxygen through the blood. The average amount of hemoglobin in erythrocytes averages about 12–16 g/dl in females and about 14–18 g/dl in males. Medically, this is an important value, because a decreased amount of hemoglobin can indicate conditions such as *iron-deficiency anemia*. In a hospital lab, the amount of hemoglobin in the blood is measured with an instrument known as a *hemoglobinometer*. However, in this lab we will employ an older (and less expensive) method using *Tallquist paper*, which provides an estimate of the blood's hemoglobin content.

1 Squeeze your finger to continue to stimulate bleeding. If you need to lance your finger again, obtain a new lancet, and follow the same steps from the first procedure.

2 Obtain a piece of Tallquist paper. Roll your bleeding finger on the paper.

3 Compare the color the paper turns with the scale on the container while the paper is still slightly wet—do not let the paper dry, or you will need to repeat the procedure.

Estimated hemoglobin value: _____

4 Dispose of any remaining sharps in the sharps container and all other blood-containing materials, including the Tallquist paper, in the red biohazard bag. Clean your work area with the disinfectant provided by your lab instructor.

12

Exercise 12-6

Lymphatic System

MATERIALS

❏ Human torso models

❏ Head and neck models

❏ Intestinal villus model

❏ Laminated outline of the human body

❏ Water-soluble marking pens

Now let's turn our attention to the lymphatic system, which consists of organs that have three primary functions:

1. **Transporting excess interstitial fluid back to the heart.** Approximately 1.5 ml/min. of fluid is lost from the circulation in the blood capillaries to the interstitial fluid. This may not sound like a lot, but if this fluid were not returned to the blood vessels, we could lose our entire plasma volume in about a day! Fortunately, the lymphatic system picks up this lost fluid, carries it through lymphatic vessels, and returns it to the cardiovascular system. The fluid is picked up first by small, blind-ended **lymph capillaries** that surround blood capillary beds. These lymph capillaries are distinct from blood capillaries and contain highly permeable walls that allow large substances and large volumes of fluid to enter and exit. After it is inside the lymph capillaries, the fluid is called **lymph** and is delivered to larger **lymph-collecting vessels**. Lymph-collecting vessels drain the fluid into larger **lymph trunks**, and these drain into **lymph ducts** that return the lymph to the cardiovascular system (Figure 12.5A). Note in Figure 12.5A that there are two lymph ducts—the **right lymphatic duct**, which drains the right arm and the right side of the head, neck, and thorax, and the **thoracic duct**, which drains lymph from the remainder of the body. The right lymphatic and thoracic ducts drain lymph into the blood at the junctions of the right and left subclavian and internal jugular veins, respectively.

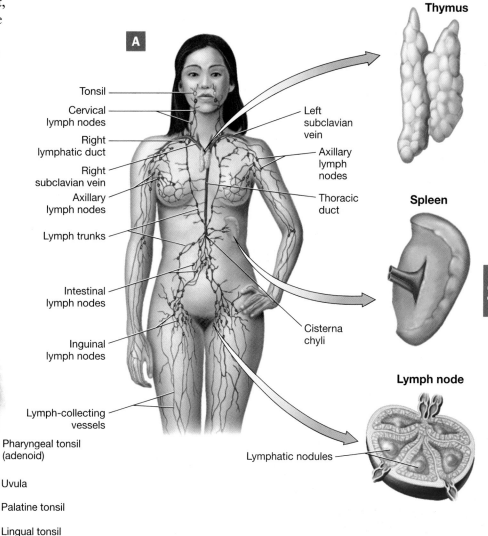

FIGURE **12.5** Lymphoid organs: (**A**) overview of the lymphatic organs and vessels; (**B**) tonsils

12

2. **Activating the immune system.** Several of the lymphatic organs activate the immune system. These include the **thymus**, the organ in which T lymphocytes mature; the **spleen**, which filters the blood and houses phagocytes; and the **tonsils**, aggregates of unencapsulated lymphoid tissue found in the oropharynx and nasopharynx (Figure 12.5B). As you can see in Figure 12.5B, there are three main sets of tonsils: the **pharyngeal tonsils**, located in the posterior nasopharynx; the **palatine tonsils**, located in the posterior oropharynx; and the **lingual tonsil**, located at the base of the tongue. Clusters of lymphatic tissue similar in structure to the tonsils are scattered throughout the gastrointestinal tract, where it is called **mucosal-associated lymphoid tissue**, or **MALT**. The lymphoid organs called **lymph nodes** are similar to tonsils and MALT, but they are surrounded by a connective tissue capsule (note that lymph nodes are often called "lymph glands," but this is a misnomer because they do not secrete any products). Lymph nodes are found along lymphatic vessels, where they filter lymph and remove pathogens, toxins, and cells (such as cancer or virally infected cells).

3. **Absorbing dietary fats.** Fats are not absorbed from the small intestine directly into the blood capillaries because they are too large to enter these small vessels. Instead, fats enter a lymphatic capillary called a **lacteal**. The lacteal delivers the fats to the lymph in a large lymphatic vessel called the **cisterna chyli** (sis-TUR-nuh KY-lee), which then drains into the thoracic duct.

In the following activities you will identify structures of the lymphatic system, and then trace the flow of lymph through the vessels on its way back to the cardiovascular system. Your instructor may also wish you to dissect a preserved small mammal to identify some of the structures difficult to see on models, such as the thymus. If so, follow the procedure outlined in Unit 1 (p. 12) to open the animal and identify the required structures.

Procedure 1 Model Inventory for the Lymphatic System

Identify the following structures of the lymphatic system on models and diagrams, using your textbook and this unit for reference. As you examine the anatomical models and diagrams, record on the model inventory in Table 12.4 the name of the model and the structures you were able to identify.

1. Lymph vessels
   a. Thoracic duct
   b. Right lymphatic duct
   c. Lymph trunks
   d. Lacteal
   e. Cisterna chyli
2. Lymph nodes
   a. Cervical lymph nodes
   b. Axillary lymph nodes
   c. Inguinal lymph nodes
   d. Intestinal lymph nodes

3. Spleen
4. Thymus (this is best viewed on a fetal pig)
5. Mucosal-associated lymphoid tissue (MALT)
6. Tonsils
   a. Palatine tonsil
   b. Pharyngeal tonsil
   c. Lingual tonsil

TABLE **12.4** Model Inventory for the Lymphatic System

Model	Structures Identified

12

Procedure 2 Tracing the Flow of Lymph through the Body

In this procedure you will trace the pathway of lymph flow from the starting point to the point at which the lymph is delivered to the cardiovascular system. You will trace the flow through the major lymph-collecting vessels, trunks, and ducts, and highlight clusters of lymph nodes through which the lymph passes as it travels.

1 Write the sequence of the flow.

2 Then use differently colored water-soluble markers to draw the pathway on a laminated outline of the human body. If no outline is available, use colored pencils and Figure 12.6. Trace the flow from the following locations:

Start: Right foot_____

_____

_____

_____

_____

_____

_____

_____

Start: Right arm_____

_____

_____

_____

_____

_____

_____

_____

Start: Intestines (with fat)_____

_____

_____

_____

_____

_____

_____

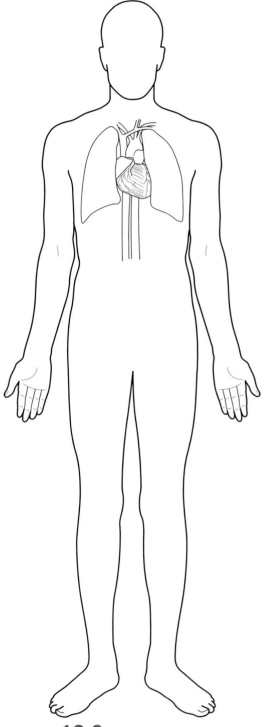

FIGURE **12.6** Outline of human body, anterior view

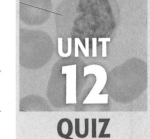

1 *Mark the following statements as true (T) or false (F). If the statement is false, correct it to make it a true statement.*

_____ a. Red blood cells are also known as leukocytes.

_____ b. White blood cells with granules in their cytoplasm are known as agranulocytes.

_____ c. The granulocytes include the neutrophils, eosinophils, and basophils.

_____ d. Erythrocytes carry oxygen through the body on the protein hemoglobin.

_____ e. Both lymphocytes and monocytes are granulocytes.

_____ f. Platelets are fully formed cells involved in blood clotting.

2 Label the formed elements on the peripheral blood smear in Figure 12.7.

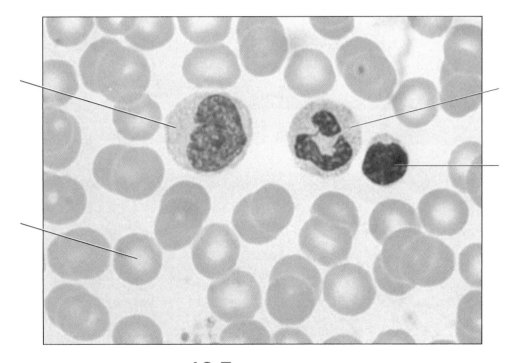

FIGURE **12.7** Peripheral blood smear

3 Which of the following is not an antigen that may be found on the surface of an erythrocyte?

a. A antigen

b. B antigen

c. O antigen

d. Rh antigen

4 A person with type A blood has

    a. anti-A antibodies.

    b. anti-B antibodies.

    c. anti-O antibodies.

    d. no antibodies.

5 A person with type B− blood has which of the following antibodies? (Assume the person has been exposed to Rh antigens. Circle all that apply.)

    a. anti-A antibodies

    b. anti-B antibodies

    c. anti-Rh antibodies

    d. no antibodies

6 List all of the blood types to which the following people could donate:

    a. Person 1: Type A− _____

    _____

    b. Person 2: Type O+ _____

    _____

    c. Person 3: Type AB− _____

    _____

    d. Person 4: Type B+ _____

    _____

7 The disease *erythroblastosis fetalis* (also called *hemolytic disease of the newborn*) develops in a fetus or a newborn infant with Rh-positive blood and an Rh-negative mother. Symptoms result when maternal anti-Rh antibodies cross the placenta and interact with the fetus' erythrocytes. Why are the children of Rh-positive mothers not at risk for this disease? Why are Rh-negative fetuses not at risk for this disease?

_____

_____

_____

_____

_____

8 Explain why a person who is blood type AB+ can receive blood from any blood type but can only donate to individuals who are also blood type AB+.

_____

_____

_____

_____

_____

12

9 When Col. Lemon arrived at the hospital, the staff determined that his blood had been mistyped, and he was in fact blood type AB−. Which of our three suspects (Mrs. Blanc, Ms. Feather, and/or Professor Purple) could safely donate blood to Col. Lemon now? (Refer to p. 324 for their blood types.)

_____

_____

_____

_____

_____

10 Label Figure 12.8 with the terms below.

Figure 12.8A

❑ Cisterna chyli
❑ Lymph nodes: cervical, axillary, intestinal, and inguinal
❑ Spleen
❑ Thoracic duct
❑ Thymus

Figure 12.8B

❑ Lingual tonsil
❑ Palatine tonsil
❑ Pharyngeal tonsil

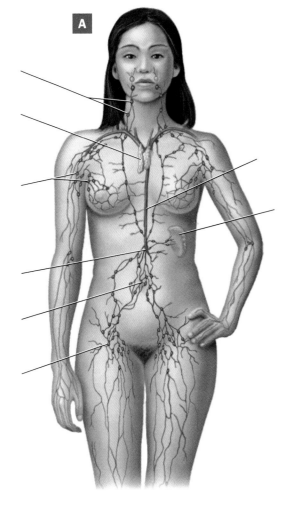

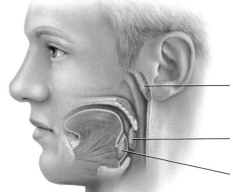

FIGURE **12.8** Lymphoid organs: (**A**) overview of the lymphatic organs and vessels; (**B**) tonsils

11 Which of the following is not a function of the lymphatic system?

a. Maintaining blood pressure

b. Absorbing dietary fats

c. Activating the immune system

d. Transporting excess interstitial fluid back to the heart

12 Lymph nodes filter _____, and the spleen filters _____.

a. lymph; lymph

b. blood; blood

c. lymph; blood

d. blood; lymph

13 Explain why blockage or removal of the lymphatic vessels can result in significant *edema* (accumulation of fluid in a limb or body part).

_____

_____

_____

_____

_____

_____

_____

12

Respiratory System

13

OBJECTIVES

Once you have completed this unit, you should be able to:

1. Describe and identify structures of the respiratory system.

2. Trace the pathway of gases through the respiratory system.

3. Describe the anatomical changes associated with inflation of the lungs.

4. Describe the pressure-volume relationships in the lungs.

5. Measure and define respiratory volumes and capacities.

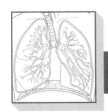

Name _____ Section _____ Date _____

PRE-LAB EXERCISES

Complete the following exercises prior to coming to lab, using your textbook and lab manual for reference.

Pre-Lab Exercise **13-1**

✎ Key Terms

You should be familiar with the following terms before coming to lab.

Term	Definition
General Structures of the Respiratory System	
Respiratory tract	
Pleural cavity	
Lungs	
Structures of the Respiratory Tract	
Nasal cavity	
Pharynx	
Larynx	
Trachea	
Bronchi	
Bronchioles	
Alveoli	

13

Pulmonary Ventilation Terms

Inspiration _____

_____

Expiration _____

_____

Boyle's law _____

_____

Intrapulmonary pressure _____

_____

Atmospheric pressure _____

_____

Spirometer _____

_____

Respiratory volume _____

_____

Respiratory capacity _____

_____

13

Pre-Lab Exercise **13-2**

Respiratory System Anatomy

Label and color the diagrams of the structures of the respiratory system in Figure 13.1 with the following terms from Exercise 13-1. Use your text and Exercise 13-1 in this unit for reference.

❑ Nasal cavity
❑ Larynx
❑ Trachea

Right Lung
  ❑ Upper, middle, lower lobes
  ❑ Horizontal fissure
  ❑ Oblique fissure

Left Lung
  ❑ Upper and lower lobes
  ❑ Oblique fissure

Pharynx
  ❑ Nasopharynx
  ❑ Oropharynx
  ❑ Laryngopharynx

Bronchi
  ❑ Primary bronchi
  ❑ Secondary bronchi

Bronchioles
  ❑ Terminal bronchioles
  ❑ Respiratory bronchioles
  ❑ Alveolar duct
  ❑ Alveoli

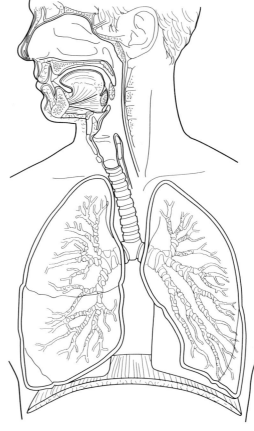

A

B

FIGURE **13.1** Structures of the respiratory system: (**A**) lungs and respiratory tract; (**B**) bronchiole and alveolar sac

13

Pre-Lab Exercise 13-3

Defining Pulmonary Volumes and Capacities

Define and give the normal value for males and females for each of the following respiratory volumes and capacities listed in Table 13.1.

TABLE **13.1** Respiratory Volumes and Capacities

Volume/Capacity	Definition	Normal Value
Tidal volume		Male: _____ ml Female: _____ ml
Inspiratory reserve volume		Male: _____ ml Female: _____ ml
Expiratory reserve volume		Male: _____ ml Female: _____ ml
Residual volume		Male: _____ ml Female: _____ ml
Inspiratory capacity		Male: _____ ml Female: _____ ml
Functional residual capacity		Male: _____ ml Female: _____ ml
Vital capacity		Male: _____ ml Female: _____ ml
Total lung capacity		Male: _____ ml Female: _____ ml

13

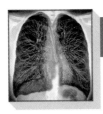

EXERCISES

Cells require oxygen in the reactions that synthesize ATP, and these reactions produce carbon dioxide as a waste product. The respiratory system and the cardiovascular system work together to supply the cells the oxygen they need and to rid them of carbon dioxide.

The first exercise in this unit will familiarize you with the anatomy of the respiratory system, including the paired **lungs** and the collection of airway passages known as the **respiratory tract**. Exercises 13-2 and 13-3 focus on the physiology of the respiratory system and the process known as **ventilation**.

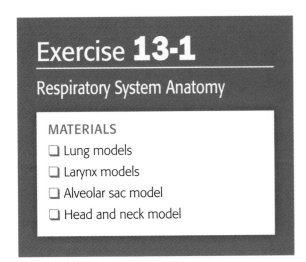

Exercise **13-1**

Respiratory System Anatomy

MATERIALS

❑ Lung models

❑ Larynx models

❑ Alveolar sac model

❑ Head and neck model

The lungs are composed of elastic connective tissue and tiny air sacs called **alveoli** (al-vee-OH-lye; singular, *alveolus*), where gas exchange takes place. Each lung is divided into smaller structures called **lobes**. The right lung has three lobes (upper, middle, and lower), and the left lung has two lobes (upper and lower) (Figure 13.2). The lobes are separated from one another by deep indentations called **fissures**. The **horizontal fissure** separates the right upper and right middle lobes; the **right oblique fissure** separates the right middle and right lower lobes; and the **left oblique fissure** separates the left upper and left lower lobes.

Each lung is surrounded by serous membranes similar to the pericardial membranes called the **pleural** (PLOO-rul) **membranes**. There are two layers of the pleural membranes:

1. **Parietal pleura.** The outer parietal pleura lines the interior of the thoracic cavity and the superior surface of the diaphragm.

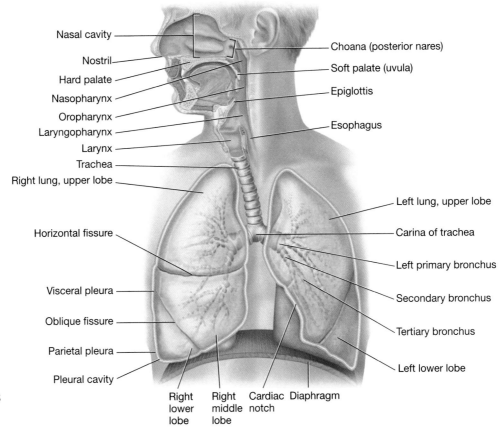

Labels (left, top to bottom): Nasal cavity, Nostril, Hard palate, Nasopharynx, Oropharynx, Laryngopharynx, Larynx, Trachea, Right lung, upper lobe, Horizontal fissure, Visceral pleura, Oblique fissure, Parietal pleura, Pleural cavity

Labels (right, top to bottom): Choana (posterior nares), Soft palate (uvula), Epiglottis, Esophagus, Left lung, upper lobe, Carina of trachea, Left primary bronchus, Secondary bronchus, Tertiary bronchus, Left lower lobe

Labels (bottom): Right lower lobe, Right middle lobe, Cardiac notch, Diaphragm

FIGURE **13.2** Lungs and respiratory tract

13

2. **Visceral pleura.** When the parietal pleura reaches the structures of the mediastinum, it folds inward to become the visceral pleura. The visceral pleura adheres tightly to the surface of the lung.

There is a very thin potential space between the parietal and visceral pleurae called the **pleural cavity**. The space is only a "potential" space because it is filled with a thin layer of serous fluid that reduces friction as the lungs change in shape and size during ventilation.

Air is delivered to the lungs' alveoli through the passageways of the respiratory tract. The respiratory tract may be divided into two regions according to structure:

1. The **upper respiratory tract**, which consists of the passages superior to the thoracic cavity, and

2. the **lower respiratory tract**, which consists of the passages within the thoracic cavity.

The upper respiratory tract begins with the **nasal cavity** and the **paranasal sinuses**, which filter, warm, and humidify the inhaled air (**Figure 13.3**). Air from the nasal cavity next enters the **pharynx** (FAIR-inx), also known as the throat, which has the following three divisions:

1. **Nasopharynx.** The nasopharynx (NAYZ-oh-fair-inx) is the region posterior to the nasal cavity. The muscles of the soft palate move superiorly to close off

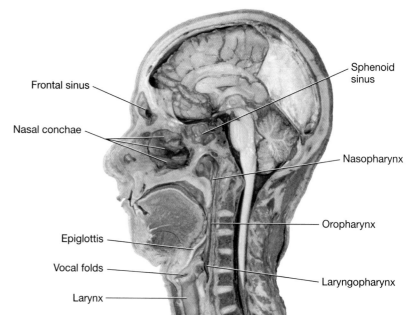

Frontal sinus
Sphenoid sinus
Nasal conchae
Nasopharynx
Oropharynx
Epiglottis
Vocal folds
Laryngopharynx
Larynx

FIGURE **13.3** Midsagittal section of the head and neck

the nasopharynx during swallowing to prevent food from entering the passage. Sometimes this mechanism fails (such as when a person is laughing and swallowing simultaneously), and the unfortunate result is that food or liquid comes out of the nose. The nasopharynx is lined with pseudostratified ciliated columnar epithelium with copious mucus-secreting **goblet cells**, a type of tissue known as *respiratory epithelium.*

2. **Oropharynx.** The oropharynx (OHR-oh-fair-inx) is the region posterior to the oral cavity. Both food and air pass through the oropharynx, and it is lined with stratified squamous epithelium. This tissue provides more resistance to mechanical and thermal stresses.

3. **Laryngopharynx.** The laryngopharynx (lair-ING-oh-fair-inx) is the intermediate region between the larynx and the esophagus. As with the oropharynx, both food and air pass through the laryngopharynx, and it is lined with stratified squamous epithelium.

Air passes from the pharynx to the **larynx** (LAIR-inx), a short passage framed by nine cartilages (**Figure 13.4**). The "lid" of the larynx is a piece of elastic cartilage called the **epiglottis** (ep-ih-GLAH-tis). During swallowing, muscles of the pharynx and larynx move the larynx superiorly, and the epiglottis seals off the larynx from food and liquids. The largest cartilage of the larynx is the shield-like **thyroid cartilage**, which forms the larynx's anterior and lateral walls. Inferior to the thyroid cartilage is a smaller cartilage called the **cricoid** (KRY-koyd) **cartilage**. Between the two is a soft piece of connective tissue called the **cricothyroid** (kry-koh-THY-royd) **ligament**.

As its common name, "voice box," implies, the larynx is the structure where sound is produced. It contains two sets of elastic ligaments known as the **vocal folds**, or **vocal cords**. The superior vocal folds, the **false vocal cords** (also called the *vestibular folds*), play no role in sound production. They do, however, serve an important sphincter function and can constrict to close off the larynx. The inferior vocal folds, called the **true vocal cords**, vibrate as air passes over them to produce sound.

Inspired air passes from the larynx into a tube supported by C-shaped rings of hyaline cartilage called the **trachea** (TRAY-kee-uh). The trachea bifurcates in the mediastinum into two **primary bronchi** (BRAHNK-eye; singular, *bronchus*) that begin the large and branching **bronchial** (BRAHNK-ee-ul) **tree**. The right primary bronchus is short, fairly straight, and wide, and the left primary bronchus is long, more horizontal, and narrow because of the position of the heart.

13

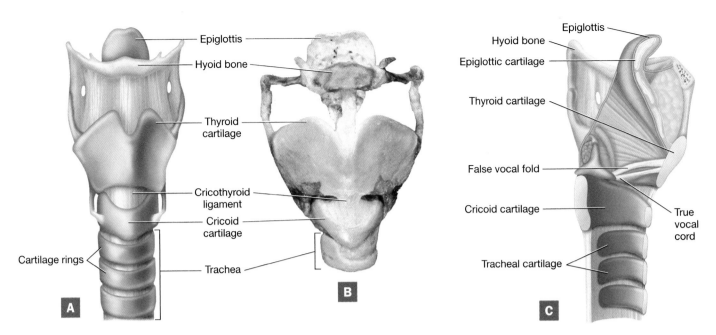

FIGURE **13.4** Larynx: (**A**) anterior view; (**B**) anterior view; (**C**) midsagittal section

Each primary bronchus divides into smaller **secondary bronchi**; the two left secondary bronchi serve the two lobes of the left lung, and the three right secondary bronchi serve the three lobes of the right lung. The bronchi continue to branch and become tertiary bronchi, quaternary bronchi, and so on until the air reaches tiny air passages smaller than 1 millimeter in diameter called **bronchioles** (BRAHNK-ee-ohlz; Figure 13.5).

Bronchioles smaller than 0.5 mm in diameter are called **terminal bronchioles**, which give off small branches called **respiratory bronchioles** that have alveoli in their walls. As the respiratory bronchioles progressively branch, the number of alveoli in the wall increases until the wall is made up exclusively of alveoli, at which point it is termed an **alveolar duct**. The terminal portions of the respiratory tract, called **alveolar sacs**, are grapelike clusters of alveoli surrounded by **pulmonary capillaries**. This junction is where pulmonary gas exchange takes place: Oxygen from the alveoli diffuses into the blood, and carbon dioxide in the blood diffuses into the alveoli to be exhaled. The structure of the alveolar sacs creates a huge surface area (around 1,000 square feet on average). This large surface area is necessary for gas exchange to take place rapidly and efficiently.

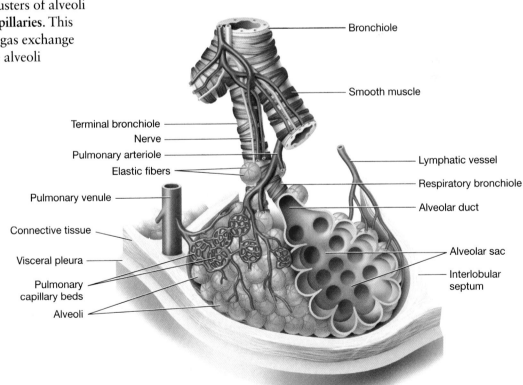

FIGURE **13.5** Bronchiole and alveolar sac

Procedure 1 Model Inventory for the Respiratory System

Identify the following structures of the respiratory system on models and diagrams, using your textbook and this unit for reference. As you examine the anatomical models and diagrams, record on the model inventory in Table 13.2 the name of the model and the structures you were able to identify.

1. Lungs
   a. Parietal pleura
   b. Visceral pleura
   c. Pleural cavity
2. Right lung
   a. Upper, middle, lower lobes
   b. Horizontal fissure
   c. Oblique fissure
3. Left lung
   a. Upper and lower lobes
   b. Oblique fissure
   c. Cardiac notch
4. Nasal cavity

5. Paranasal sinuses
   a. Sphenoid sinus
   b. Ethmoid sinus
   c. Frontal sinus
   d. Maxillary sinus
6. Pharynx
   a. Nasopharynx
   b. Oropharynx
   c. Laryngopharynx
7. Larynx
   a. Epiglottis
   b. Thyroid cartilage
   c. Cricoid cartilage
   d. Cricothyroid ligament
   e. False vocal cords
   f. True vocal cords

8. Trachea
9. Bronchi
   a. Right and left primary bronchi
   b. Secondary bronchi
   c. Tertiary bronchi
10. Bronchioles
    a. Terminal bronchioles
    b. Respiratory bronchioles
    c. Alveolar duct
11. Alveoli and alveolar sacs
12. Vascular structures
    a. Pulmonary arteries
    b. Pulmonary capillaries
    c. Pulmonary veins

TABLE **13.2** Model Inventory for the Respiratory System

Model/Diagram	Structures Identified

Procedure 2 Time to Trace

You are a molecule of oxygen floating happily through the atmosphere when all of a sudden you are inhaled by Ms. Magenta.

1 Trace your pathway through Ms. Magenta's respiratory tract beginning in her nasal cavity to the point where you enter the pulmonary capillaries.

Start: _____

_____

_____

_____

_____

_____ End

The cardiovascular system delivers you to a cell in Ms. Magenta's liver, where you are used in the process of cellular respiration as an electron acceptor as the cell generates ATP. While in her cell, you notice that a molecule of carbon dioxide has just been produced.

2 Trace the carbon dioxide's pathway from Ms. Magenta's inferior vena cava through her heart and to her pulmonary capillaries. You will likely need to review Unit 11 (p. 263) for some help with this.

Start: _____

_____

_____

_____

_____

_____

_____ End

3 Trace the pathway of the carbon dioxide from the pulmonary capillaries through the respiratory tract to the point where it exits from Ms. Magenta's body through her nose.

Start: _____

_____

_____

_____

_____

_____

_____ End

13

Exercise 13-2

Respiratory Physiology: Pressure-Volume Relationships in the Lungs

MATERIALS

❏ Bell-jar model of the lungs
❏ Air hose
❏ Air compressor
❏ Fresh lungs

Respiration consists of four basic physiological processes:

1. **pulmonary ventilation**, the physical movement of air into and out of the lungs,
2. **pulmonary gas exchange**, the movement of gases across the respiratory membrane,
3. **gas transport**, the movement of gases through the blood, and
4. **tissue gas exchange**, the exchange of gases between the blood and the tissues.

Of these four processes, the easiest one to examine in the lab is pulmonary ventilation, which consists of two phases:

1. **inspiration**, during which air is brought into the lungs, and
2. **expiration**, during which air is expelled from the lungs.

The movement of air during inspiration and expiration is driven by changes in the lungs' volume and pressure (Figure 13.6). The relationship of gas pressure and volume is expressed in what is known as **Boyle's law**, expressed mathematically as:

$$P_1V_1 = P_2V_2 \text{ or } P = 1/V$$

Stated simply, this means that pressure and volume are inversely proportional: As the volume of a container increases, the pressure decreases, and as the volume of a container decreases, the pressure increases.

The changes in volume during the phases of ventilation are driven by the inspiratory muscles. The main inspiratory muscle is the **diaphragm,** and it is assisted by the **external intercostal muscles**. During forced inspiration, several other muscles, termed *accessory muscles of inspiration*, assist the diaphragm and external intercostals. When the inspiratory muscles contract, they increase both the height and the diameter of the thoracic cavity, which increases its volume. Recall that the lungs are attached to the thoracic cavity directly by the pleural membranes. Therefore, the lungs increase in volume when the thoracic cavity increases in volume. As the lungs' volume increases, the pressure within them, called the **intrapulmonary pressure**, decreases. When intrapulmonary pressure is lower than the **atmospheric pressure**, inspiration occurs, and air rushes into the lungs. Because the intrapulmonary pressure must be *lower* than the atmospheric pressure for inspiration to occur, it sometimes is referred to as *negative pressure*.

Expiration is achieved primarily by the elastic recoil of the lungs. As the inspiratory muscles relax, the lungs' elastic tissue causes them to recoil to their original, smaller size. This decreases the volume of the lungs and increases the intrapulmonary pressure. When the intrapulmonary pressure is higher than the atmospheric pressure, expiration occurs, and air exits the lungs. In the event of forced expiration, several accessory muscles of expiration, including the internal intercostals, will decrease the height and diameter of the thoracic cavity.

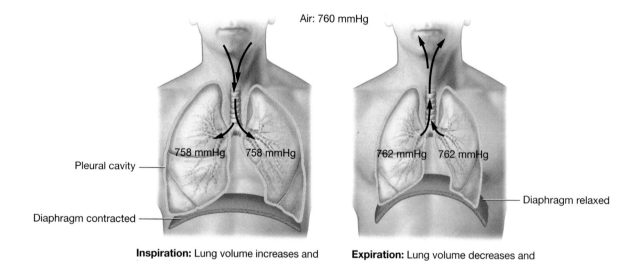

Inspiration: Lung volume increases and intrapulmonary pressure decreases.

Expiration: Lung volume decreases and intrapulmonary pressure increases.

FIGURE **13.6** Pressure-volume relationships in the lungs during inspiration and expiration

13

Procedure 1 Model Ventilation with the Bell-Jar Model

In this procedure we will use a bell-jar model of the lungs, shown in Figure 13.7, to view the effects of pressure and volume on ventilation. The bell-jar model has two balloons, each representing one lung, and a flexible membrane on the bottom that represents the diaphragm.

1 Apply upward pressure to the diaphragm. This represents how the diaphragm looks when it is relaxed. What has happened to the pressure of the system (has it increased or decreased)? What happened to the volume of the lungs?

_____

_____

_____

2 Now slowly release the diaphragm. This represents the diaphragm flattening out as it contracts. What is happening to the pressure as you release the diaphragm? What happened to the volume of the lungs?

_____

_____

_____

_____

FIGURE **13.7** Bell-jar model of the lungs, simulated inspiration

3 If your bell-jar model has a rubber stopper in the top, you can use it to demonstrate the effects of a **pneumothorax** (noo-muh-THOHR-ax) on lung tissue. A pneumothorax generally is caused by a tear in the pleural membranes that allows air to enter the pleural cavity. With the diaphragm flat and the lungs (balloons) inflated, loosen the rubber stopper. What happens to the lungs? Why?

_____

_____

_____

_____

_____

13

Procedure 2 Lung Inflation

Now let's see what the lungs look like as they inflate and deflate during inspiration and expiration. In this procedure, you will use fresh lungs from a sheep, a pig, or a cow and inflate them with an air hose. As you perform the procedure, note the difference in the textures and appearances of the lungs as they inflate and deflate.

1 Obtain a fresh specimen and a large air hose.

2 Examine the specimen for structures covered in Exercise 13-1 (p. 341), in particular the epiglottis and vocal folds, the trachea and its hyaline cartilage rings, and the pleural membranes.

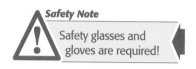

Safety Note

Safety glasses and gloves are required!

3 Squeeze the deflated lungs between your fingertips, and record their texture below. Deflated lungs are shown in Figure 13.8A.

_____

_____

_____

4 Insert the air hose into the larynx, and feed it down into the trachea. Take care not to get the hose stuck in one of the primary bronchi.

5 Attach the hose to the air outlet, and turn it on slowly. You may have to squeeze the trachea and the hose to prevent air leakage.

6 Observe the lungs as they inflate, shown in Figure 13.8B. You may inflate the lungs quite fully. Don't worry—they're very unlikely to pop.

7 Squeeze the inflated lungs between your fingers, and note their texture:

_____

_____

8 Crimp the air hose, and watch the lungs deflate. Again feel the lungs, and note changes in texture:

_____

_____

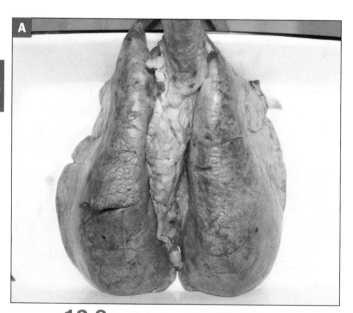
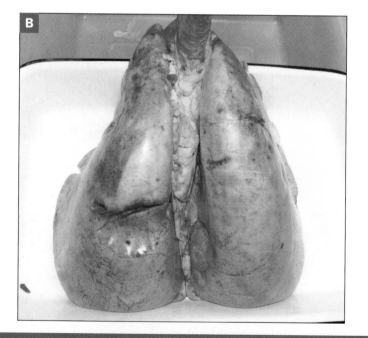

FIGURE **13.8** Fresh lungs: **(A)** deflated; **(B)** inflated

Exercise 13-3

Measuring Pulmonary Volumes and Capacities

MATERIALS

❑ Wet or handheld spirometer

❑ Disposable mouthpiece

Respiratory volumes are the volumes of air exchanged with each breath. These volumes of air are measured with an instrument called a **spirometer** (spy-RAH-met-ur) and include the following (Figure 13.9):

1. **Tidal volume (TV).** The tidal volume, or TV, is the amount of air exchanged with each breath during normal, quiet breathing. It measures about 500 ml in a healthy adult.

2. **Expiratory reserve volume (ERV).** The expiratory reserve volume, or the ERV, is the volume of air that may be expired after a tidal expiration. It averages between 700 and 1,200 ml of air.

3. **Inspiratory reserve volume (IRV).** The inspiratory reserve volume, or the IRV, is the amount of air that may be inspired after a tidal inspiration. It averages between 1,900 and 3,100 ml of air.

Note that there is also a fourth volume, called the **residual volume (RV)**, that cannot be measured with a spirometer. It is defined as the amount of air that remains in the lungs after maximal expiration and is generally equal to about 1,100–1,200 ml of air. This amount of air accounts for the difference between the IRV and the ERV.

Two or more respiratory volumes may be combined to give **respiratory capacities.** As you can see in Figure 13.9, there are four respiratory capacities:

1. **Inspiratory capacity (IC).** The inspiratory capacity, or IC, is equal to the TV plus the IRV and is the amount of air a person can maximally inspire after a tidal expiration. It averages between 2,400 and 3,600 ml of air.

2. **Functional residual capacity (FRC).** The functional residual capacity, or the FRC, is the amount of air normally left in the lungs after a tidal expiration. It is the sum of the ERV and the RV and averages between 1,800 and 2,400 ml of air. It is not measurable with general spirometry.

3. **Vital capacity (VC).** The vital capacity, or VC, represents the total amount of exchangeable air that moves in and out of the lungs. It is equal to the sum of the TV, IRV, and ERV and averages between 3,100 and 4,800 ml of air.

4. **Total lung capacity (TLC).** The total lung capacity, or TLC, represents the total amount of exchangeable and nonexchangeable air in the lungs. It is the total of all four respiratory volumes and is not measurable with general spirometry. It averages between 4,200 and 6,000 ml of air.

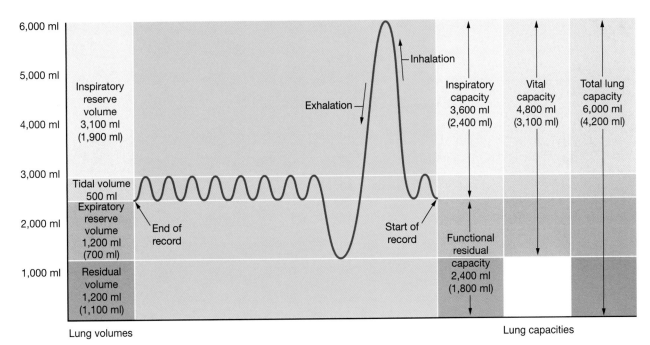

FIGURE **13.9** Respiratory volumes and capacities (note that the top value in the figure is the average value for males, and the value in parentheses is the average value for females)

Spirometry is a useful tool with which to assess pulmonary function. The respiratory volumes and capacities are especially helpful in differentiating the two primary types of respiratory disorders—**restrictive diseases** and **obstructive diseases**. Restrictive diseases, such as pulmonary fibrosis, are characterized by a loss of elasticity (decreased compliance) of the lung tissue. As a result, patients' ability to inspire is affected adversely. This decreases the IRV, IC, VC, and TLC.

Obstructive diseases, such as chronic obstructive pulmonary disease (COPD) and asthma, are characterized by increased airway resistance caused by narrowing of the bronchioles, increased mucus secretion, and/or an obstructing body, such as a tumor. It may seem counterintuitive, but obstructive diseases make expiration difficult. This is because the increased intrapulmonary pressure during expiration naturally tends to shrink the diameter of the bronchioles. When the bronchioles are already narrowed, as in an obstructive disease, the increased intrapulmonary pressure can actually collapse the bronchioles and trap oxygen-poor air in the distal respiratory passages. Therefore, patients with obstructive diseases often exhale slowly and through pursed lips to minimize the pressure changes and maximize the amount of air exhaled. This decreases the ERV and VC and increases the RV and FRC.

 ## Procedure 1 Measuring Respiratory Volumes with a Wet Spirometer

Three types of spirometers are commonly found in anatomy and physiology labs:

1. a bell, or "wet" spirometer,

2. a computerized spirometer, and

3. a handheld spirometer (shown in Figure 13.10).

Many types of wet and handheld spirometers allow you to assess only expiratory volumes, whereas computerized spirometers typically allow you to assess both inspiratory and expiratory volumes. All types of devices allow measurement of one or more respiratory capacities.

The following procedure is intended for a wet or handheld spirometer. If your lab has a computerized spirometer, however, you can either follow the procedure below or follow the prompts by the computer program.

Safety Note

> ⚠ You should not be the subject of this experiment if you have cardiovascular or pulmonary disease or are prone to dizziness or fainting.

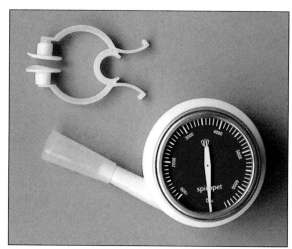

FIGURE **13.10** Handheld spirometer

1 Obtain a disposable mouthpiece, and attach it to the end of the tube.

2 Before you begin, practice exhaling through the tube several times. Note that you are supposed to only *exhale* into the tube, because it likely has no filter.

3 *Measure the tidal volume*: Sit in a chair with your back straight and your eyes closed. Inhale a normal tidal inspiration, and exhale this breath through the tube. Getting a true representation of the tidal volume is often difficult, because people have a tendency to force the expiration. To get the most accurate tidal volume, take several measurements and average the numbers.

Measurement 1: _____

Measurement 2: _____

Measurement 3: _____

Average Tidal Volume: _____

Note that some handheld spirometers are not terribly sensitive, so they give a value for the tidal volume that is too low. If you find this is the case, you may need to take extra readings to get an approximately accurate measurement.

4 *Measure the expiratory reserve volume*: Before taking this measurement, inhale and exhale a series of tidal volumes. Then inspire a normal tidal inspiration, breathe out a normal tidal expiration, put the mouthpiece to your mouth, and exhale as forcibly as possible. Don't cheat by taking in a large breath first! As before, perform several measurements, and average the numbers.

Measurement 1: _____

Measurement 2: _____

Measurement 3: _____

Average Expiratory Reserve Volume: _____

5 *Measure the vital capacity*: As before, inhale and exhale a series of tidal volumes. Then bend over, and exhale maximally. Once you have exhaled as much air as you can, raise yourself upright, and inhale as much air as you possibly can (until you feel like you are about to "pop"). Quickly place the mouthpiece to your mouth, and exhale as forcibly and as long as possible. Take several measurements (you may want to give yourself a minute to rest between measurements), and record the data below.

Measurement 1: _____

Measurement 2: _____

Measurement 3: _____

Average Vital Capacity: _____

6 *Calculate the inspiratory reserve volume*: Even though the bell spirometer cannot measure inspiratory volumes, you can calculate this volume now that you have the vital capacity (VC), tidal volume (TV), and expiratory reserve volume (ERV). Recall that VC = TV + IRV = ERV. Rearrange the equation: IRV = VC − (TV + ERV).

Average IRV: _____

7 How do your values compare with the average values? What factors, if any, do you think may have affected your results?

_____

_____

_____

_____

_____

_____

8 Pool the results for your class, and divide the results into four categories: female cigarette smokers, female nonsmokers, male cigarette smokers, and male nonsmokers. Calculate the average TV, ERV, and VC for each group, and record these data in Table 13.3.

13

TABLE **13.3** Respiratory Volumes and Capacities for Smokers and Nonsmokers

Group	Tidal Volume	Expiratory Reserve Volume	Inspiratory Reserve Volume	Vital Capacity
Female smokers				
Female nonsmokers				
Male smokers				
Male nonsmokers				

9 Interpret your results:

a How did the average values differ for males and females?

_____

_____

_____

b How did the average values differ for smokers and nonsmokers?

_____

_____

_____

c What disease pattern would you expect to see with the smokers? Did your results follow this expectation?

_____

_____

_____

13

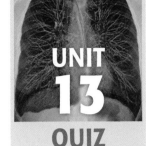
Name _____

Section _____ Date _____

1 Label **Figure 13.11** with the terms below.

- ❏ Epiglottis
- ❏ Laryngopharynx
- ❏ Larynx
- ❏ Left primary bronchus
- ❏ Nasal cavity
- ❏ Nasopharynx
- ❏ Pleural cavity
- ❏ Right primary bronchus
- ❏ Secondary bronchi

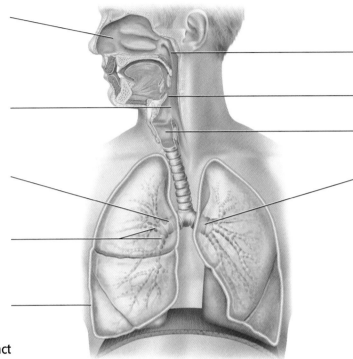

FIGURE **13.11** Lungs and respiratory tract

2 Label **Figure 13.12** with the terms below.

- ❏ Alveolar duct
- ❏ Alveolus
- ❏ Pulmonary arteriole
- ❏ Pulmonary capillaries
- ❏ Pulmonary venule
- ❏ Respiratory bronchiole

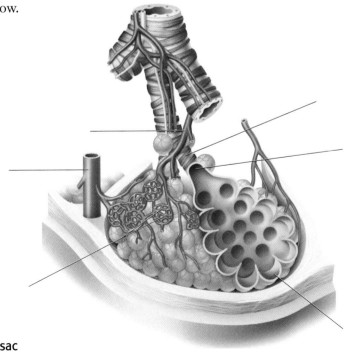

FIGURE **13.12** Bronchiole and alveolar sac

13

3 *Fill in the blanks:* The _____ is the lungs' outer serous membrane, which adheres to the inner wall of the thoracic cavity. At the lungs' root, it folds inward on itself to become the inner membrane called the

_____, which adheres to the lungs' surface. Between the two layers of membrane is the

_____.

4 Number the following structures of the respiratory tract in the proper order. The structure that comes into contact with oxygenated air first should be number 1, and the structures where gas exchange takes place should be number 11.

_____ Oropharynx

_____ Trachea

_____ Nasal cavity

_____ Bronchiole

_____ Alveolar sac

_____ Larynx

_____ Nasopharynx

_____ Bronchi

_____ Terminal bronchiole

_____ Laryngopharynx

_____ Respiratory bronchiole

5 The piece of elastic cartilage that seals off the larynx during swallowing is called the
a. uvula.
b. false vocal cord.
c. true vocal cord.
d. epiglottis.

6 Passages in the respiratory tract smaller than 1 mm in diameter are called
a. bronchi.
b. bronchioles.
c. alveolar ducts.
d. paranasal sinuses.

7 *Fill in the blanks:* According to Boyle's law, as the volume of a container increases, the pressure _____.

Conversely, as the volume of a container decreases, the pressure _____.

8 Air moves into the lungs when
a. intrapulmonary pressure is less than atmospheric pressure.
b. intrapulmonary pressure is more than atmospheric pressure.
c. blood pressure is more than intrapulmonary pressure.
d. blood pressure is less than intrapulmonary pressure.

13

9 Passive expiration is achieved primarily by the

    a. contraction of the diaphragm and external intercostals.

    b. decrease in intrapulmonary pressure.

    c. increase in atmospheric pressure.

    d. elastic recoil of the lungs.

10 Why do you think the hyaline cartilage rings of the trachea are C-shaped rather than O-shaped? (*Hint:* Think about the structure behind the trachea.)

_____

_____

_____

_____

_____

_____

11 Conditions such as pneumonia and lung cancer can result in what is known as a *pleural effusion*, in which the pleural cavity becomes filled with a large amount of fluid. What effects do you think a pleural effusion would have on ventilation? Explain.

_____

_____

_____

_____

_____

_____

12 The condition *emphysema* results in loss of elastic recoil of the lung tissue. Would this make inspiration or expiration difficult? Explain.

_____

_____

_____

_____

_____

_____

_____

13

13 A male patient presents with the following respiratory volumes and capacities: TV = 500 ml, ERV = 1,200 ml, IRV = 1,100 ml. What is this patient's VC? Are these values normal? If not, are they more consistent with an obstructive or restrictive disease pattern? Explain.

_____

_____

_____

_____

_____

_____

_____

_____

13

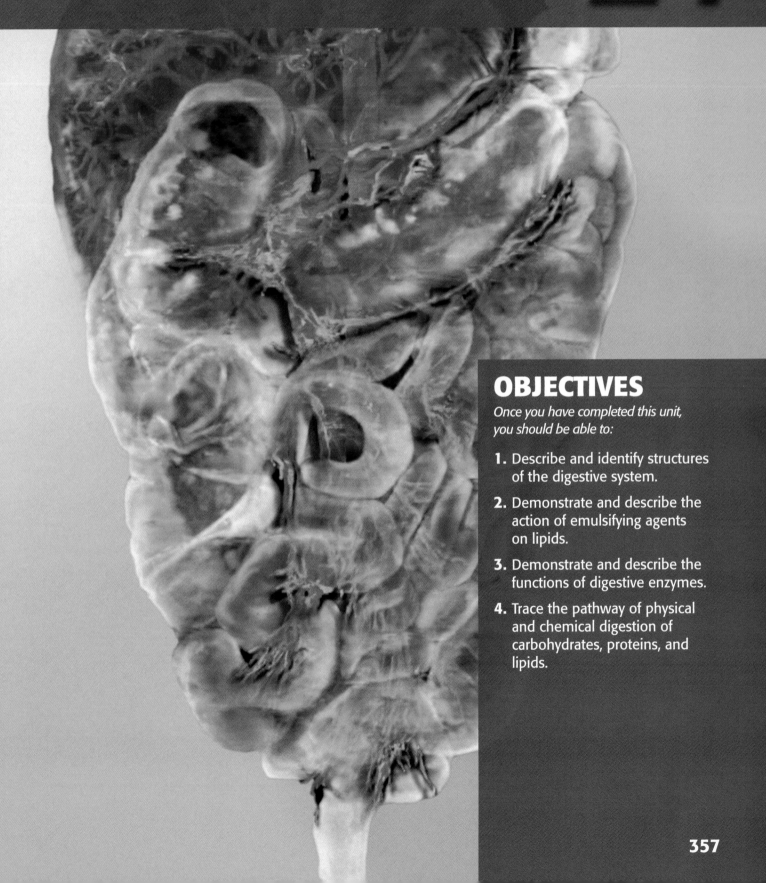

Digestive System

14

OBJECTIVES

Once you have completed this unit, you should be able to:

1. Describe and identify structures of the digestive system.

2. Demonstrate and describe the action of emulsifying agents on lipids.

3. Demonstrate and describe the functions of digestive enzymes.

4. Trace the pathway of physical and chemical digestion of carbohydrates, proteins, and lipids.

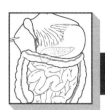

Name _____ Section _____ Date _____

PRE-LAB EXERCISES

Complete the following exercises prior to coming to lab, using your textbook and lab manual for reference.

Pre-Lab Exercise **14-1**

✎ Key Terms

You should be familiar with the following terms before coming to lab. Please note that this list is not all-inclusive, because the terminology for the digestive system is extensive.

Term	Definition

Digestive System Structures

Alimentary canal _____

_____

Accessory organ _____

_____

Peritoneal cavity _____

_____

Esophagus _____

_____

Stomach _____

_____

Small intestine _____

_____

Large intestine _____

_____

Salivary glands _____

_____

Pancreas _____

_____

Liver _____

_____

Gallbladder _____

_____

14

Digestive Physiology

Digestive enzyme _____

_____

Chemical digestion _____

_____

Salivary amylase _____

_____

Emulsification _____

_____

Bile _____

_____

14

Pre-Lab Exercise **14-2**

Anatomy of the Digestive System

Label and color the structures of the digestive system depicted in Figures 14.1 and 14.2 with the following terms from Exercise 14-1. Use your text and Exercise 14-1 in this unit for reference.

❏ Esophagus
❏ Stomach
❏ Small intestine

Salivary Glands
   ❏ Parotid gland
   ❏ Submandibular gland
   ❏ Sublingual gland

Pharynx
   ❏ Oropharynx
   ❏ Laryngopharynx

Large Intestine
   ❏ Cecum
   ❏ Vermiform appendix
   ❏ Ascending colon
   ❏ Transverse colon
   ❏ Descending colon
   ❏ Sigmoid colon
   ❏ Rectum
   ❏ Anal canal

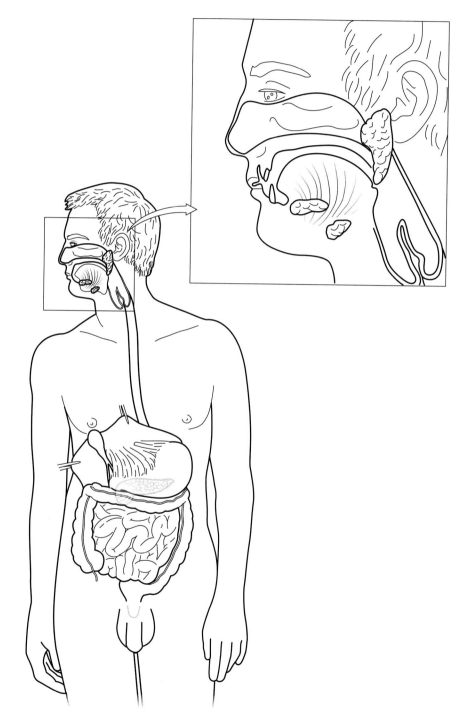

FIGURE **14.1** Organs of the digestive system

❏ Pancreas
  ❏ Pancreatic duct
❏ Liver
  ❏ Common hepatic duct
❏ Gallbladder
  ❏ Cystic duct
  ❏ Common bile duct
❏ Duodenum

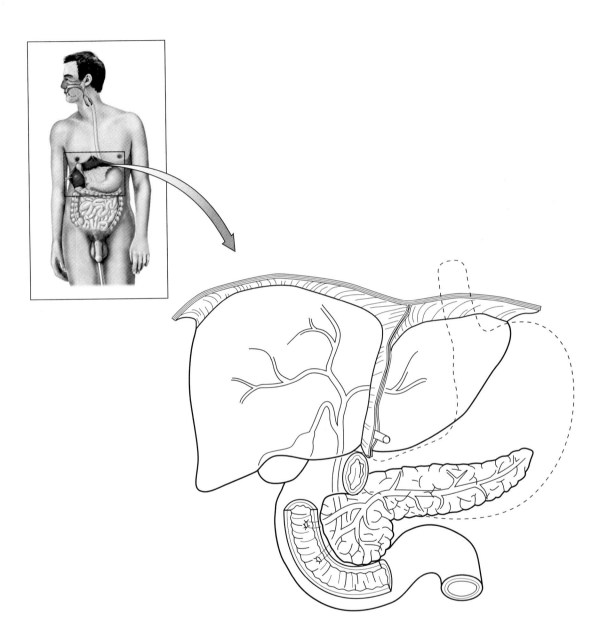

FIGURE **14.2** Liver, gallbladder, pancreas, and duodenum

14

EXERCISES

The food we eat contains nutrients our cells use to build and repair body tissues and to make ATP. Food macromolecules, however, are typically too large for the body to absorb and use, so they must be broken down into smaller molecules. This process of breaking down foods into smaller substances that can enter cells is called **digestion** and is carried out by the **digestive system**. In general, the functions of the digestive system include taking in food, breaking down food mechanically and chemically into nutrients, absorbing these nutrients into the bloodstream, and eliminating indigestible substances.

We begin this unit with an introduction to the anatomy of the organs of the digestive system. Next we examine the physiological processes of chemical digestion and emulsification. We conclude with a "big picture" view of digestion through a tracing exercise.

Exercise **14-1**

Digestive System Anatomy

> **MATERIALS**
> ❑ Digestive system models
> ❑ Head and neck models
> ❑ Human torso models
> ❑ Human skulls with teeth
> ❑ Digestive organ models (stomach, pancreas, liver, and duodenum)

The digestive system is composed of two types of organs: (1) the organs of the **alimentary canal**, also known as the **gastrointestinal (GI) tract**, through which food travels, and (2) the **accessory organs**, which assist in mechanical or chemical digestion. The alimentary canal consists of the following organs (Figure 14.3):

1. **Mouth.** The alimentary canal begins with the mouth. In and around the mouth we find numerous accessory organs, including the **teeth**, the **tongue**, and the **salivary glands**. These accessory organs help the mouth carry out mechanical digestion and chemical digestion.

FIGURE **14.3**
Digestive system:
(A) alimentary canal and accessory organs;
(B) dissected abdominopelvic cavity

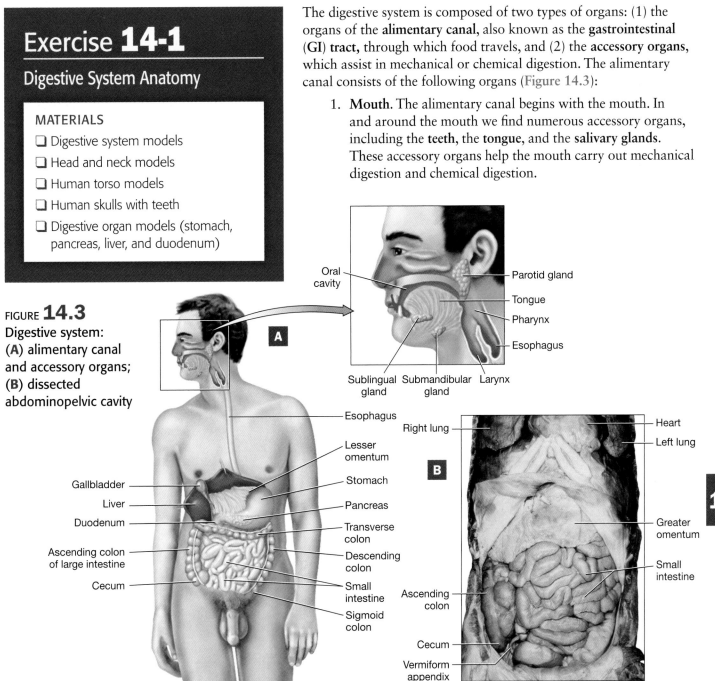

14

2. **Pharynx.** The food next enters the pharynx (FAIR-inx), also known as the throat. The muscles surrounding the pharynx propel swallowed food into the next portion of the alimentary canal.

3. **Esophagus.** The esophagus (e-SAH-fuh-gus) is a narrow tube posterior to the heart and the trachea in the thoracic cavity. The esophagus contains both smooth and skeletal muscle fibers that undergo rhythmic contractions called **peristalsis** (pair-ih-STAHL-sis) that propel food into the stomach. A sphincter at the inferior end of the esophagus called the **gastroesophageal** (gas-troh-e-sah-fuh-GEE-ul) **sphincter** prevents the contents of the stomach from regurgitating into the esophagus.

4. **Stomach.** The stomach, shown in Figure 14.4, has the following regions:
   a. the dome-shaped **fundus,**
   b. the **cardia,** near the gastroesophageal sphincter,
   c. the middle **body,** and
   d. the **pylorus** (py-LOHR-us). A sphincter called the **pyloric sphincter** separates the stomach from the initial portion of the small intestine.

   Note in Figure 14.4 that the stomach has interior folds called **rugae** (ROO-gee) that allow it to expand considerably when filled with food.

5. **Small intestine.** The small intestine is the portion of the alimentary canal where most chemical digestion and absorption take place. It has three portions:
   a. the initial **duodenum** (doo-AH-den-um),
   b. the middle **jejunum** (je-JOO-num), and
   c. the terminal **ileum** (IL-ee-um).

   Of the three divisions, the duodenum is the shortest, measuring only about 10 inches. The jejunum and the ileum measure about 8 feet and 12 feet long, respectively.

6. **Large intestine.** The large intestine is named for its large diameter rather than its length, which only measures about 5.5 feet. The large intestine may be divided into five regions:
   a. the **cecum** (SEE-kum; Figure 14.5), the pouch that receives contents from the ileum, from which it is separated by the **ileocecal** (il-ee-oh-SEE-kul) **valve,**
   b. the **vermiform appendix,** also visible in Figure 14.5, a blind-ended sac that extends from the cecum and contains lymphatic nodules,
   c. the **colon,** which itself has four divisions (the *ascending, transverse, descending,* and *sigmoid colon*),
   d. the **rectum,** the straight part of the large intestine, which runs along the sacrum, and
   e. the **anal canal,** the terminal portion of the large intestine with two sphincters—the involuntary **internal anal sphincter** and the voluntary **external anal sphincter.**

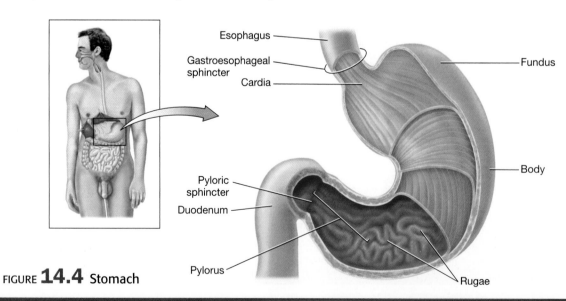

FIGURE **14.4** Stomach

The accessory digestive organs generally do not come into direct contact with ingested food (the teeth and tongue are exceptions). Most of them instead secrete substances such as bile salts and enzymes that travel through a duct to the alimentary canal. The accessory digestive organs are the following:

1. **Teeth and tongue.** The teeth and the tongue are accessory organs located in the mouth that assist in mechanical digestion of ingested food. The tongue contains keratinized papillae called **filiform papillae** that provide a rough surface, which helps to break down food physically. Note that filiform papillae do not contain taste buds, which are located only on circumvallate, foliate, and fungiform papillae.

2. **Salivary glands.** The three types of salivary glands are located around the mouth, and their secretions pass through a duct into the mouth.

    a. The largest salivary glands are the paired **parotid** (pair-AH-tid) **glands,** superficial to the masseter muscle.

    b. The smaller **submandibular glands** are located anterior and inferior to the parotid glands.

    c. The **sublingual** (sub-LING-wul) **gland** is located under the tongue, as its name implies.

    All three types of glands secrete saliva, which contains water, mucus, an enzyme called *salivary amylase,* and antimicrobial molecules, such as *lysozyme.*

3. **Liver and gallbladder.** The liver and gallbladder are organs located on the right side of the abdominal cavity (Figure 14.6).

    a. The liver consists of four lobes—the large *right* and *left lobes* and the small, posterior *caudate* and *quadrate lobes* (not visible in Figure 14.6). The liver has a multitude of functions in the body, most of which are metabolic in nature. For example, recall from Unit 11 that all blood from the digestive organs and the spleen travels via the hepatic portal vein to the hepatic portal system of the liver. There, the absorbed nutrients and

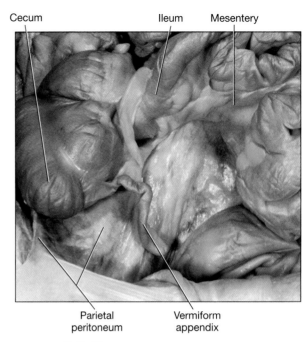

FIGURE **14.5** Cecum and vermiform appendix

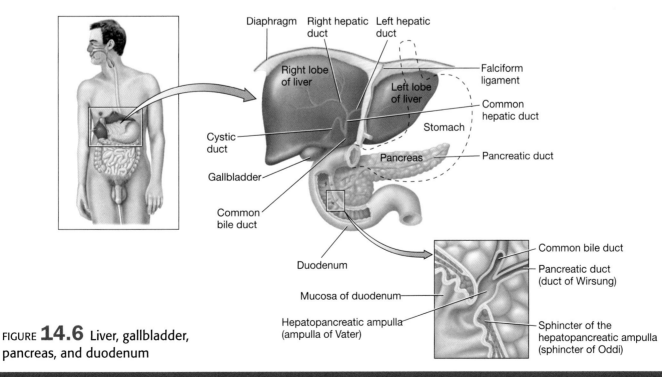

FIGURE **14.6** Liver, gallbladder, pancreas, and duodenum

14

chemicals are processed before they enter the general circulation. One of the liver's main digestive functions is to produce a chemical called *bile* required for the digestion and absorption of fats.

b. Bile leaves the liver via a duct called the **common hepatic duct,** after which much of it enters the gallbladder on the posterior side of the liver for storage. When stimulated by certain hormones, the gallbladder contracts, and the bile contained within it is ejected through the **cystic (SIS-tik) duct.** Note in Figure 14.6 that the cystic duct joins with the common hepatic duct to form the **common bile duct,** which empties into the duodenum at the **hepatopancreatic ampulla (hep-at-oh-pank-ree-A-tik am-PYOO-luh).**

4. **Pancreas.** The **pancreas (PAYN-kree-us)** is an exocrine and endocrine gland that sits posterior and inferior to the stomach. Its exocrine functions are digestive, whereas its endocrine functions are metabolic. The exocrine portion of the pancreas produces a fluid called **pancreatic juice** that contains water, bicarbonate to neutralize the acid produced by the stomach, and multiple digestive enzymes. Pancreatic juice is released through the **pancreatic duct** and enters the duodenum at the hepatopancreatic ampulla.

Much of the alimentary canal and many of the accessory organs reside inside a cavity known as the **peritoneal (pair-ih-toh-NEE-ul; Figure 14.7) cavity.** Like the pleural and pericardial cavities, the peritoneal cavity is found between a double-layered serous membrane that secretes serous fluid, which allows the organs to slide over one another and expand and contract without friction. The two peritoneal layers include the:

1. **Parietal peritoneum.** The outer parietal peritoneum is a thin membrane functionally fused to the abdominal wall and certain organs.

2. **Visceral peritoneum.** The inner visceral peritoneum adheres to the surface of many digestive organs. The visceral peritoneum around the intestines folds over on itself to form a thick membrane known as the **mesentery (MES-en-tair-ee;** Figure 14.8). The mesentery houses blood vessels, nerves, and lymphatic vessels and anchors these structures and the intestines in place. Some mesenteries have specific names, including the **greater omentum (oh-MEN-tum),** which covers the abdominal organs like an apron. The smaller lesser omentum runs from the liver to the medial surface of the stomach.

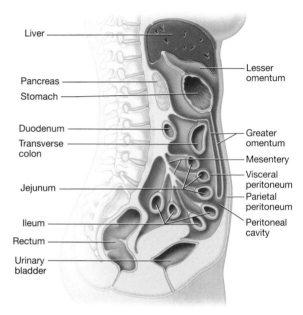

FIGURE **14.7** Peritoneal membranes and cavity

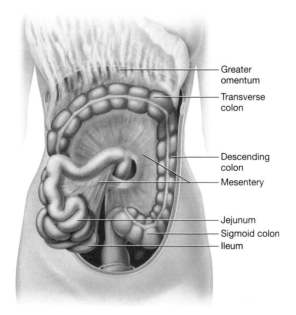

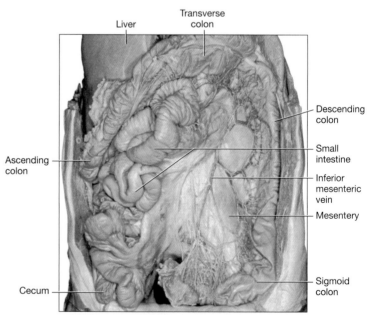

FIGURE **14.8** Mesentery and greater omentum

14

Procedure 1 Model Inventory for the Digestive System

Identify the following structures of the digestive system on models and diagrams, using your textbook and this unit for reference. As you examine the anatomical models and diagrams, record the name of the model and the structures you were able to identify on the model inventory in Table 14.1.

Alimentary Canal

1. Mouth
   a. Oral cavity
   b. Hard palate
   c. Soft palate
   d. Uvula
2. Pharynx
   a. Oropharynx
   b. Laryngopharynx
3. Esophagus
   a. Gastroesophageal sphincter
4. Stomach
   a. Cardia
   b. Fundus
   c. Body
   d. Pylorus
   e. Pyloric sphincter
   f. Rugae
5. Small intestine
   a. Duodenum
      (1) Hepatopancreatic ampulla
   b. Jejunum
   c. Ileum
   d. Ileocecal valve
6. Large intestine
   a. Cecum
   b. Vermiform appendix
   c. Ascending colon
   d. Transverse colon
   e. Descending colon
   f. Sigmoid colon
   g. Rectum
   h. Anal canal

Accessory Organs

1. Teeth
2. Tongue
3. Salivary glands
   a. Parotid gland
   b. Submandibular gland
   c. Sublingual gland
4. Pancreas
   a. Pancreatic duct
5. Liver
   a. Right lobe, left lobe, caudate lobe, and quadrate lobe
   b. Common hepatic duct
6. Gallbladder
   a. Cystic duct
   b. Common bile duct

Other Structures

1. Peritoneal cavity
2. Peritoneum
   a. Visceral peritoneum
   b. Parietal peritoneum
   c. Mesentery
3. Greater omentum

Your instructor may wish to omit certain structures or add structures not included in these lists. List any additional structures below:

_____

_____

_____

_____

14

TABLE **14.1** Model Inventory for the Digestive System

Model	Digestive Structures Identified

Exercise 14-2

Digestion

MATERIALS

- ❏ Graduated cylinders
- ❏ Starch solution
- ❏ Amylase enzyme
- ❏ Distilled water
- ❏ Water bath set to 37°C
- ❏ Glass stirring rod
- ❏ Lugol's iodine solution
- ❏ Benedict's reagent
- ❏ Test-tube rack
- ❏ Vegetable oil
- ❏ Rubber stopper
- ❏ Sudan red stain
- ❏ Liquid detergent
- ❏ Laminated outline of the human body
- ❏ Water-soluble marking pens

We now turn our attention to the physiology of food breakdown and absorption. Three major types of nutrients are broken down and absorbed in the alimentary canal: *carbohydrates*, *proteins*, and *lipids*. Carbohydrate digestion begins in the mouth with the enzyme **salivary amylase** (AM-uh-layz), which catalyzes the reactions that digest polysaccharides into smaller oligosaccharides. The remaining polysaccharides and oligosaccharides are digested in the small intestine with the help of many enzymes, including pancreatic amylase and enzymes associated with enterocytes, the cells of the small intestine.

Protein digestion begins in the stomach with the enzyme **pepsin**, secreted from chief cells in the gastric glands as the inactive pre-enzyme **pepsinogen**. Pepsinogen becomes the active enzyme pepsin when it encounters the hydrochloric acid secreted by cells of the stomach. Pepsin begins digesting proteins into polypeptides and some free amino acids. The remainder of protein digestion occurs in the small intestine with pancreatic enzymes and enzymes produced by enterocytes.

Lipid digestion does not begin until the lipids reach the small intestine. It is more complicated than protein or carbohydrate digestion because lipids are nonpolar molecules that do not dissolve in the water-based environment of the small intestine. This causes the lipids to clump together and form large fat "globules" in the small intestine. In this form, it is nearly impossible for the enzyme **pancreatic lipase** (LY-payz) to catalyze the breakdown of lipids into monoglycerides and free fatty acids because it has only a small surface area on which to work. Therefore, the first step in lipid digestion is to break up this large fat globule into smaller pieces, a process called **emulsification** (ee-mul-sih-fih-KAY-shun; Figure 14.9).

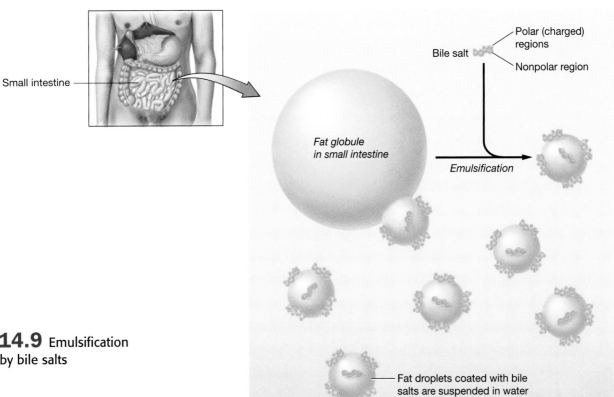

Small intestine

Bile salt

Polar (charged) regions

Nonpolar region

Fat globule in small intestine

Emulsification

Fat droplets coated with bile salts are suspended in water

FIGURE **14.9** Emulsification of fats by bile salts

14

Emulsification is accomplished by chemicals called **bile salts**, produced by the liver and stored in the gallbladder. Bile salts are molecules that have both nonpolar and polar parts. Notice in Figure 14.9 what happens to the fat globule when bile salts come into contact with it: The bile salts' nonpolar parts interact with the lipids, but their polar parts repel other lipids. The overall effect is that the fat globule is physically broken down into smaller fat pieces. This gives pancreatic lipase much more surface area on which to work, and the fats are digested into monoglycerides and free fatty acids.

After chemical digestion is complete, all three nutrients are absorbed through the plasma membranes of the enterocytes lining the small intestine. Both monosaccharides and amino acids are absorbed into the enterocytes via facilitated diffusion or secondary active transport mechanisms. These nutrients then exit the other side of the enterocytes and enter the capillaries in the small intestine.

Lipid absorption, like lipid digestion, is more complicated because lipids are nonpolar and cannot be transported as free fatty acids through the water-filled plasma of the blood. In the small intestinal lumen, digested lipids remain associated with bile salts to form clusters of lipids and other nonpolar chemicals called **micelles** (my-SELZ). Micelles escort the lipids to the enterocytes' plasma membranes; they are able to do so because of their polar outer surface. The lipids then leave the micelles and enter the enterocytes by simple diffusion. Note that in the absence of bile salts, nearly all of the lipids will simply pass through the small intestine unabsorbed and be excreted in the feces.

In the enterocytes, lipids associate with other nonpolar substances and proteins to form protein-coated droplets called **chylomicrons** (ky-loh-MY-krahnz). Chylomicrons exit the enterocytes by exocytosis, but they are too large to enter the blood capillaries. Instead, they enter a lymphatic vessel called a *lacteal* and join the lymph in the lymphatic system. The chylomicrons travel within the lymphatic vessels until they enter the blood at the junction of the left subclavian vein and the left internal jugular vein.

Procedure 1 Test Carbohydrate Digestion

In the following procedure you will test for carbohydrate digestion using a starch solution and the enzyme amylase. You will check for digestion using two reagents: Lugol's iodine, which turns dark blue in the presence of starch, and Benedict's reagent, which forms a precipitate (solid) in the presence of simple sugars. You may interpret the results of your tests as follows:

▪ If the solution turns dark blue with Lugol's iodine, *no* or limited carbohydrate digestion occurred because starch is still present.

▪ If the solution develops a greenish-brownish red precipitate with Benedict's reagent, monosaccharides are present, and carbohydrate digestion *did* occur.

1 Obtain six glass test tubes, and number them 1 through 6.

2 Place 3 ml of starch solution into tube 1 and tube 2.

3 Add 3 ml of amylase to tube 1.

4 Add 3 ml of distilled water to tube 2.

5 Set tubes 1 and 2 into a 37°C water bath, and leave them in there for 30 minutes.

6 Remove the tubes from the water bath, and mix the contents of each tube thoroughly with stirring rods (be certain to use two separate rods so you don't contaminate the contents of the tubes).

7 Divide the mixture in tube 1 equally into tubes 3 and 4 (each tube should contain about 3 ml of the mixture).

8 Divide the mixture in tube 2 equally into tubes 5 and 6 (each tube should contain about 3 ml of the mixture).

9 Add two drops of Lugol's iodine solution to tube 3 and tube 5. Record the results in Table 14.2.

10 Add 10 drops of Benedict's reagent to tube 4 and tube 6. Swirl the tubes gently to mix the contents.

11 Place tubes 4 and 6 into a boiling water bath for three minutes. *Use caution* to prevent the mixture from splattering and burning you or your classmates.

12 Remove the tubes from the boiling water, and record the results of the test in Table 14.2.

Safety Note

Safety glasses and gloves are required!

14

TABLE **14.2** Results of Carbohydrate Digestion Experiment

Tube	Reaction with Lugol's Iodine
Tube 3 (starch + amylase)	
Tube 5 (starch + water)	

Tube	Reaction with Benedict's Reagent
Tube 4 (starch + amylase)	
Tube 6 (starch + water)	

13 Interpret your results:

a In which tube(s) did carbohydrate digestion occur? How do you know?

_____

_____

_____

_____

b In which tube(s) did no carbohydrate digestion occur? How do you know?

_____

_____

_____

_____

c What conclusions can we draw?

_____

_____

_____

_____

14

Procedure 2 Demonstrate Lipid Emulsification

Let's now examine what happens during the process of emulsification. In this procedure you will use four compounds to observe emulsification in action:

▮ *Lipids*: The source of lipids for this procedure is vegetable oil.

▮ *Emulsifying agent*: Detergents are considered emulsifiers because they have both polar parts and nonpolar parts, similar to bile salts. The emulsifying agent in this procedure, therefore, will be a liquid detergent.

▮ *Distilled water*.

▮ *Sudan red stain*: This is a stain that binds only to lipids. The sole purpose of this stain is to make the lipids more visible during the procedure.

1 Obtain a glass test tube, and add approximately 2 ml of distilled water to it.

2 Add about 2 ml of vegetable oil to the water.

3 Place a rubber stopper into the tube, and shake it vigorously for 15 seconds. Allow it to stand for two minutes. What happens to the oil and water?

Safety Note

Safety glasses and gloves are required!

_____

_____

_____

4 Add three or four drops of Sudan red stain, and shake the tube again for 15 seconds. What color is the oil? What color is the water?

_____

_____

5 Add about 1 ml of liquid detergent to the mixture, and shake the tube vigorously for 15 seconds. Allow the tube to stand for two minutes. What has happened to the solution? Is it still two distinct colors? Explain your results.

_____

_____

_____

_____

_____

_____

_____

14

Procedure 3 Time to Trace!

Now it's time to put all of the digestive anatomy and physiology together to get a "big picture" view of the digestive system. In this procedure you will trace the pathways of three different nutrients from their ingestion at the mouth to their arrival in the blood or lymph. You will trace a cookie (primarily carbohydrates), an egg (primarily protein), and greasy fried food (primarily lipids).

Along the way, detail the following for each:

1. The *anatomical pathway* each takes from ingestion through its passage through the alimentary canal to its absorption into the blood or lymph.

2. The *physical* and *chemical processes* that break down each substance, including enzymatic breakdown, churning, chewing, and emulsification.

Some hints:

▍ Remember that digestion and absorption are quite different for lipids. For example, fats are not absorbed into the same structures as proteins and carbohydrates.

▍ Use the text in this exercise for reference about the enzymes involved in the chemical digestion of each nutrient.

Tracing Steps

1 Cookie: Start: mouth → _____

_____

_____

_____

_____

_____

_____

_____

_____

_____

_____ blood End

2 **Egg:** Start: mouth → _____

_____

_____

_____

_____

_____

_____

_____

_____ blood **End**

3 **Greasy fried food:** Start: mouth → _____

_____

_____

_____

_____

_____

_____

_____

_____

_____ lymph **End**

14

1 Label the following structures on Figure 14.10.

- ❏ Cecum
- ❏ Esophagus
- ❏ Gallbladder
- ❏ Liver
- ❏ Parotid gland
- ❏ Sigmoid colon
- ❏ Sublingual gland
- ❏ Transverse colon

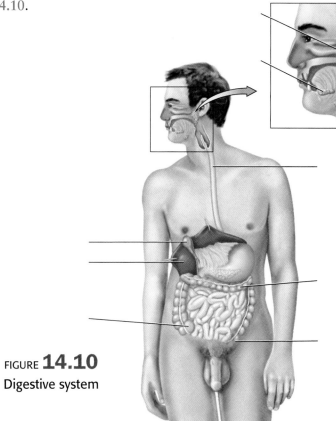

FIGURE **14.10**
Digestive system

2 Label the following structures on Figure 14.11.

- ❏ Body
- ❏ Cardia
- ❏ Fundus
- ❏ Gastroesophageal sphincter
- ❏ Pyloric sphincter
- ❏ Pylorus
- ❏ Rugae

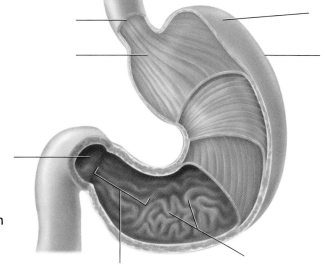

FIGURE **14.11** Stomach

14

3 Label the following structures on Figure 14.12.

- ❏ Common bile duct
- ❏ Common hepatic duct
- ❏ Cystic duct
- ❏ Duodenum
- ❏ Pancreas
- ❏ Pancreatic duct

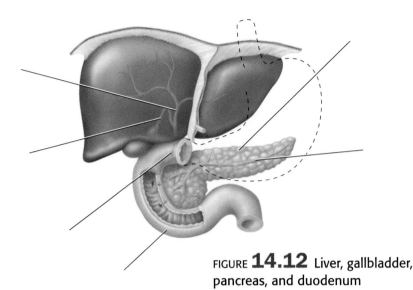

FIGURE **14.12** Liver, gallbladder, pancreas, and duodenum

4 Which of the following organs is *not* part of the alimentary canal?

a. Esophagus

b. Gallbladder

c. Cecum

d. Ileum

5 Which of the following digestive functions is performed by the organs in the alimentary canal, but not by accessory organs?

a. Absorption

b. Mechanical digestion

c. Chemical digestion

d. Ingestion

6 *Mark the following statements as true (T) or false (F). If the statement is false, correct it so it becomes a true statement.*

_____ a. The peritoneal cavity is located between the visceral peritoneum and the mesentery.

_____ b. The longest segment of the small intestine is the duodenum.

_____ c. The stomach has three layers of smooth muscle that contract to churn food into chyme.

_____ d. The gallbladder produces and stores bile.

_____ e. Bile leaves the liver through the cystic duct.

14

7 *Matching:* Match the following with the correct definition.

_____ Salivary amylase

_____ Bile salts

_____ Micelles

_____ Pancreatic lipase

_____ Hydrochloric acid

_____ Pepsin

A. Clusters of bile salts and digested lipids

B. Enzyme(s) that digest(s) lipids into free fatty acids and monoglycerides

C. Chemical required to activate pepsinogen

D. Protein-digesting enzyme(s) produced by the stomach

E. Emulsifies/emulsify fats

F. Begin(s) carbohydrate digestion in the mouth

8 How does the absorption of lipids differ from the absorption of carbohydrates and proteins?

a. Lipids are absorbed into capillaries; carbohydrates and proteins are absorbed into lacteals.

b. Lipids are absorbed by bile salts; carbohydrates and proteins are absorbed by micelles.

c. Lipids, carbohydrates, and proteins are absorbed the same way.

d. Lipids are absorbed into lacteals; carbohydrates and proteins are absorbed into capillaries.

9 Would removal of the gallbladder affect the production of bile? Why or why not?

_____

_____

_____

_____

_____

_____

10 The condition known as heartburn is most often caused by acid regurgitating from the stomach into the esophagus. Some of the drugs that treat heartburn work by decreasing the secretion of acid by the cells of the stomach. Could this affect the chemical digestion of certain nutrients? Explain.

_____

_____

_____

_____

_____

_____

14

11 Many dietary supplements contain digestive enzymes the manufacturers claim are necessary to digest food properly. What will happen to these enzymes in the stomach? (*Hint:* Enzymes are proteins.) Will the enzymes continue to function once they have reached the small intestine? Why or why not?

_____

_____

_____

_____

_____

_____

_____

12 One of the common consequences of gallstones is blockage of the common bile duct, which prevents bile from being emptied into the duodenum. Predict the possible consequences of this condition. (*Hint:* Think about the functions of bile and what would happen if bile were absent.)

_____

_____

_____

_____

_____

_____

_____

14

Urinary System

15

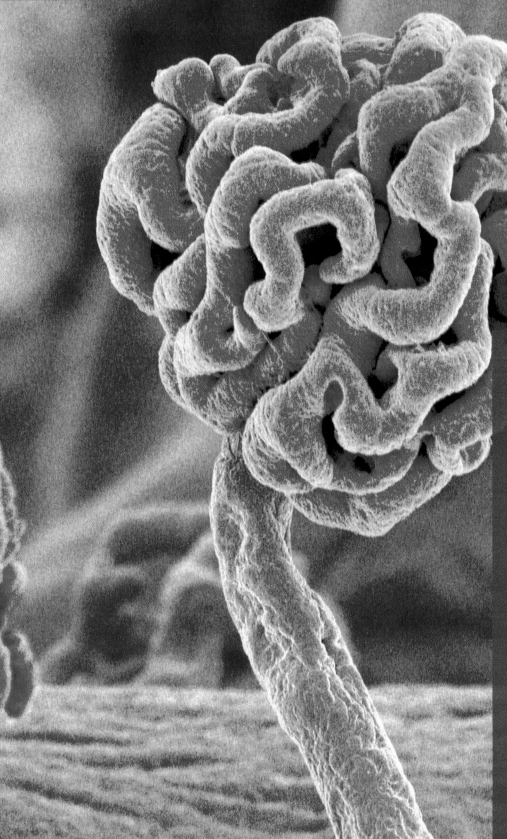

OBJECTIVES

Once you have completed this unit, you should be able to:

1. Describe and identify gross and microscopic structures of the urinary system.

2. Model the physiology of the kidney, and test for chemicals in the filtrate.

3. Perform and interpret urinalysis on simulated urine specimens.

4. Trace an erythrocyte, a glucose molecule, and a urea molecule through the gross and microscopic anatomy of the kidney.

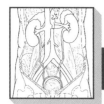
PRE-LAB EXERCISES

Complete the following exercises prior to coming to lab, using your textbook and lab manual for reference.

Pre-Lab Exercise **15-1**

✎ Key Terms

You should be familiar with the following terms before coming to lab.

Term	Definition

Gross Structures of the Kidney

Renal cortex _____

_____

Renal medulla _____

_____

Renal pelvis_____

_____

Major and minor calyces _____

_____

Other Structures of the Urinary System

Ureter _____

_____

Urinary bladder _____

_____

Urethra _____

_____

Blood Vessels and Tubules of the Nephron

Nephron _____

_____

Glomerulus _____

_____

Peritubular capillaries _____

_____

Renal tubule _____

_____

Collecting duct _____

_____

Urinary Physiology Terms

Glomerular filtration _____

_____

Tubular reabsorption _____

_____

Tubular secretion _____

_____

Filtrate _____

_____

Urine _____

_____

Urinalysis _____

_____

Pre-Lab Exercise **15-2**

Structures of the Urinary System

Label and color the structures of the urinary system depicted in Figures 15.1 and 15.2 with the following terms from Exercise 15-1. Use your text and Exercise 15-1 in this unit for reference.

❏ Ureter
❏ Urinary bladder
❏ Urethra

Regions of the Kidney

❏ Renal cortex
❏ Renal medulla
    ❏ Renal columns
    ❏ Renal pyramids
❏ Minor calyces
❏ Major calyces
❏ Renal pelvis

Blood Supply

❏ Renal artery
❏ Renal vein

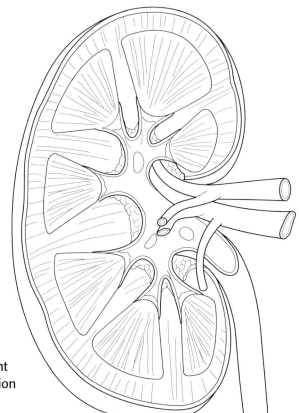

FIGURE **15.1** Right kidney, frontal section

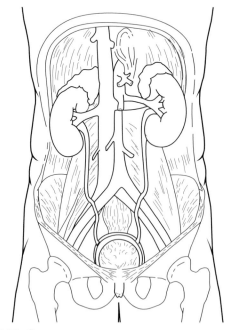

FIGURE **15.2** Organs of the urinary system, anterior view

Pre-Lab Exercise **15-3**

Structures of the Nephron

Label and color the structures of the nephron depicted in Figure 15.3 with the following terms from Exercise 15-1. Use your text and Exercise 15-1 in this unit for reference.

Renal Corpuscle
❑ Glomerulus
  ❑ Afferent arteriole
  ❑ Efferent arteriole
  ❑ Peritubular capillaries

Glomerular Capsule
  ❑ Parietal layer
  ❑ Visceral layer

Renal Tubule
  ❑ Proximal tubule
  ❑ Nephron loop
  ❑ Distal tubule
❑ Collecting duct

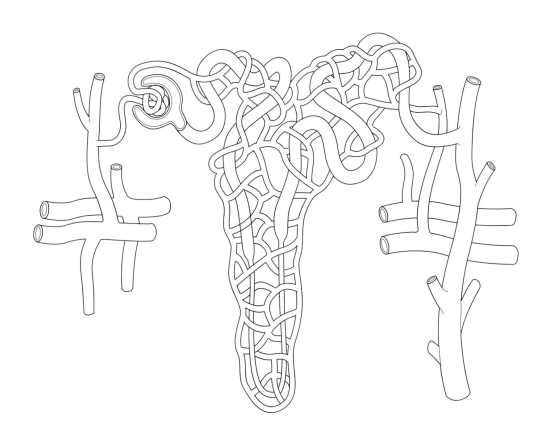

FIGURE **15.3** Nephron

Pre-Lab Exercise 15-4

Glomerular Filtration and Tubular Reabsorption

Table 15.1 lists chemicals and cells found in blood. Do the following for each chemical, using your textbook for reference:

1 Determine whether each listed substance is filtered at the glomerulus (i.e., if it is able to leave the blood and enter the nephron to become part of the filtrate).

2 If the substance is found in the filtrate, determine if the substance is reabsorbed into the blood or if it is found in the urine.

3 If the substance is reabsorbed into the blood, determine where this substance is reabsorbed in the nephron.

TABLE **15.1** Substances Found in the Blood and Their Filtration and Reabsorption by the Nephron

Substance	Filtered in the Glomerulus? (yes/no)	Reabsorbed? (yes/no)	Location Where Reabsorption Takes Place
Cells			
Water			
Glucose			
Proteins			
Urea			
Creatinine			
Electrolytes (sodium, potassium, chloride ions)			
Uric acid			

EXERCISES

The urinary system performs many functions critical to homeostasis, including removing waste products from the blood; regulating the body's fluid, electrolyte, and acid-base balance; and producing the hormone erythropoietin (e-rith-roh-POY-e-tin), which regulates blood cell formation. In addition to these roles, the urinary system helps the liver detoxify certain compounds and makes glucose during times of starvation. These critical functions are carried out primarily by the main organs of the urinary system—the kidneys. The other organs in the urinary system include the ureters, the urinary bladder, and the urethra.

In this unit you will become acquainted with the anatomy and the physiology of the urinary system. You will first examine the gross and microscopic structures of its organs, after which you will construct a model kidney and test samples of simulated urine. In the final exercise you will trace the pathway of substances through the general circulation and the microanatomy of the kidney to contrast the filtration and reabsorption of three substances: erythrocytes, urea, and glucose.

Exercise 15-1

Urinary System Anatomy

MATERIALS
- ❏ Urinary system models
- ❏ Kidney models
- ❏ Nephron models
- ❏ Preserved kidney
- ❏ Dissection equipment
- ❏ Dissecting tray

The paired **kidneys** are situated against the posterior body wall posterior to the peritoneal membranes (i.e., they are *retroperitoneal*). They are encased within three layers of connective tissue, the thickest of which is a middle layer of adipose tissue. The innermost layer of connective tissue encases each kidney like plastic wrap and is called the **renal** (REE-nul) **capsule**.

Internally, each kidney has three distinct regions that can be seen in a frontal section (Figure 15.4):

1. **Renal cortex.** The most superficial region is known as the renal cortex. It is dark brown because it consists of many blood vessels that serve the tiny functional units of the kidney, the **nephrons** (NEF-rahnz).

2. **Renal medulla.** The kidney's middle region is known as the medulla and contains triangular structures known as **renal,** or **medullary, pyramids.** The medullary pyramids are separated from one another by inward extensions of the renal cortex called **renal columns.** Like the renal cortex, the renal columns contain many blood vessels. Each pyramid contains looping tubules of the nephron as well as structures that drain fluid from the nephron. These tubes give the pyramids a striped (or *striated*) appearance.

3. **Renal pelvis.** The tubes that drain the fluid from the nephron drain into larger tubes called **minor calyces** (KAL-ih-seez) that in turn drain into even larger **major calyces.** The major calyces drain into the kidney's inner-most region, called the renal pelvis, which serves as a basin for collecting urine.

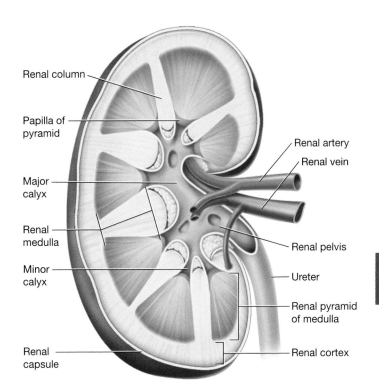

FIGURE **15.4** Right kidney, frontal section

15

The blood flow through the kidney follows a unique pattern that allows it to carry out its function of maintaining the homeostasis of the blood (Figure 15.5). The large **renal arteries** deliver about 1,200 milliliters of blood per minute to the kidney to be filtered. The renal arteries branch into progressively smaller arteries as they pass through the medulla to the cortex, including the **segmental arteries** in the renal pelvis, the **interlobar arteries** between the medullary pyramids, the **arcuate** (AHR-kyoo-it) **arteries** that curve around the top of the pyramids, and finally the small **interlobular arteries** in the renal cortex. The interlobular arteries branch into tiny **afferent arterioles**, each of which supplies a ball of capillaries known as the **glomerulus** (gloh-MAIR-yoo-lus). This is where the blood is filtered. Note that the glomerulus is not the primary site for gas and nutrient exchange for the tissues of the kidneys.

You learned in Unit 11 that a capillary bed generally drains into a venule, but note in Figure 15.5 that the capillaries of the glomerulus drain into a second *arteriole* called the **efferent arteriole**. The efferent arteriole then branches to form a second capillary bed containing the **peritubular capillaries**. These capillaries surround the tubules of the nephron, where they provide them with oxygen and nutrients and also take substances reabsorbed by the tubules back into the blood. In some nephrons, a second set of capillaries called the **vasa recta** (VAY-zah REK-tah) is found surrounding the nephron loop. The peritubular capillaries then drain out through the small **interlobular veins**, which drain into **arcuate veins**, then into **interlobar veins**, and finally into the large **renal vein**. This pattern of blood flow allows the kidneys both to filter blood and to reclaim most of the fluid and solutes filtered.

Microscopically, each kidney is composed of more than a million tiny nephrons (Figure 15.6). Blood first enters the high-pressure circuit of the glomerulus, where fluid and small solutes are forced out of the capillaries and into a space called the **capsular space**. The capsular space is found within a structure known as the **glomerular capsule**. Note in Figure 15.6 that the glomerular capsule has two layers: (a) the outer **parietal layer**, which is simple squamous epithelium, and (b) the inner **visceral layer**, which consists of cells called **podocytes** (POH-doh-sytz) that surround the capillaries of the glomerulus. The glomerulus and its surrounding capsule together are known as the **renal corpuscle**.

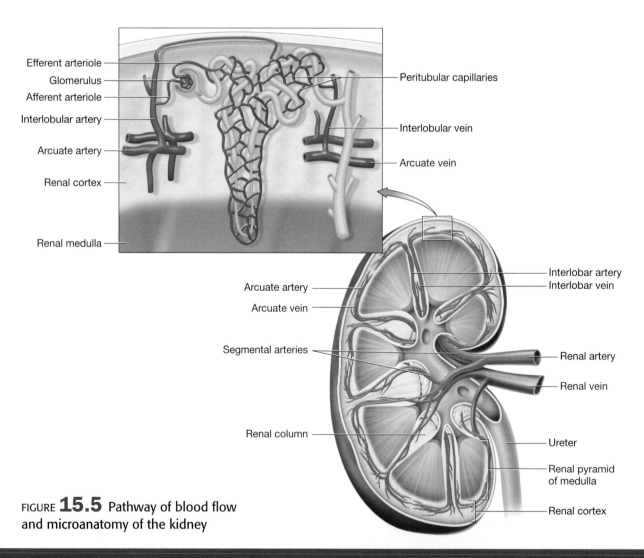

FIGURE **15.5** Pathway of blood flow and microanatomy of the kidney

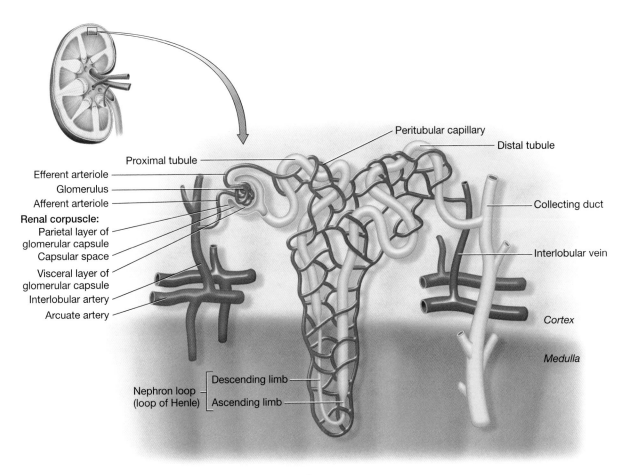

FIGURE **15.6** Nephron

The fluid in the capsular space, known as **filtrate**, next enters a series of small tubes, or *tubules,* that can be likened to the "plumbing" of the kidney. These tubes collectively are called the **renal tubule**, which consists of three parts:

1. the **proximal tubule** (sometimes called the *proximal convoluted tubule*),
2. the ascending and descending limbs of the **nephron loop** (also called the **loop of Henle**), and
3. the **distal tubule** (sometimes called the *distal convoluted tubule*).

Several distal tubules drain into one **collecting duct** not technically part of the nephron. Note that the majority of the renal tubule is confined to the renal cortex; only the nephron loops of certain nephrons dip down into the renal medulla.

Filtrate in the renal tubule and collecting duct is modified, and most of the water and solutes are reclaimed. From the collecting ducts, filtrate drains into larger tubules called **papillary ducts**, where more water is reclaimed. After the fluid leaves the papillary ducts, it is known as **urine** and drains into the minor calyces, major calyces, and finally the renal pelvis. From the renal pelvis, urine enters the next organs of the urinary system—the tubes called the **ureters** (YOO-re-turz; Figure 15.7). Ureters are lined by a type of epithelium called **transitional epithelium**, and their walls contain smooth muscle that massages the urine inferiorly via peristalsis. The ureter exits the kidney through a slit in its medial surface known as the **hilum** (HY-lum).

The ureters drain urine into the posteroinferior wall of the organ known as the **urinary bladder** (Figure 15.8). Like the ureters, the urinary bladder is lined with transitional epithelium and contains smooth muscle, sometimes called the **detrusor** (de-TROO-sohr) **muscle**, in its wall. The majority of the urinary bladder contains folds called **rugae** that allow it to expand when it is filled with urine. The smooth inferior portion of the urinary bladder wall, a triangular-shaped area known as the **trigone** (TRY-gohn), contains the opening called the **internal urethral orifice**. This opens into the final organ of the urinary system—the **urethra**. The urethra contains two rings of muscle—the involuntary **internal urethral sphincter** and the voluntary **external urethral sphincter**. When both of these sphincters relax, urine is expelled from the body via a process called **micturition** (mik-chur-ISH-un).

15

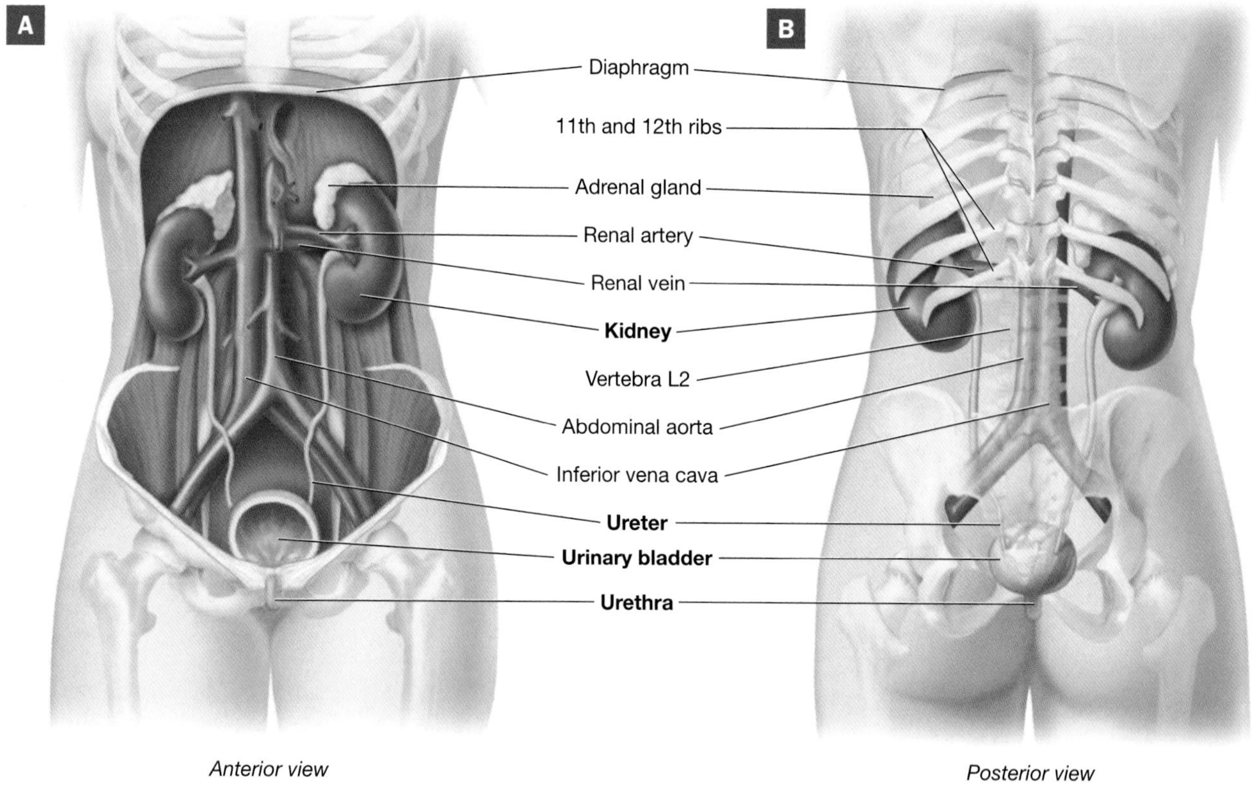

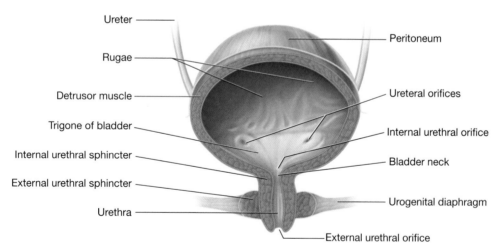

Anterior view

Posterior view

FIGURE **15.7** Organs of the female urinary system: **(A)** anterior view; **(B)** posterior view

Diaphragm

11th and 12th ribs

Adrenal gland

Renal artery

Renal vein

Kidney

Vertebra L2

Abdominal aorta

Inferior vena cava

Ureter

Urinary bladder

Urethra

Ureter

Rugae

Detrusor muscle

Trigone of bladder

Internal urethral sphincter

External urethral sphincter

Urethra

Peritoneum

Ureteral orifices

Internal urethral orifice

Bladder neck

Urogenital diaphragm

External urethral orifice

FIGURE **15.8** Female urinary bladder, frontal section

Procedure 1 Model Inventory for the Urinary System

Identify the following structures of the urinary system on models and diagrams, using your textbook and this unit for reference. As you examine the anatomical models and diagrams, record on the model inventory in Table 15.2 the name of the model and the structures you were able to identify.

Kidney Anatomy

1. Hilum
2. Regions
   a. Renal cortex
   b. Renal medulla
      (1) Renal columns
      (2) Renal pyramids
      (3) Renal papillae
   c. Minor calyces
   d. Major calyces
   e. Renal pelvis
3. Blood supply
   a. Renal artery
   b. Renal vein

Structures of the Nephron

1. Renal corpuscle
   a. Glomerulus
      (1) Afferent arteriole
      (2) Efferent arteriole
      (3) Peritubular capillaries
      (4) Vasa recta
   b. Glomerular capsule
      (1) Parietal layer
      (2) Visceral layer
2. Renal tubule
   a. Proximal tubule
   b. Nephron loop
   c. Distal tubule
3. Collecting duct
4. Papillary duct

Other Urinary Structures

1. Ureter
2. Urinary bladder
   a. Detrusor muscle
   b. Ureteral orifices
   c. Internal urethral orifice
   d. Trigone
3. Urethra
   a. Internal urethral sphincter
   b. External urethral sphincter
   c. External urethral orifice

TABLE **15.2** Model Inventory for Urinary Anatomy

Model/Diagram	Structures Identified

15

Procedure 2 Kidney Dissection

In this procedure you will identify several of the structures you just identified on models and diagrams by dissecting a preserved kidney.

1 Obtain a fresh or preserved kidney specimen and dissection supplies.

2 If the thick surrounding connective tissue coverings are intact, note their thickness and amount of adipose tissue.

3 Use scissors to cut through the connective tissue coverings, and remove the kidney.

4 List surface structures you are able to identify (see **Figure 15.9A** for reference):

_____

_____

_____

5 Distinguishing between the ureter, the renal artery, and the renal vein is often difficult. Following are some hints to aid you:

▌ The renal artery typically has the thickest and most muscular wall, and it branches into several segmental arteries prior to entering the kidney.

▌ The renal vein is thinner, flimsier, and often larger in diameter than the renal artery.

▌ The ureter has a thick, muscular wall, too, but it does not branch after it leaves the kidney. Also, its diameter is usually smaller than either the renal artery or the renal vein.

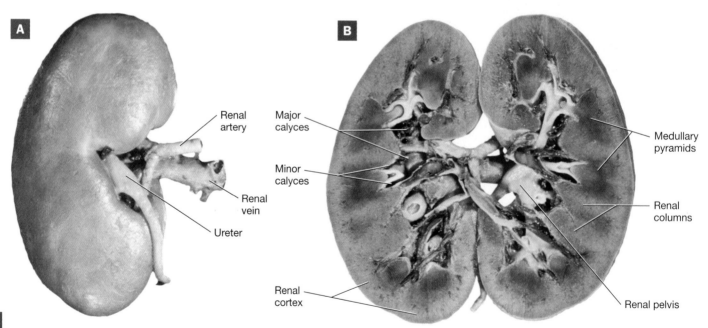

FIGURE **15.9** Preserved kidney: **(A)** anterior view; **(B)** frontal section

15

Keeping these points in mind, determine the location of the renal artery, the renal vein, and the ureter on your specimen. Sketch the arrangement of the three structures below:

6 Use a scalpel to make a frontal section of the kidney. List the internal structures you are able to identify (Figure 15.9B):

_____   _____

_____   _____

_____   _____

_____   _____

_____   _____

_____   _____

Renal Physiology: The Model Kidney

MATERIALS

❏ 4-inch piece of dialysis tubing
❏ 2 pieces of string
❏ Animal blood or simulated blood
❏ 200 ml beaker
❏ Deionized water
❏ URS-10 and bottle with key

The glomeruli filter the blood delivered to them. Fluid is forced from the glomerular capillaries into the capsular space by a pressure called the **net filtration pressure** (NFP). The fluid that results from this filtration process enters the proximal tubule and is called **filtrate**. Filtrate is similar in composition to blood, but it lacks most of the proteins and cells we find in blood. This selectivity is possible because of the **filtration membrane**, which consists of the glomerular endothelial cells, the basal lamina, and the podocytes of the visceral layer of the glomerular capsule (Figure 15.10). The filtration membrane acts in a similar manner to the filter in your coffeemaker: It prevents large substances, such as proteins and cells, from leaving the blood while allowing small substances, such as water, glucose, amino acids, electrolytes, and waste products, to leave the blood and enter the filtrate.

The filtrate contains a number of substances our bodies need to reclaim in a process known as **tubular reabsorption**. About 99% of the water in the filtrate and most of the solutes are reabsorbed through the epithelium of the nephron tubules and returned to the blood. The importance of this function cannot be overstated. If the water were not reabsorbed in the renal tubule and the collecting duct, we would lose our entire plasma volume in less than 30 minutes! In addition to tubular reabsorption, the nephron tubules remove substances from the blood not filtered at the glomerulus and put them into the filtrate, a process known as **tubular secretion**.

In this exercise you will examine the process of glomerular filtration by constructing a model kidney and testing for substances that appear in the filtrate. A kidney is easily modeled with either animal blood or simulated blood and simple dialysis tubing, which has a permeability similar to that of the filtration membrane. Glomerular filtration is mimicked by immersing the blood-filled tubing in water. Substances to which the "filtration membrane" is permeable will enter the surrounding water (the "filtrate"), whereas those to which the membrane is not permeable will remain in the tubing.

The results of this test are analyzed using **urinalysis reagent test strips** (URS-10; Figure 15.11). Each strip consists of 10 small, colored pads that change color in the presence of certain chemicals. The strip is interpreted by watching the pads for color changes and comparing the color changes with a color-coded key on the side of the bottle. The color closest to the color on the strip is recorded as your result. Please note that for this exercise you will read only 4 of the 10 boxes: blood, leukocytes, protein, and glucose.

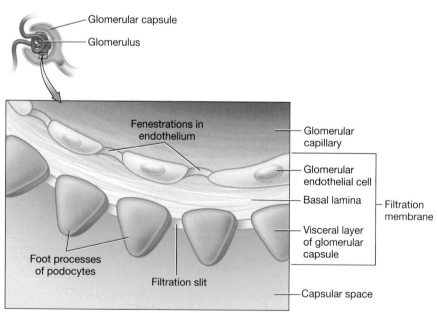

FIGURE **15.10** Filtration membrane

FIGURE **15.11** URS-10 vial and strip

15

Procedure 1 Making a Model Kidney and Testing Glomerular Filtration

Now let's construct our model kidneys. The model kidney must sit in water for 25 minutes while you wait for your results.

1 Cut a 4-inch piece of dialysis tubing.

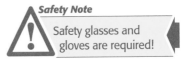

Safety Note

Safety glasses and gloves are required!

2 Securely tie off one end of the tubing with string. Open the other end of the tubing by wetting the end of the tube and rubbing it between your fingers.

3 Fill the dialysis tubing about half-full with either animal blood or simulated blood, and securely tie off the open end of the tube with string.

4 Place the tied-off tube in a 200 ml beaker containing about 150 ml of deionized water.

5 Leave the tubing in the water for approximately 25 minutes.

6 After 25 minutes have passed, remove the tubing from the water.

7 Dip a URS-10 in the water, and remove it quickly. Turn the bottle on its side, and compare the colors of the pads for glucose, blood, leukocytes, and protein. You will notice that on the side of the bottle, time frames are listed for each substance tested. Wait this amount of time to watch for a reaction; otherwise, you could obtain a false negative result. If you wait too long to read the results, though, the colors will tend to darken and may blend with adjacent colors.

8 Record your results below.

    a Glucose: _____

    b Erythrocytes (blood): _____

    c Leukocytes: _____

    d Protein: _____

9 Which substances were filtered out? Which substances stayed in the tubing?

_____

_____

_____

_____

_____

15

Exercise 15-3

Urinalysis

MATERIALS

❑ Samples of simulated urine

❑ Graduated cylinder or test tube

❑ URS-10 and bottle with key

For hundreds of years, health-care providers have recognized the utility of testing urine, called urinalysis, as a diagnostic tool. Historically, the urine was evaluated for color, translucency, odor, and taste (yes, taste!). Today, although these characteristics are still examined (except, thankfully, taste), we also use urinalysis test strips, as we did in Exercise 15-2, to test for the presence of various chemicals in the urine. Both normal and abnormal readings give a health-care provider a wealth of information about a patient's renal function and overall health.

In this exercise you will analyze different urine samples using a URS-10. For each urine sample, one or more results will be read as abnormal. In the second part of the exercise, you will research potential causes of the abnormalities you detected.

Procedure 1 Urinalysis Part One

Test a minimum of five samples of simulated urine using your urinalysis test strips. Use a new strip for each sample, and take care to clean your graduated cylinder thoroughly between each sample you test. Please note that this is *simulated* urine rather than real urine, but it contains the same chemicals as real urine and should be handled with equal caution.

1 Randomly choose one sample of simulated urine, and pour approximately 3 ml of the sample into a test tube or graduated cylinder.

2 Submerge one URS-10 in the urine, and quickly remove it.

3 Compare the resulting colors and patterns on the test strip with those on the key on the bottle. Be sure to wait the appropriate amount of time to read the results.

4 Record your results in Table 15.3, and note any abnormal results.

5 Repeat this procedure for the remaining samples.

15

TABLE **15.3** Urinalysis Results

Reading	Sample 1	Sample 2	Sample 3	Sample 4	Sample 5
pH					
Leukocytes					
Nitrite					
Urobilinogen					
Protein					
Blood					
Specific gravity					
Ketones					
Bilirubin					
Glucose					

15

Procedure 2 Urinalysis Part Two

Each sample you tested should have had at least one abnormality. Use your textbook and/or the Internet as a resource to determine which disease state(s) could lead to the abnormality you detected in each sample. Record your results in Table 15.4.

TABLE **15.4** Urinalysis Abnormalities and Disease States

Sample	Primary Abnormality	Potential Causes
1		
2		
3		
4		
5		

Exercise 15-4

Time to Trace!

MATERIALS

☐ Anatomical models of the kidney and nephron

It's time to trace again! In this exercise you will trace the pathway of different molecules through the vasculature of the kidney and the microanatomy of the kidney. You will examine three different substances:

1. An erythrocyte,
2. A molecule of glucose, and
3. A molecule of urea.

Following are some hints to use as you trace:

> ▍ Don't forget the basic rules of blood flow: You must pass through a capillary bed in order to get from an artery to a vein.

▍ Refer to Table 15.1 in Pre-Lab Exercise 15-4 (p. 384) before you trace each substance. This will help you determine if the substance gets filtered at the glomerulus or if it remains in the blood, if a filtered substance gets reabsorbed, and where the reabsorption occurs.

▍ Refer to anatomical models of the kidney and nephron and Figures 15.5 and 15.6 (pp. 386–387) for help with the pathway of blood flow through the kidney and its microanatomy.

Part 1: Erythrocyte

Trace an erythrocyte from the renal artery to the renal vein.

_____ → _____ →

_____ → _____ →

_____ → _____ →

_____ → _____ →

_____ → _____ →

_____ → _____ →

_____ .

Part 2: Glucose

Trace a molecule of glucose from the renal artery to the renal vein.

_____ → _____ →

_____ → _____ →

_____ → _____ →

_____ → _____ →

_____ → _____ →

_____ → _____ →

_____ → _____ .

15

Part 3: Urea

Trace a molecule of urea from the renal artery to its final destination outside the body.

_____ → _____ →

_____ → _____ →

_____ → _____ →

_____ → _____ →

_____ → _____ →

_____ → _____ →

_____ → _____ →

_____ → _____ →

_____ → _____ →

_____ → _____ →

_____ → _____ .

15

1 Label the following parts of the kidney on Figure 15.12.

- ❑ Major calyx
- ❑ Minor calyx
- ❑ Renal artery
- ❑ Renal column
- ❑ Renal cortex
- ❑ Renal medulla
- ❑ Renal pelvis
- ❑ Renal (medullary) pyramid
- ❑ Renal vein
- ❑ Ureter

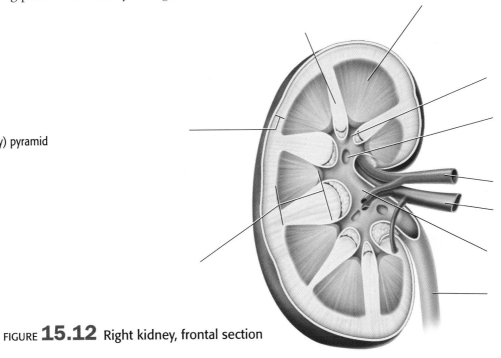

FIGURE **15.12** Right kidney, frontal section

2 Label the following parts of the nephron on Figure 15.13.

- ❑ Afferent arteriole
- ❑ Collecting duct
- ❑ Distal tubule
- ❑ Efferent arteriole
- ❑ Glomerular capsule
- ❑ Glomerulus
- ❑ Nephron loop
- ❑ Peritubular capillaries
- ❑ Proximal tubule

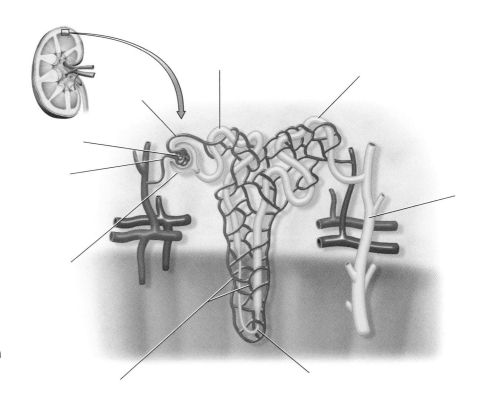

FIGURE **15.13** Nephron

15

3 Which of the following is *not* one of the urinary system's functions?

   a. Regulating fluid, electrolyte, and acid-base balance

   b. Regulating blood cell formation

   c. Regulating production of insulin and glucagon

   d. Removing waste products from the blood

4 The blood flow through the kidney is special because

   a. its first capillary beds drain into arterioles.

   b. its second capillary beds drain into arterioles.

   c. it is supplied by three renal arteries.

   d. it contains no capillary beds.

5 Number the following from the point the filtrate is first formed (with a number 1) to the point it drains into the renal pelvis (with a number 7).

   _____ Minor calyx

   _____ Proximal tubule

   _____ Collecting duct

   _____ Capsular space

   _____ Nephron loop

   _____ Papillary duct

   _____ Distal tubule

6 Urine drains from the kidneys via the

   a. urinary bladder.

   b. urethra.

   c. ureters.

   d. papillary calyces.

7 Urine is expelled from the body by a process called

   a. micturition.

   b. parturition.

   c. defecation.

   d. procrastination.

8 Predict the effects renal failure might have on the body's overall homeostasis.

_____

_____

_____

_____

_____

15

9 Which of the following is *true*?

a. The fluid and solutes in the filtrate have been removed from the blood and are located in the renal tubules.

b. The filtration membrane allows blood cells and other large substances to pass but prevents small substances from moving through it.

c. Tubular secretion involves the reclamation of substances in the filtrate and their return to the blood.

d. Substances such as glucose, proteins, and erythrocytes are secreted into the filtrate.

10 Which of the following substances would you *not* expect to find in the filtrate in significant amounts?

a. Erythrocytes

b. Glucose

c. Electrolytes

d. Amino acids

11 Urinalysis can tell you

a. if there is an infection in the kidney or urinary tract.

b. if blood sugar is elevated.

c. if a person is dehydrated.

d. if a person's kidneys function normally.

e. All of the above.

12 Should glucose, erythrocytes, leukocytes, and protein appear in the urine in large amounts? Why or why not? What happens to each of these substances in the kidney?

_____

_____

_____

_____

_____

_____

_____

Reproductive Systems

16

PRE-LAB EXERCISES

Complete the following exercises prior to coming to lab, using your textbook and lab manual for reference.

Pre-Lab Exercise 16-1

✎ Key Terms

You should be familiar with the following terms before coming to lab.

Term	Definition

Structures of the Male Reproductive System

Testes _____

_____

Seminiferous tubules _____

_____

Epididymis _____

_____

Vas (ductus) deferens _____

_____

Spermatic cord _____

_____

Prostate gland _____

_____

Structures of the Female Reproductive System

Ovaries _____

_____

Uterine tube _____

_____

Uterus _____

_____

Vagina _____

_____

Vulva _____

_____

Mammary glands _____

_____

Gametogenesis Terms

Meiosis _____

_____

Haploid _____

_____

Spermatogenesis _____

_____

Oogenesis _____

_____

Development

Fertilization _____

_____

Zygote _____

_____

Embryo _____

_____

Fetus _____

_____

Fetal Structures

Chorion_____

_____

Amnion _____

_____

Placenta _____

_____

Pre-Lab Exercise **16-2**

Male Reproductive Anatomy

Label and color the structures of the male reproductive system depicted in Figure 16.1 with the following terms from Exercise 16-1. Use your text and Exercise 16-1 in this unit for reference.

❏ Scrotum
❏ Testes
❏ Epididymis
❏ Vas (ductus) deferens
❏ Ejaculatory duct

❏ Urethra
   ❏ Prostatic urethra
   ❏ Membranous urethra
   ❏ Spongy urethra

❏ Glands
   ❏ Seminal vesicle
   ❏ Prostate gland
❏ Penis
   ❏ Corpora cavernosa
   ❏ Corpus spongiosum
      ❏ Glans penis

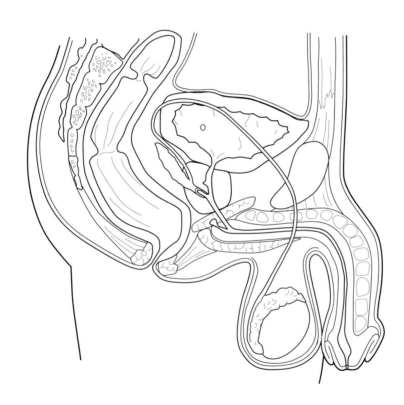

FIGURE **16.1** Midsagittal section of the male pelvis

Pre-Lab Exercise **16-3**

Female Reproductive Anatomy

Label and color the structures of the female reproductive system depicted in Figure 16.2 with the following terms from Exercise 16-2. Use your text and Exercise 16-2 in this unit for reference.

❏ Ovary
❏ Uterine tube
❏ Uterus
   ❏ Fundus
   ❏ Body
   ❏ Cervix

❏ Vagina
❏ Vulva
   ❏ Labium majus
   ❏ Labium minus
   ❏ Clitoris
   ❏ Urethral orifice

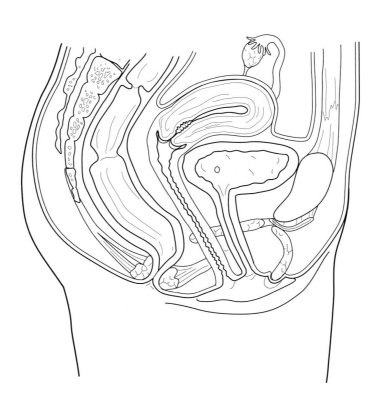

FIGURE **16.2** Midsagittal section of the female pelvis

Label and color the structures of the fetal cardiovascular system depicted in Figure 16.3 with the following terms from Exercise 16-6. Use your text and Exercise 16-6 in this unit for reference.

- ❏ Placenta
- ❏ Umbilical cord
  - ❏ Umbilical arteries
  - ❏ Umbilical vein
- ❏ Foramen ovale
- ❏ Ductus venosus
- ❏ Ductus arteriosus

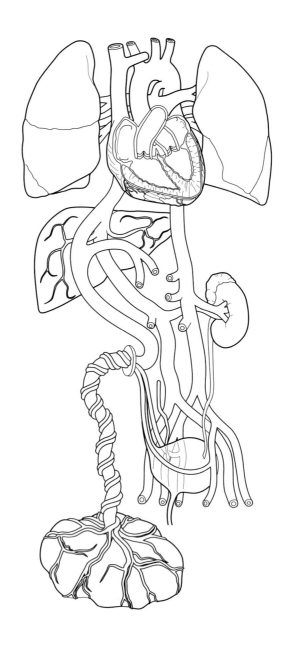

FIGURE **16.3** Fetal cardiovascular anatomy

EXERCISES

The other organ systems in the human body we have discussed all function in some manner to help maintain homeostasis of the body. The reproductive system, however, plays few roles in maintaining homeostasis and instead functions to perpetuate the species. The main organs of the reproductive system are the **gonads** (GOH-nadz)—the testes and the ovaries—which produce **gametes** (GAM-eetz), or sex cells, for reproduction.

We begin this unit with the anatomy of the male and female reproductive systems. Then we turn to the main functions of these organs: **gametogenesis** (gam-e-toh-JEN-e-sis), the formation of new gametes, the process of development, and the unique anatomy and structures of the developing human.

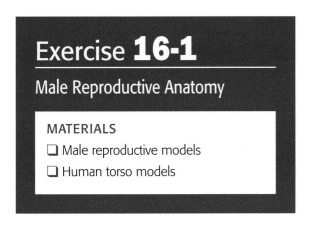

Exercise **16-1**

Male Reproductive Anatomy

MATERIALS
❑ Male reproductive models
❑ Human torso models

The **testes** (TES-teez), the gamete-producing organs of the male, are situated outside the body in a sac of skin and connective tissue called the **scrotum** (Figure 16.4). They are located externally because sperm production requires a temperature lower than body temperature of about 34°C (about 94°F). Smooth muscle tissue called the **cremaster muscle** surrounds each testis in the scrotum, helping control its height and therefore its temperature.

The testes are surrounded by an outer connective tissue sheath called the **tunica vaginalis** and an inner sheath called the **tunica albuginea** (al-byoo-JIN-ee-uh) that divides the interior of the testes into **lobules**. Each lobule contains a tightly coiled **seminiferous tubule** where **spermatogenesis** takes place.

The seminiferous tubules converge near the superior part of the testis to form a structure called the **rete testis** (REET TES-tis). The rete testis exits the testis to join the first segment of the duct system of the male reproductive tract, the **epididymis** (ep-ih-DID-ih-mis; Figures 16.4 and 16.5). Immature sperm produced by the seminiferous tubules migrate to the epididymis to finish their maturation, after which they exit via a long tube called the **vas** (or **ductus**) **deferens** (DEF-ur-unz). The vas deferens travels superiorly through the **spermatic cord**, a structure that also carries the testicular artery, testicular veins (the pampiniform plexus), and nerves.

Note in Figure 16.5 that after the vas deferens enters the pelvic cavity, it crosses superiorly and posteriorly over the urinary bladder to join a gland called the **seminal vesicle**. At this point, the vas deferens merges with the duct from the seminal vesicle to form the **ejaculatory duct**. This duct passes through the **prostate** (PRAHS-tayt) **gland**, where it joins with the **prostatic urethra**. The prostatic urethra becomes the **membranous urethra** as it exits the prostate, and then becomes the **spongy urethra** as it enters the penis.

The **penis** is composed of three erectile bodies: the single **corpus spongiosum** and the paired, dorsal **corpora cavernosa**. The corpus spongiosum, which surrounds the spongy urethra, enlarges distally to form the **glans penis**. All three bodies consist of vascular spaces that fill with blood during an erection.

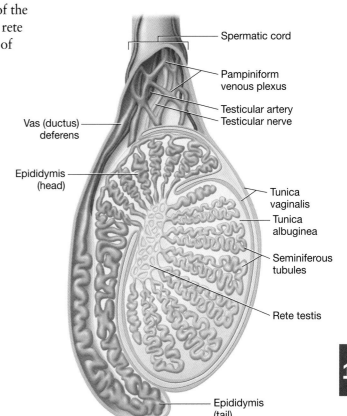

Spermatic cord

Pampiniform venous plexus

Testicular artery
Testicular nerve

Vas (ductus) deferens

Epididymis (head)

Tunica vaginalis

Tunica albuginea

Seminiferous tubules

Rete testis

Epididymis (tail)

FIGURE **16.4** Midsagittal section through the testis

16

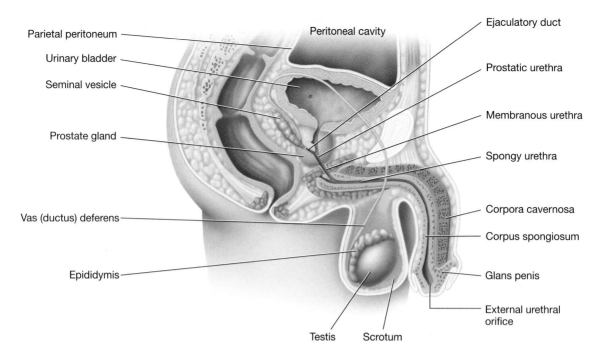

Parietal peritoneum

Urinary bladder

Seminal vesicle

Prostate gland

Vas (ductus) deferens

Epididymis

Peritoneal cavity

Ejaculatory duct

Prostatic urethra

Membranous urethra

Spongy urethra

Corpora cavernosa

Corpus spongiosum

Glans penis

External urethral orifice

Testis   Scrotum

FIGURE **16.5** Midsagittal section through the male pelvis

16

Procedure 1 Model Inventory for the Male Reproductive System

Identify the following structures of the male reproductive system on models and diagrams using your textbook and this unit for reference. As you examine the anatomical models and diagrams, record on the model inventory in Table 16.1 the name of the model and the structures you were able to identify.

1. Scrotum
2. Testes
   a. Tunica albuginea
   b. Tunica vaginalis
   c. Seminiferous tubules
   d. Rete testis
3. Epididymis
4. Spermatic cord

5. Cremaster muscle
6. Vas (ductus) deferens
7. Ejaculatory duct
8. Urethra
   a. Prostatic urethra
   b. Membranous urethra
   c. Spongy urethra

9. Glands
   a. Seminal vesicle
   b. Prostate gland
10. Penis
   a. Corpora cavernosa
   b. Corpus spongiosum
      (1) Glans penis

TABLE **16.1** Model Inventory for the Male Reproductive System

Model/Diagram	Structures Identified

16

Exercise 16-2

Female Reproductive Anatomy

MATERIALS
❑ Female reproductive models
❑ Human torso models

The female reproductive organs lie in the pelvic cavity, with the exception of the almond-shaped **ovaries**, located in the peritoneal cavity (Figures 16.6 and 16.7). The ovaries, the female gonads, produce gametes, or eggs, called **oocytes** (OH-oh-sytz) that travel through the reproductive tract to be fertilized.

Developing oocytes within the ovaries are encased in structures called **follicles**. Follicles are present in various stages, ranging from the immature **primordial follicles** to the mature **vesicular follicle**, from which an oocyte is released during ovulation. Unlike the male reproductive tract, the tubule system of the female reproductive tract is not continuous. Therefore, the oocyte actually is released into the pelvic cavity, and the fingerlike extensions of the **uterine** (YOO-tur-in) tube, called **fimbriae** (FIM-bree-ay), must "catch" the oocyte and bring it into the uterine tube.

The uterine tubes join the superolateral portion of the **uterus**. The uterus is situated between the urinary bladder and the rectum. The uterus consists of three portions: the dome-shaped **fundus**, the central **body**, and the narrow **cervix**. The wall of the uterus has three layers: the inner epithelial and connective tissue lining called the **endometrium** (en-doh-MEE-tree-um), in which a fertilized ovum implants; the middle, muscular **myometrium**; and the outermost connective tissue lining, the **perimetrium**.

The inferiormost portion of the cervix is the **cervical (external) os**. The **vagina** extends inferiorly from the cervical os and terminates at the vaginal orifice. The external anatomy of the female is collectively called the **vulva**, and consists of the **labia majora** and **labia minora** (singular: labium majus and minus, respectively), the **clitoris** (KLIH-tohr-us), and the urethral and vaginal orifices. The labia are paired skin folds analogous to the scrotum in the male.

The **mammary glands** are not true reproductive organs but do have an associated reproductive function in milk production (Figure 16.8). Mammary glands are present in both males and females (males can produce milk too), but their anatomy is most appropriately discussed with female anatomy. Internally, mammary glands consist of 15–25 **lobes**, each of which has smaller **lobules** that contain milk-producing **alveoli**. Milk leaves through the **nipple**, which is surrounded by a darkly pigmented area called the **areola** (air-ee-OH-lah).

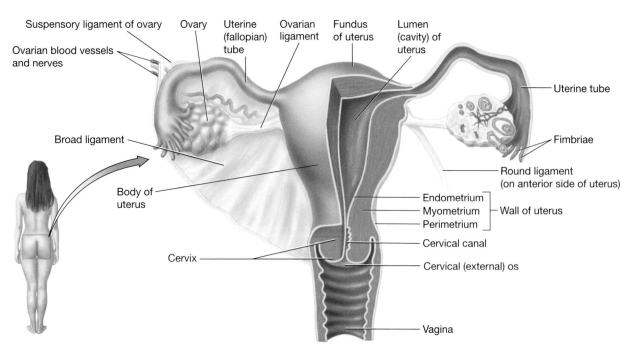

FIGURE **16.6** Posterior view of the female reproductive organs

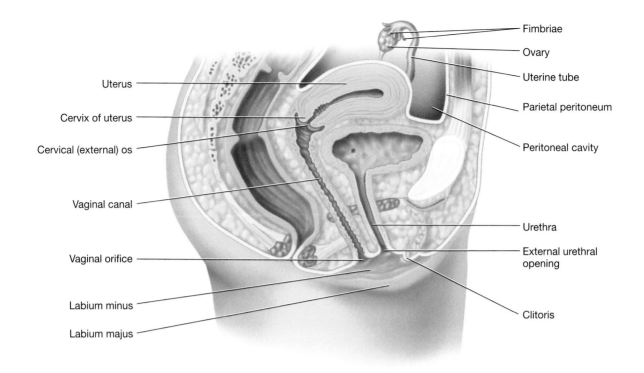

FIGURE **16.7** Midsagittal section of the female pelvis

Fimbriae

Ovary

Uterine tube

Uterus

Parietal peritoneum

Cervix of uterus

Cervical (external) os

Peritoneal cavity

Vaginal canal

Urethra

External urethral opening

Vaginal orifice

Labium minus

Clitoris

Labium majus

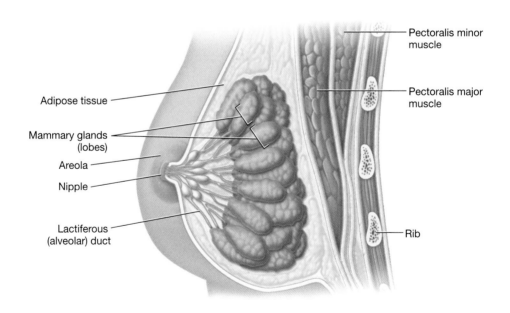

FIGURE **16.8** Mammary gland

Pectoralis minor muscle

Pectoralis major muscle

Adipose tissue

Mammary glands (lobes)

Areola

Nipple

Lactiferous (alveolar) duct

Rib

Procedure 1 Model Inventory for the Female Reproductive System

Identify the following structures of the female reproductive system on models and diagrams, using your textbook and this unit for reference. As you examine the anatomical models and diagrams, record on the model inventory in Table 16.2 the name of the model and the structures you were able to identify.

1. Ovary
2. Ovarian follicles
3. Uterine tube
   a. Fimbriae
4. Uterus
   a. Fundus
   b. Body
   c. Cervix

   d. Layers
      (1) Endometrium
      (2) Myometrium
      (3) Perimetrium
5. Vagina

6. Vulva
   a. Labia majora
   b. Labia minora
   c. Clitoris
   d. Urethral orifice
7. Mammary glands
   a. Areola
   b. Nipple
   c. Lobe

TABLE **16.2** Model Inventory for the Female Reproductive System

Model/Diagram	Structures Identified

16

Exercise **16-3**

Meiosis

MATERIALS

❏ Meiosis models

❏ Mitosis models

❏ 4 colors of pop beads

As you may recall from Unit 3, somatic cells divide by a process called mitosis. During mitosis, a cell replicates its 23 pairs of homologous chromosomes and divides its DNA and organelles into two identical daughter cells. Each new **diploid** cell is identical to the original cell. Gametogenesis (oogenesis and spermatogenesis), however, must proceed in a different way for two reasons:

1. If each gamete were to have the same genetic material, we all would be genetically identical to our siblings.

2. If each gamete were to have two sets of chromosomes, our offspring would have four sets of chromosomes.

For this reason, gametes undergo a process known as **meiosis** (my-OH-sis) rather than mitosis.

In meiosis, gametes proceed through two rounds of cell division, and each gamete ends up with only one set of chromosomes (a **haploid** cell). As you can see in Figure 16.9, meiosis begins in a manner similar to mitosis: The homologous chromosomes have replicated during the S phase of the cell cycle to yield two pairs of sister chromatids.

The cell then goes through **meiosis I**, during which replicated chromosomes line up next to one another so closely that they overlap, or **cross over**, in several places. As anaphase I begins, the chromosomes exchange pieces of genetic material at the points of crossover.

After telophase I and cytokinesis are complete, the gametes have 23 sets of sister chromatids, and the amount of genetic material is halved because of the separation of homologous chromosomes. They then go through the second round of division, **meiosis II**, during which the sister chromatids separate. Meiosis II is similar to meiosis I with one major exception: The DNA does *not* replicate prior to the start of prophase II. At the end of telophase II, each gamete has only 23 chromosomes and is a haploid cell.

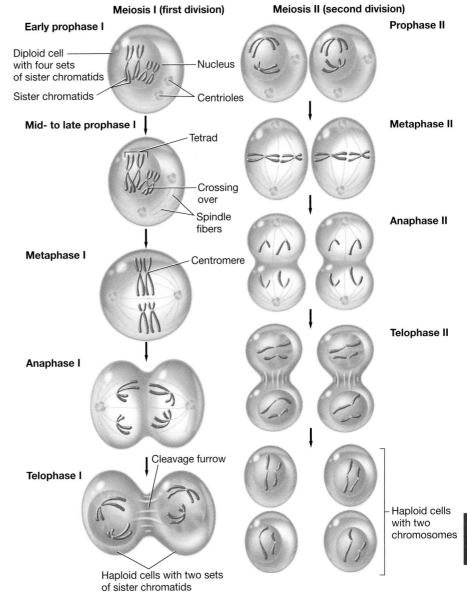

FIGURE 16.9 Meiosis

Procedure 1 Model Meiosis

In the following procedure you will model meiosis with either a set of cell meiosis models or with pop-bead chromosomes.

1 Obtain a set of meiosis and mitosis models.

2 Arrange the mitosis models in the correct order.

3 Now arrange the meiosis models in the correct order.

4 Compare the models of the two processes. List all of the differences you can see between meiosis and mitosis below.

_____

_____

_____

_____

_____

_____

_____

_____

16

Exercise 16-4

Spermatogenesis and Oogenesis

Gametogenesis is really two separate processes: spermatogenesis, which takes place in the seminiferous tubules of the testes, and oogenesis, which takes place in the ovary and uterine tube. Spermatogenesis, shown in Figure 16.10, begins with stem cells located at the outer edge of the seminiferous tubules called **spermatogonia**. Before puberty, these diploid cells undergo repeated rounds of mitosis to increase their numbers. As puberty begins, each spermatogonium divides into two different cells—one cell that stays a spermatogonium and another cell that becomes a **primary spermatocyte**.

The primary spermatocyte then undergoes meiosis I and divides into two **secondary spermatocytes** that migrate closer to the lumen of the tubule. The two secondary spermatocytes undergo meiosis II and give rise to four haploid **spermatids**. The spermatids move to the lumen of the seminiferous tubule, at which point they are called spermatozoa, or sperm cells. These cells then move to the epididymis to mature into functional gametes. Mature sperm contain three parts: the **head,** in which the DNA resides, the **midpiece,** and the **flagellum** (Figure 16.11).

Like spermatogenesis, oogenesis proceeds through meiosis to yield a haploid gamete, the **ovum** (Figure 16.12). But the two processes differ in some notable ways:

- *The number of oocytes is determined before birth.* During the fetal period, stem cells called **oogonia** undergo mitosis, increasing their numbers to about 500,000 to 700,000. This is the total number of oocytes a woman will ever produce. This is in sharp contrast to spermatogenesis, which begins at puberty and continues throughout a male's lifetime.

- *Meiosis I begins during the fetal period but is arrested.* Still during the fetal period, the oogonia become encased in a **primordial follicle,** enlarge, and become **primary oocytes.** The primary oocytes begin prophase I but are arrested at this stage. Meiosis I does not resume until puberty.

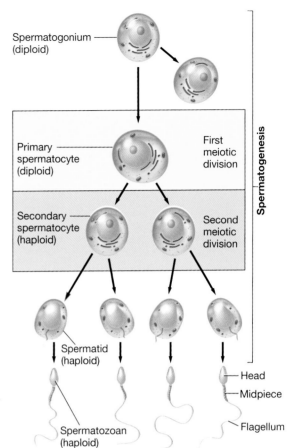

FIGURE **16.10** Spermatogenesis

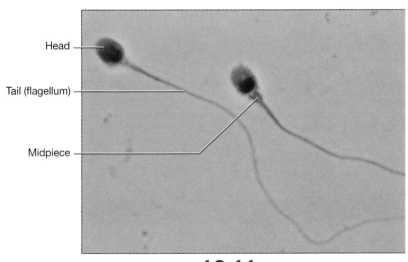

FIGURE **16.11** Sperm cells

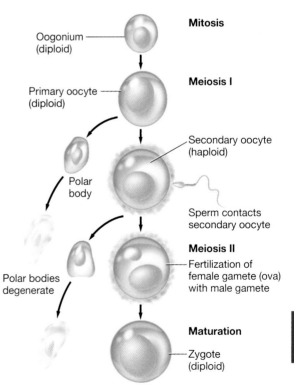

FIGURE **16.12** Oogenesis

16

■ *The first meiotic division results in one secondary oocyte and one polar body.* At puberty, one primary oocyte enlarges and becomes encased in a **primary follicle**. This primary oocyte then completes meiosis I to produce a **secondary oocyte** and a small bundle of nuclear material called a **polar body**. The formation of a polar body allows the oocyte to conserve cytoplasm, which will have to sustain the cell if fertilization occurs. The secondary oocyte, initially encased in a **secondary follicle**, enlarges to form a **vesicular** follicle that contains a large, fluid-filled space called the **antrum** (Figure 16.13).

■ *Meiosis II completes only if fertilization takes place.* The secondary oocyte begins meiosis II and is released when the vesicular follicle ruptures during ovulation. Note that the ruptured follicle then becomes an endocrine organ called a **corpus luteum** (KOHR-pus LOO-tee-um). But the secondary oocyte completes meiosis II to form an ovum and a second polar body only if fertilization occurs. If fertilization does not occur, the secondary oocyte degenerates without ever completing meiosis II.

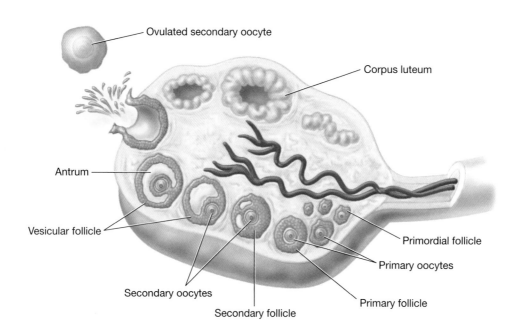

FIGURE **16.13** Ovary

Procedure 1 Time to Trace!

In this exercise, you will trace the male and female gametes from their production in the gonads to the point at which they meet in the uterine tube, where fertilization takes place.

Step 1: Male Gamete

Trace the male gamete from its earliest stage—the spermatogonium in the seminiferous tubule—through the stages of spermatogenesis to a mature sperm, and then through the male reproductive tract until it exits the body and enters the uterine tube of the female reproductive tract. Trace the pathway using Figure 16.14, and also fill in the space below.

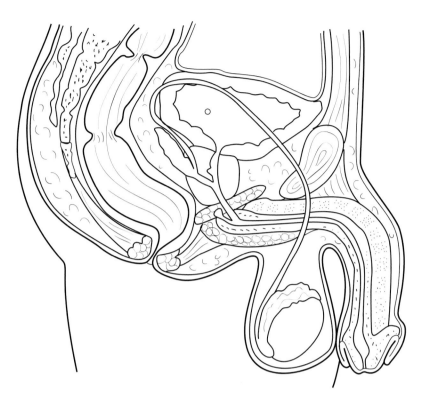

FIGURE **16.14** Male reproductive tract

Start: Spermatogonium_____

_____

_____

_____

_____

_____

_____

_____

_____ End: Uterine tube

Step 2: Female Gamete

Trace the female gamete from its earliest stage, the oogonium in a primordial follicle, to the time at which it is ovulated and enters the uterine tube. Trace the pathway using Figure 16.15, and also fill in the space below.

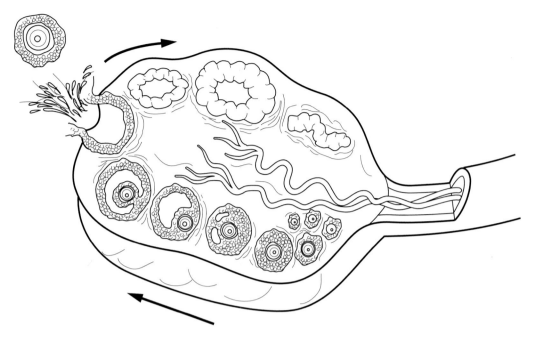

FIGURE **16.15** Ovary and follicles

Start: Oogonium _____

_____

_____

_____

_____

_____

_____

_____

_____

_____ End: Uterine tube

Exercise 16-5

Fertilization and Implantation

The first event in human development is **fertilization**, which takes place in the uterine tube when sperm cells encounter a secondary oocyte. Fertilization begins with a process called the **acrosomal reaction**, in which the acrosomes in the heads of the sperm release digestive enzymes by exocytosis. The acrosomal enzymes digest the secondary oocyte's outer coverings.

When the head and midpiece of a single sperm enter the oocyte, it completes meiosis II, yielding an ovum and a second polar body. The sperm and ovum nuclei swell to become **pronuclei**, and their nuclear membranes rupture. The two sets of exposed chromosomes then fuse to form a single-celled structure called a **zygote** (ZY-goht) (Figure 16.16).

The zygote, also called a **conceptus**, undergoes multiple changes during the period of time known as **gestation**. Gestation is considered a 40-week period extending from the mother's last menstrual period to birth. The changes the conceptus undergoes can be divided into three processes:

1. an increase in cell number,
2. cellular differentiation, and
3. the development of organ systems.

The increase in cell number begins about 30 hours after fertilization as the zygote travels down the uterine tube. At this time a process called **cleavage** occurs, in which the cell undergoes a series of mitotic divisions to produce two cells, then four, and so on. At about day 3, the conceptus reaches the uterus as a 16-cell ball that floats around the uterus for another 2 to 3 days and continues to divide until it becomes a hollow sphere called a **blastocyst**. The blastocyst has two populations of cells: the rounded **inner cell mass** and an outer layer of cells called the **trophoblast** (TROH-foh-blast).

At about day 6, the blastocyst adheres to the endometrium and begins the process of **implantation**. The implanting blastocyst secretes digestive enzymes that eat away the endometrial lining, and the endometrium reacts to the injury by growing over and enclosing the blastocyst. The process of implantation is generally complete by the second week, about the time a woman's menstrual period would begin.

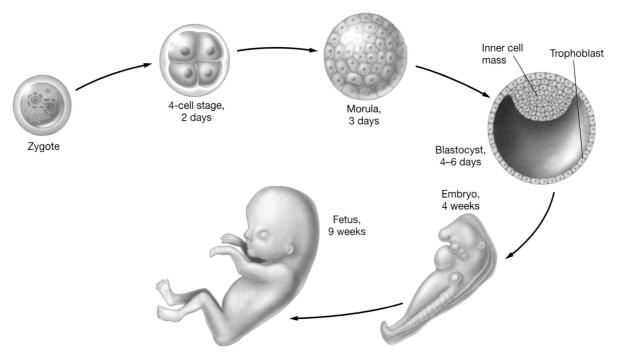

FIGURE **16.16** The stages of development

Procedure 1 Time to Trace!

In this exercise you will be tracing the gametes from the point at which the male and female gametes meet to form a zygote to the point at which it implants into the endometrium. Trace the pathway using Figure 16.17, and also fill in the space below.

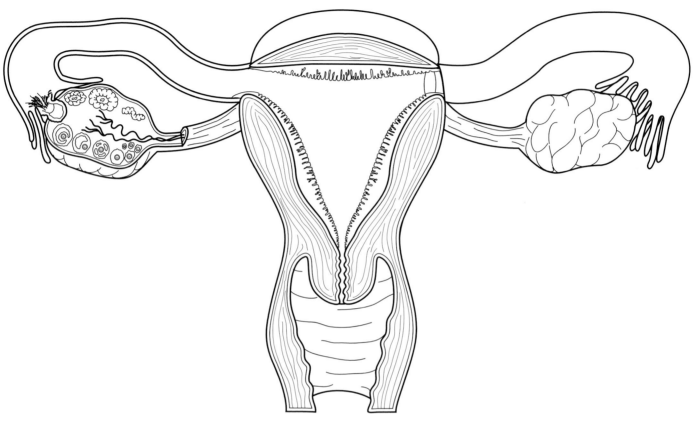

FIGURE **16.17** Female reproductive tract

Start: Sperm and ovum meet in uterine tube _____

_____

_____

_____

_____

_____

_____

_____

End: Implanted blastocyst

16

Exercise 16-6

Embryogenesis, Fetal Development, and Fetal Cardiovascular Anatomy

MATERIALS

- ❏ Sequence of embryonic development model
- ❏ Female reproductive system with fetus model
- ❏ Fetal circulation model

As the blastocyst implants, it begins a process known as **embryogenesis** during which cellular differentiation takes place. During embryogenesis, the inner cell mass differentiates into three primary tissue layers known as **germ layers,** from which all other tissues arise. The three primary germ layers are formed by the end of the second week, at which point the conceptus is considered an **embryo.**

The next six weeks of the embryonic period are marked by development of the **placenta,** formation of the extraembryonic membranes, and differentiation of the germ layers into rudimentary organ systems (**Figure 16.18**). The placenta begins to form at day 11, when the trophoblast forms the **chorion** (KOHR-ee-ahn), the fetal part of the placenta. Note in **Figure 16.18** that the chorion develops elaborate projections called the **chorionic villi** that eat into uterine blood vessels to create a space filled with maternal blood called the **placental sinus.** Nutrients and oxygen from maternal blood diffuse from the placental sinus to the chorionic villi and are delivered to the embryo by the large **umbilical vein.** Note that the umbilical vein is red, which reflects the fact that it carries oxygenated blood. Wastes are drained from the embryo via the paired **umbilical arteries.** All three vessels travel through the **umbilical cord.**

During this period the extraembryonic membranes develop. The innermost membrane is called the **amnion** (AM-nee-ahn). The amnion completely surrounds the embryo (and later the fetus) and suspends it in **amniotic fluid** within the **amniotic cavity.** The amniotic fluid protects the embryo from trauma by allowing it to remain buoyant and also protects it from fluctuations in temperature. In addition, the cavity provides the embryo ample space in which to move, which is critical to early muscle development.

As the placenta and extraembryonic membranes form, the primitive organ systems develop. This process completes by the end of the eighth week, at which point the conceptus is considered a **fetus.** For the duration of gestation, the organ systems become progressively more specialized, and the fetus continues to grow and develop.

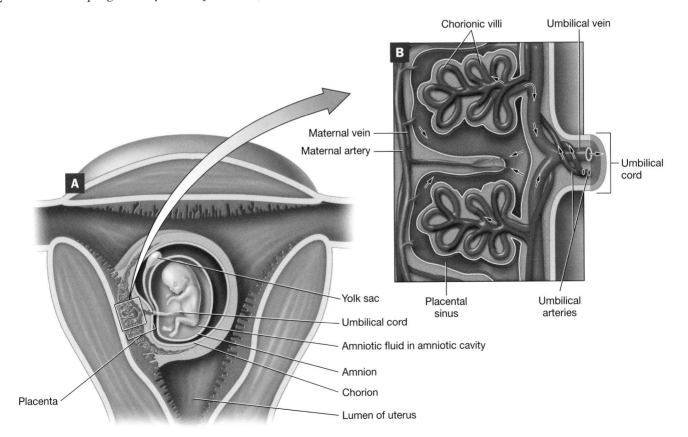

FIGURE **16.18** Embryo and membranes (**A**) embryo in uterus; (**B**) chorionic villi

16

The fetus's cardiovascular system differs significantly from that of the neonate. Within the fetal cardiovascular system are three **shunts** that bypass the relatively inactive lungs and liver and reroute the blood to other, more metabolically active organs. The three shunts include the following (Figure 16.19):

1. **Ductus venosus.** The ductus venosus (DUK-tus vee-NOH-sus) is a shunt that bypasses the liver. The umbilical vein delivers a small amount of blood to the liver but sends the majority of the blood through the ductus venosus to the fetal inferior vena cava. It closes around the time of birth and becomes the *ligamentum venosum*.

2. **Foramen ovale.** The foramen ovale (foh-RAY-men oh-VAL-ee) is a hole in the interatrial septum that shunts blood from the right atrium to the left atrium. This allows the blood to bypass the collapsed fetal lungs. The foramen ovale closes about the time of birth, leaving a permanent indentation in the interatrial septum called the *fossa ovalis*.

3. **Ductus arteriosus.** The ductus arteriosus (DUK-tus ahr-tih-ree-OH-sus) is a vascular bridge between the pulmonary artery and the aorta that bypasses the pulmonary circuit. It also closes around the time of birth and leaves behind a remnant called the *ligamentum arteriosum*.

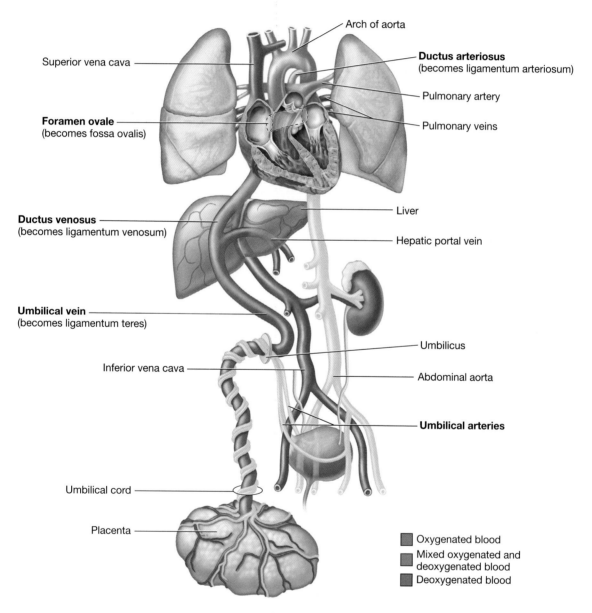

FIGURE **16.19** Fetal circulatory system

16

Procedure 1   Model Inventory for Fetal Development

Identify the following structures of development on models and diagrams, using your textbook and this unit for reference. As you examine the anatomical models and diagrams, record on the model inventory in Table 16.3 the name of the model and the structures you were able to identify.

1. Stages of development
   a. Zygote
   b. Blastocyst
   c. Implanted blastocyst
   d. Embryo
   e. Fetus

2. Fetal membranes
   a. Amnion
      (1) Amniotic cavity
      (2) Amniotic fluid
   b. Chorion
      (1) Chorionic villi

3. Vascular structures
   a. Placenta
      (1) Placental sinus
      (2) Maternal arteries and veins
   b. Umbilical cord
      (1) Umbilical arteries
      (2) Umbilical vein
   c. Foramen ovale
   d. Ductus venosus
   e. Ductus arteriosus

TABLE **16.3** Model Inventory for the Stages of Development and Fetal Structures

Model/Diagram	Structures Identified

1 Label the following structures on Figure 16.20.

❏ Corpora cavernosa
❏ Corpus spongiosum
❏ Ejaculatory duct
❏ Epididymis
❏ Glans penis
❏ Prostate gland
❏ Scrotum
❏ Vas (ductus) deferens

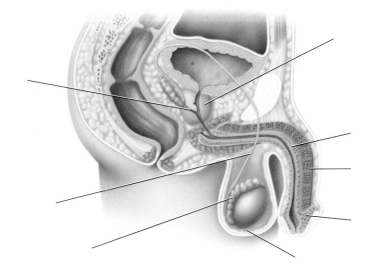

FIGURE **16.20** Midsagittal section through the male pelvis

2 Label the following structures on Figure 16.21.

❏ Cervical os
❏ Labium majus
❏ Labium minus
❏ Ovary
❏ Uterine tube
❏ Uterus
❏ Vaginal canal

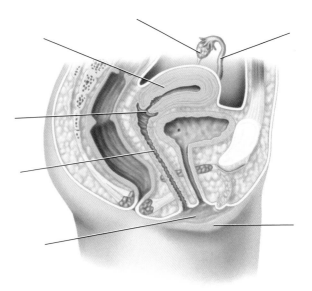

16

FIGURE **16.21** Midsagittal section through the female pelvis

3 Label the following structures on Figure 16.22.

❏ Body of uterus   ❏ Fimbriae   ❏ Ovary

❏ Cervical canal   ❏ Fundus of uterus   ❏ Perimetrium

❏ Endometrium   ❏ Myometrium   ❏ Uterine tube

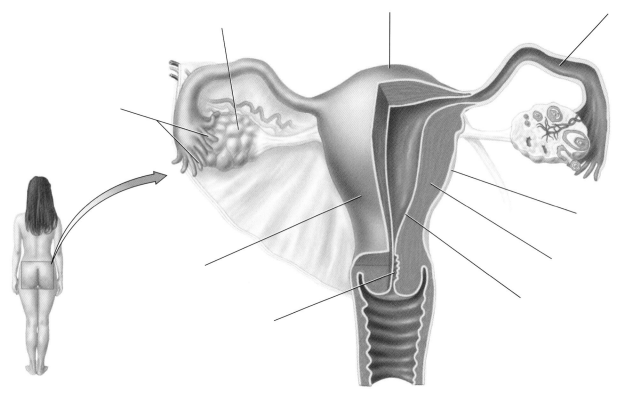

FIGURE **16.22** Posterior view of the female reproductive organs

4 Which of the following statements about meiosis is *false*?

a. Gametes proceed through two rounds of cell division.

b. Crossover occurs during meiosis, which increases genetic diversity.

c. The DNA replicates before both meiosis I and meiosis II.

d. Meiosis is carried out only in the gonads to produce gametes.

5 *Fill in the blanks:* The daughter cells produced by mitosis are _____ with _____

set(s) of chromosomes, whereas the gametes produced by meiosis are _____ with _____

set(s) of chromosomes.

6 Which of the following statements about spermatogenesis and oogenesis is *false*?

a. Meiosis II does not complete in oogenesis unless fertilization takes place.

b. Meiosis I begins during the fetal period but is arrested in oogenesis.

c. Spermatogenesis begins at puberty and continues throughout the male's lifetime, whereas the total number of oocytes a woman will produce is determined before birth.

d. Spermatogenesis results in one spermatid and two polar bodies, whereas oogenesis results in four ova.

16

7 A condition called *testicular torsion* results when the spermatic cord becomes twisted. Why would this condition be a surgical emergency?

_____

_____

_____

_____

_____

_____

8 A tubal (or ectopic) pregnancy results from implantation of a fertilized ovum in the uterine tube instead of the uterus. Why is this dangerous?

_____

_____

_____

_____

_____

_____

9 Which of the following is *not* one of the three basic changes a conceptus undergoes during development?
   a. An increase in cell number
   b. Cellular differentiation
   c. Development of organ systems
   d. Neoplasia

10 A condition called *placenta previa* occurs when the placenta is too low in the uterus. Why do you think this is a cause for concern?

_____

_____

_____

_____

_____

_____

16

11 *Fill in the blanks:* The umbilical _____ carries oxygenated blood to the fetus, and the _____ carries deoxygenated blood away from the fetus. The _____ bypasses the fetal liver, and the _____ and _____ bypass the fetal lungs.

12 Label **Figure 16.23** with the terms below.

❏ Ductus arteriosus
❏ Ductus venosus
❏ Foramen ovale
❏ Placenta
❏ Umbilical arteries
❏ Umbilical vein

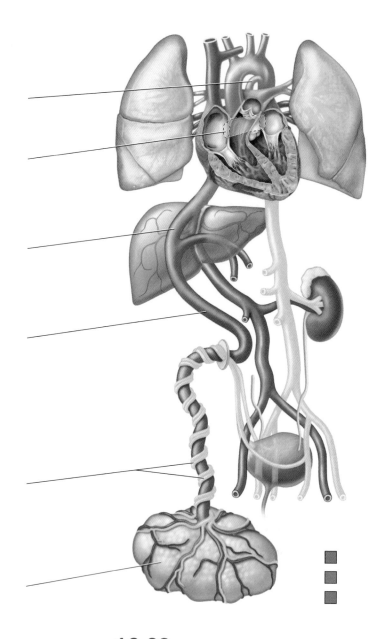

FIGURE **16.23** Fetal circulatory system

Photo Credits

Morton Publishing expresses thanks to the following sources for allowing us to use their photos.

Unit 1

Opener: SPL/Science Source

Fig. 1.7, Fig. 1.8: Kent M. Van De Graaff and John Crawley, *A Photographic Atlas for the Anatomy and Physiology Laboratory*, 6E © Morton Publishing

Fig. 1.11A–B: Neil Borden/Science Source

Fig. 1.11C: SPL/Science Source

Unit 2

Opener: Ken Eward/Science Source

Fig. 2.2: SPL/Science Source

Fig. 2.3: Justin Moore

Fig. 2.4: GIPhotoStock/Science Source

Unit 3

Opener: SPL/Science Source

Fig. 3.2: Courtesy of Olympus America

Fig. 3.5: GIPhotoStock/Science Source

Fig. 3.7: Michael Abbey/Science Source

Unit 4

Opener: SPL/Science Source

Fig. 4.2A: Biophoto Assoc./Science Source

Fig. 4.2B: Biology Pics/Science Source

Fig. 4.2C: Spike Walker/Science Source

Fig. 4.2D: Biophoto Assoc./Science Source

Fig. 4.2E: David Phillips/Science Source

Fig. 4.2F: SPL/Science Source

Fig. 4.2G: Biophoto Assoc./Science Source

Fig. 4.3A: Biophoto Assoc./Science Source

Fig. 4.3B: Visuals Unlimited

Fig. 4.3C: Erin Amerman

Fig. 4.3D: Biophoto Assoc./Photo Researcher

Fig. 4.3E: Erin Amerman

Fig. 4.3F: Spike Walker/Science Source

Fig. 4.3G: Chuck Brown/Science Source

Fig 4.3H: SPL/Science Source

Fig. 4.3I: Biophoto Assoc./Science Source

Fig. 4.4A: Eric Grave/Science Source

Fig. 4.4B: SPL/Science Source

Fig. 4.4C: Getty Images

Fig. 4.4D: Biophoto Assoc./Science Source

Fig. 4.5: Spike Walker/Science Source

Unit 5

Opener: SPL/Science Source

Fig. 5.4A: SPL/Science Source

Fig. 5.4B: Garry Delong/Science Source

Unit 6

Opener: SPL/Science Source

Fig. 6.7: A. Travelogue/Science Source

Fig. 6.8: VideoSurgery/Science Source

Fig. 6.9: David Bassett/Science Source

Fig. 6.10: Getty Images

Fig. 6.11: SPL/Science Source

Fig. 6.12: VideoSurgery/Science Source

Fig. 6.13: Martin Shields/Science Source

Fig. 6.14: SPL/Science Source

Fig. 6.16: SPL/Science Source

Fig. 6.18: Kent M. Van De Graaff and John Crawley, *A Photographic Atlas for the Anatomy and Physiology Laboratory*, 6E © Morton Publishing

Fig. 6.21, Fig. 6.22: VideoSurgery/Science Source

Fig. 6.27A: Kent M. Van De Graaff and John Crawley, *A Photographic Atlas for the Zoology Laboratory*, 6E © Morton Publishing

Fig. 6.27B: VideoSurgery/Science Source

Fig. 6.28: VideoSurgery/Science Source

Fig. 6.31: VideoSurgery/Science Source

Fig. 6.40: SPL/Science Source

Unit 7

Opener: SPL/Science Source

Fig. 7.4B: VideoSurgery/Science Source

Fig. 7.6B: Mike Leboffe

Unit 8

Opener: 3D4Medical/Science Source

Fig. 8.8: Spike Walker/Science Source

Fig. 8.14: SPL/Science Source

Fig. 8.17, Fig. 8.18, Fig. 8.19: Kent M. Van De Graaff and John Crawley, *A Photographic Atlas for the Anatomy and Physiology Laboratory*, 6E © Morton Publishing

Fig. 8.29: SPL/Science Source

Unit 9

Opener: VideoSurgery/Science Source

Fig. 9.5, Fig. 9.6, Fig. 9.7: Kent M. Van De Graaff and John Crawley, *A Photographic Atlas for the Anatomy and Physiology Laboratory*, 6E © Morton Publishing

Unit 10

Opener: A. Travelogue/Science Source

Unit 11

Opener: BSIP/Science Source

Fig. 11.4: VideoSurgery/Science Source

Fig. 11.6, Fig. 11.7, Fig. 11.8: Justin Moore

Unit 12

Opener: SPL/Science Source

Fig. 12.2: Biophoto Assoc./Science Source and Michael Ross/Science Source

Fig. 12.3: Justin Moore

Fig. 12.7: Biophoto Assoc./Science Source

Unit 13

Opener: SPL/Science Source

Fig. 13.3, Fig. 13.4B: VideoSurgery/Science Source

Fig. 13.7: SPL/Science Source

Fig. 13.8: Justin Moore

Fig. 13.10: Justin Moore

Unit 14

Opener: A. Travelogue/Science Source

Fig. 14.3B: Visuals Unlimited

Fig. 14.5: VideoSurgery/Science Source

Fig. 14.8B: Visuals Unlimited

Unit 15

Opener: SPL/Science Source

Fig. 15.9: VideoSurgery/Science Source

Fig. 15.11: Scott Camazine/Science Source

Unit 16

Opener: Petit Format/Science Source

Fig. 16.11: Michael Abbey/Science Source

Index

Face
    muscles moving, 159, 165, 172
    musculature of, 159f
Facial bones, 107, 118, 126
Facial nerve, 189, 207
Fascicles, 154, 161
Fats, 366
    emulsification of, 369f
Feedback, negative, 248, 255, 256, 260
Femoral artery, 269, 282, 283, 296
Femoral nerve, 213
Femoral vein, 270, 286, 288, 305
Femur, 107, 117, 117f, 135, 135f, 136, 136f, 138
Fertilization, 405, 419, 421
Fetal pig
    abdominopelvic cavity of, 15f
    ventral view of, 14f
Fetus, 405, 423, 430
Fibroblasts, 78
Fibrocartilage, 78, 81f, 82, 84, 92
Fibrous joint, 107, 141, 141f
Fibula, 107, 135f, 136, 136f, 138
Fibular nerve, common, 213
Filtrate, 381, 384, 387, 392, 400, 401
Fimbriae, 412
Flagellum, 45, 52, 417
Flat bones, 106, 115, 116
Flexor retinaculum, 212
Follicles, 420f
    hair, 95, 98, 102
    ovarian, 412, 414
    primary, 418
    primordial, 412, 417
    secondary, 418
    thyroid, 252
    vesicular, 412
Follicle-stimulating hormone, 251
Fontanel, anterior/posterior, 124, 126
Food coloring, diffusion results for, 57t
Foot, 136f, 330
Foramen magnum, 118
Foramen ovale, 408, 424
Forearm
    anterior view of, 150f, 242
    muscles moving, 159, 166, 172
Forearm flexors, 178, 212
Formed elements, 309, 311, 311t, 313
Fossa ovalis, 424
Fovea centralis, 230
Fractures, 151f
FRC. See Functional residual capacity
Frontal bone, 118, 125
Frontal lobe, 195
Frontal plane, 2, 18, 19, 28
Frontal section, 19f
Frontal sinus, 118
Functional residual capacity (FRC), 340, 349, 350
Fundus, 364, 412
Funny bone nerve, 212

G1, described, 61
G2, described, 61

Gallbladder, 359, 362f, 365, 365f, 366, 367, 370, 376, 377
Gallstones, 378
Gametes, 409, 415, 419, 420, 422, 428
Gametogenesis, 405, 415, 417, 509
Ganglia, 192
Gastric artery, left, 218
Gastric veins, 284, 288
Gastrocnemius, 156, 169
Gastroesophageal reflux, 37
Gastroesophageal sphincter, 364
Gastrointestinal (GI) tract, 363
Germ layers, 423
Gestation, 421, 423
GH. See Growth hormone
Glands, 90, 97, 98, 192, 253, 406, 411
Glans penis, 409
Glenohumeral joint, 146
Glenoid cavity, 131
Globules, 369
Glomerular capsule, 383, 386
Glomerular endothelial cells, 392
Glomerular filtration, 381, 384, 392, 393
Glomerulus, 380, 384, 386, 397
Glossopharyngeal nerve, 189, 207
Glucagon, 250, 253, 255
Glucose, 255, 384, 385, 392, 393, 401
Gluteus maximus, 168
Gluteus medius, 168
Gluteus muscles, 156, 168
Goblet cells, 342
Golgi complex, 44, 52
Gonads, 409, 412, 419, 428
Gracilis, 168, 175
Granulocytes, 313, 331
Gray matter, 183, 195
    spinal, 204
Greater omentum, 366, 366f, 367
Greater sciatic notch, 135
Greater trochanter, 135
Greater tubercle, 131
Greater wings, 118
Great saphenous vein, 270, 286, 288, 305
Great vessels, 265–266, 267, 275
Ground substance, 71
Growth hormone (GH), 250, 251, 261
Gunshot wounds, locating, 17, 17t, 29f
Gyri, 195, 200

Hair, 97, 98f, 99, 234
Hamstrings group, 156, 168
Hand, 133f, 151f, 212
Haploid cells, 405, 415
Head, 131, 135, 136, 417
    arteries of, 269, 283
    muscles moving, 159, 165, 172
    skeletal muscles of, 155
    veins of, 270, 284f, 288
Hearing, 234, 236
Hearing loss, conductive/sensorineural, 236
Heart, 279f, 345
    anatomy of, 265, 267, 274, 278
    anterior view of, 267f, 273f, 276, 276f, 301f

blood flow through, 268, 279
    frontal section of, 267f, 273f, 301f
    inferior aspect of, 276
    left ventricle of, 278f
    lymphatic system and, 327
    parts of, 301
    posterior view of, 273f, 276
    right ventricle of, 277f
    sheep, 276f, 277f, 278f
    superior aspect of, 276
Heartburn, 37, 377
Heart murmur, 294
Heart rate, 294, 297
    autonomic nervous system and, 298
    calculating, 299, 300
Heart sounds, additional, 294
Heart vessels, 294
Heart wall, layers of, 265
Hematoxylin, 313
Hemipelvis, 150
Hemoglobin, 313, 325, 326, 331
Hemoglobinometer, 326
Hemolysis, 322
Hemolytic disease of the newborn, 332
Hepatic artery, common, 281
Hepatic duct, common, 366
Hepatic portal system, veins of, 270, 284, 285f, 288, 290, 304f
Hepatopancreatic ampulla, 366
Hilum, 387, 389
Hips
    extending, 178
    muscles moving, 159, 168, 172
Histology, 49, 71, 363
Homeostasis, 191, 251, 254, 255, 313, 400, 409
    fluid/electrolyte, 253
    urinary system and, 385
Horizontal fissure, 341
Horizontal plane, 18
Hormones, 248, 257, 261, 297
    antagonist, 259
    inhibiting, 251
    luteinizing, 251
    properties of, 250, 250t
    releasing, 251
    secreting, 251, 253, 255, 260
    steroid, 253
Horns
    anterior/posterior, 203
    gray matter, 183
Humerus, 107, 131, 132f, 133f, 137, 174
Hyaline cartilage, 78, 80f, 84, 92, 117, 141
    rings, 348, 355
Hydrochloric acid (HCl), 37, 38, 369, 377
Hydrogen ions, 34, 38, 42
Hyoid bone, 107, 130, 130f, 137
Hypertonic solution, 58, 60, 66
Hypodermis, 95, 97, 99
Hypoglossal nerve, 189, 207
Hypothalamus, 183, 196, 248, 249, 251, 254, 255, 259
Hypotonic solution, 58, 60, 66
Hypoxic injury, 274